Student Solutions Guide for

DISCRETE MATHEMATICS AND ITS APPLICATIONS

Kenneth H. Rosen

AT&T Information Systems Laboratories

D1089272

Random House  New York

First Edition

9876543

ISBN: 0-394-38050-9

Manufactured in the United States of America

# PREFACE

This *Student Solutions Guide for Discrete Mathematics and Its Applications* contains complete solutions to all the odd-numbered exercises in the text. It also contains, for each section, words of wisdom, advice, insight, and general hints on approaching the exercises in that section.

In many cases, more than one solution to an exercise is presented, and sometimes the solutions presented here are not the same as the answers given in the back of the text. Indeed, there is rarely only one way to solve a problem in mathematics. You may well come upon still other valid ways to arrive at the correct answers. Even if you have solved a problem completely, you will find that reviewing the solutions presented here will be valuable, since there is insight to be gained by seeing how someone else handles a problem that you have just solved.

Exercises often ask that answers be justified or verified, or they ask you to show or prove a particular statement. In all these cases your solution should be a proof, i.e., a mathematical argument based on the rules of logic. Such a proof needs to be complete, convincing, and correct. Read your proof after finishing it. Ask yourself whether you would understand and believe it if it were presented to you by your instructor.

Although I cannot personally discuss with you my philosophy on learning discrete mathematics by solving exercises, let me include a few general words of advice. The best way to learn mathematics is by solving exercises, and it is crucial that you first try to solve these exercises independently. Consequently, do not use this *Guide* as a crutch. Do not look at the solution (or even the answer) to a problem before you have worked on it yourself. Resist the temptation to consult the solution as soon as the going gets rough. Make a real effort to work the problem completely on your own—preferably to the point of *writing down* a complete solution—before checking your work with the solutions presented here. If you have reached the point where you feel it necessary to look at the answer or solution to a problem, try reading it only casually, looking for a hint as to how you might proceed; then try working on the exercise again, armed with this added information. As a last resort, study the solution in detail and make sure you could explain it to a fellow student.

I want to thank Jerry Grossman for his advice and assistance in the preparation of this *Guide*, Suzanne Zeitman for double-checking the solutions, and students at Monmouth College and Oakland University for their input on preliminary versions of solutions to the exercises. I would also like to thank the staff at Random House and especially my editor, Wayne Yuhasz, for his valuable suggestions for this *Guide*; his advice has helped make the material presented here more valuable for the students.

A tremendous amount of effort has been devoted to ensuring the accuracy of these solutions, but it is possible that a few scattered errors remain. I would appreciate hearing about all that you find, be they typographical or mathematical.

Kenneth H. Rosen

# CONTENTS

# CHAPTER 1
## The Foundations: Logic, Sets, and Functions

⇒ **SECTION 1.1    Logic**

*Manipulating propositions and constructing truth tables are straightforward. A truth table is constructed by finding the truth values of compound propositions from the inside out; see the solution to Exercise 7f, for instance. This exercise set will probably pose no difficulty, except possibly for the brain-teaser in Exercise 4 and the classical logical paradox in Exercise 14.*

1.  a) This is a true proposition.

    b) This is a false proposition (Tallahassee is the capital).

    c) This is a true proposition.

    d) This is a false proposition.

    e) This is not a proposition (it contains a variable; the truth value depends on value assigned to $x$).

    f) This is not a proposition, since it does not assert anything.

    g) This is a true proposition (the commutative law holds for real numbers).

3.  a) Here we have the conjunction $p \wedge q$.

    b) Here we have a conjunction of $p$ with the negation of $q$, namely $p \wedge \neg q$. Note that "but" logically means the same thing as "and."

    c) Again this is a conjunction: $\neg p \wedge \neg q$.

    d) Here we have a disjunction, $p \vee q$. Note that $\vee$ is the inclusive $OR$, so the "(or both)" part of the English sentence is automatically included.

    e) This sentence is an implication, $p \rightarrow q$.

    f) This is a conjunction of propositions, both of which are compound: $(p \vee q) \wedge (p \rightarrow \neg q)$.

    g) This is the biconditional $p \leftrightarrow q$.

5.  a) Many forms of the answer are possible. One that reads well in English is "I will ski tomorrow only if it snows today."

    b) Technically, this is not an implication, since the hypothesis and conclusion are not propositions (they contain variables). Nevertheless, we can treat such sentences in the same way we treat propositions. The converse here is "If $n^2 > 9$, then $n > 3$."

    c) As in part (b), there is a variable ("a positive integer") in this sentence, so technically it is not a proposition. Its converse is "A positive integer is a prime if it has no divisors other than 1 and itself."

7.  To construct the truth table for a compound proposition, we work from the inside out. In each case, we will show the intermediate steps. In part (d), for example, we first construct the truth table for $p \rightarrow q$, then the truth table for $\neg p \rightarrow q$ (using the truth table for $\neg p$), and finally combine them to get the truth table for $(p \rightarrow q) \wedge (\neg p \rightarrow q)$.

    For parts (a) and (b) we have the following table (column four for part (a), column six for part (b)).

| $p$ | $q$ | $\neg q$ | $p \rightarrow \neg q$ | $\neg p$ | $\neg p \leftrightarrow q$ |
|---|---|---|---|---|---|
| T | T | F | F | F | F |
| T | F | T | T | F | T |
| F | T | F | T | T | T |
| F | F | T | T | T | F |

For parts **(c)** and **(d)** we have the following table (columns six and seven, respectively).

| $p$ | $q$ | $p \rightarrow q$ | $\neg p$ | $\neg p \rightarrow q$ | $(p \rightarrow q) \vee (\neg p \rightarrow q)$ | $(p \rightarrow q) \wedge (\neg p \rightarrow q)$ |
|---|---|---|---|---|---|---|
| T | T | T | F | T | T | T |
| T | F | F | F | T | T | F |
| F | T | T | T | T | T | T |
| F | F | T | T | F | T | F |

For parts **(e)** and **(f)** we have the following table (this time we have not explicitly shown the columns for negation). Column five shows the answer for part **(e)**, and column seven shows the answer for part **(f)**.

| $p$ | $q$ | $p \leftrightarrow q$ | $\neg p \leftrightarrow q$ | $(p \leftrightarrow q) \vee (\neg p \leftrightarrow q)$ | $\neg p \leftrightarrow \neg q$ | $(\neg p \leftrightarrow \neg q) \leftrightarrow (p \leftrightarrow q)$ |
|---|---|---|---|---|---|---|
| T | T | T | F | T | T | T |
| T | F | F | T | T | F | T |
| F | T | F | T | T | F | T |
| F | F | T | F | T | T | T |

9. **a)** bitwise $OR = 11\ 11111$; bitwise $AND = 00\ 00000$; bitwise $XOR = 11\ 11111$

   **b)** bitwise $OR = 111\ 11010$; bitwise $AND = 101\ 00000$; bitwise $XOR = 010\ 11010$

   **c)** bitwise $OR = 10011\ 11001$; bitwise $AND = 00010\ 00000$; bitwise $XOR = 10001\ 11001$

   **d)** bitwise $OR = 11111\ 11111$; bitwise $AND = 00000\ 00000$; bitwise $XOR = 11111\ 11111$

11. For "Fred is not happy," the truth value is $1 - 0.8 = 0.2$.

    For "John is not happy," the truth value is $1 - 0.4 = 0.6$.

13. For "Fred is happy, or John is happy," the truth value is $\max(0.8, 0.4) = 0.8$.

    For "Fred is not happy, or John is not happy," the truth value is $\max(0.2, 0.6) = 0.6$ (using the result of Exercise 11).

$\Rightarrow$ **SECTION 1.2   Propositional Equivalences**

*The solutions to Exercise 1 through Exercise 10 can be routine, if we use truth tables to show propositions equivalent. The reader should do more than this, however; think about what the equivalence is saying. See Exercise 7 for this approach. Some important topics not covered in the text are introduced in this exercise set, including the notion of the* **dual** *of a proposition,* **disjunctive normal form** *for propositions,* **functional completeness,** *and two other logical connectives,* NAND *and* NOR. *Much of this material foreshadows the study of Boolean algebra in Chapter 9.*

1. First we construct the following truth tables, for the propositions we are asked to deal with.

| $p$ | $p \wedge \mathbf{T}$ | $p \vee \mathbf{F}$ | $p \wedge \mathbf{F}$ | $p \vee \mathbf{T}$ | $p \vee p$ | $p \wedge p$ |
|---|---|---|---|---|---|---|
| T | T | T | F | T | T | T |
| F | F | F | F | T | F | F |

The first equivalence, $p \wedge \mathbf{T} \iff p$ is valid because the second column $p \wedge \mathbf{T}$ is identical to the first column $p$. Similarly, part **(b)** comes from looking at columns three and one. Since column four is a column of $F$'s, and column five is a column of $T$'s, part **(c)** and part **(d)** hold. Finally, the last two parts follow from the fact that the last two columns are identical to the first column.

3. We construct the following truth tables.

| $p$ | $q$ | $p \vee q$ | $q \vee p$ | $p \wedge q$ | $q \wedge p$ |
|---|---|---|---|---|---|
| T | T | T | T | T | T |
| T | F | T | T | F | F |
| F | T | T | T | F | F |
| F | F | F | F | F | F |

Part **(a)** follows from the fact that the third and fourth columns are identical; part **(b)** follows from the fact that the fifth and sixth columns are identical.

5. We construct the following truth table and note that the fifth and eighth columns are identical.

| $p$ | $q$ | $r$ | $q \vee r$ | $p \wedge (q \vee r)$ | $p \wedge q$ | $p \wedge r$ | $(p \wedge q) \vee (p \wedge r)$ |
|---|---|---|---|---|---|---|---|
| T | T | T | T | T | T | T | T |
| T | T | F | T | T | T | F | T |
| T | F | T | T | T | F | T | T |
| T | F | F | F | F | F | F | F |
| F | T | T | T | F | F | F | F |
| F | T | F | T | F | F | F | F |
| F | F | T | T | F | F | F | F |
| F | F | F | F | F | F | F | F |

7. We could construct truth tables and verify that in each case the truth table consists of a column of **T**'s. Alternately we can argue as follows. Recall that the only way an implication can be false is for the hypothesis to be true and the conclusion to be false; hence it is sufficient to show that the conclusion must be true whenever the hypothesis is true.

**a)** If the hypothesis is true, then by the definition of $\wedge$ we know that $p$ is true. Hence the conclusion is also true.

**b)** If the hypothesis $p$ is true, then by the definition of $\vee$ the conclusion $p \vee q$ must also be true.

**c)** If the hypothesis is true, then $p$ must be false; hence the conclusion $p \to q$ is true, since *its* hypothesis is false.

**d)** If the hypothesis is true, then by the definition of $\wedge$ we know that $q$ must be true. This makes the conclusion $p \to q$ true, since *its* conclusion is true.

**e)** If the hypothesis is true, then $p \to q$ must be false. But this can only happen if $p$ is true, which is precisely what we wanted to show.

**f)** If the hypothesis is true, then $p \to q$ must be false. But this can only happen if $q$ is false, which is precisely what we wanted to show.

9. We could construct truth tables and verify that in each case the two propositions give identical columns. Alternately, we can argue as follows.

**a)** If $p$ is true, then $[p \vee (p \wedge q)]$ is true, since the first proposition in the disjunction is true. On the other hand, if $p$ is false, then both parts of the disjunction are false. Hence $[p \vee (p \wedge q)]$ always has the same truth value as $p$ does, so the two propositions are logically equivalent.

**b)** If $p$ is false, then $[p \wedge (p \vee q)]$ is false, since the first proposition in the conjunction is false. On the other hand, if $p$ is true, then both parts of the conjunction are true. Hence $[p \wedge (p \vee q)]$ always has the same truth value as $p$ does, so the two propositions are logically equivalent.

**11.** To show that these are *not* logically equivalent, we need only find one assignment of truth values to $p$, $q$, and $r$ for which the truth values of $(p \rightarrow q) \rightarrow r$ and $p \rightarrow (q \rightarrow r)$ differ. One such assignment is F for all three. Then $(p \rightarrow q) \rightarrow r$ is false and $p \rightarrow (q \rightarrow r)$ is true.

**13.** If we apply the operation for forming the dual twice to a proposition, then every symbol returns to what it originally was. The $\wedge$ changes to the $\vee$, then changes back to the $\wedge$. Similarly the $\vee$ changes to the $\wedge$, then back to the $\vee$. The same thing happens with the $\mathbf{T}$ and the $\mathbf{F}$. Thus the dual of the dual of a proposition $s$, namely $(s^*)^*$, is equal to the original proposition $s$.

**15.** Let $p$ and $q$ be two compound propositions involving only the operators $\wedge$, $\vee$, and $\neg$; we can also allow them to involve the constant $\mathbf{T}$ and $\mathbf{F}$. We want to show that if $p$ and $q$ are logically equivalent, then $p^*$ and $q^*$ are logically equivalent. The trick is to look at $\neg p$ and $\neg q$. They are certainly logically equivalent if $p$ and $q$ are. Now if $p$ is a conjunction, say $r \wedge s$, then $\neg p$ is logically equivalent, by DeMorgan's Laws, to $\neg r \vee \neg s$; a similar statement applies if $p$ is a disjunction. If $r$ and/or $s$ are themselves compound propositions, then we apply DeMorgan's Laws again to "push" the negation symbol $\neg$ deeper inside the formula, changing $\wedge$ to $\vee$ and $\vee$ to $\wedge$. We repeat this process until all the negation signs have been "pushed in" as far as possible and are now attached to the atomic (i.e., not compound) propositions in the compound propositions $p$ and $q$. Call these atomic propositions $p_1$, $p_2$, etc. Now in this process DeMorgan's Laws have forced us to change each $\wedge$ to $\vee$ and each $\vee$ to $\wedge$. Furthermore, if there are any constants $\mathbf{T}$ or $\mathbf{F}$ in the propositions, then they will be changed to their opposite when the negation operation is applied: $\neg \mathbf{T}$ is the same as $\mathbf{F}$, and $\neg \mathbf{F}$ is the same as $\mathbf{T}$. In summary, $\neg p$ and $\neg q$ look just like $p^*$ and $q^*$, except that each atomic proposition $p_i$ within them is replaced by its negation. Now we agreed that $\neg p \Longleftrightarrow \neg q$; this means that for *every* possible assignment of truth values to the atomic propositions $p_1$, $p_2$, etc., the truth values of $\neg p$ and $\neg q$ are the same. But assigning T to $p_i$ is the same as assigning F to $\neg p_i$, and assigning F to $p_i$ is the same as assigning T to $\neg p_i$. Thus, for every possible assignment of truth values to the atomic propositions, the truth values of $p^*$ and $q^*$ are the same. This is precisely what we wanted to prove.

**17.** There are three ways in which exactly two of $p$, $q$, and $r$ can be true. We write down these three possibilities as conjunctions and join them by $\vee$ to obtain the answer: $(p \wedge q \wedge \neg r) \vee (p \wedge \neg q \wedge r) \vee (\neg p \wedge q \wedge r)$. See Exercise 18 for the more general result.

**19.** Given a compound proposition $p$, we can construct its truth table and then, by Exercise 18, write down a proposition $q$ in disjunctive normal form which is logically equivalent to $p$. Since $q$ involves only $\neg$, $\wedge$, and $\vee$, this shows that $\neg$, $\wedge$, and $\vee$ form a functionally complete collection of logical operators.

**21.** Given a compound proposition $p$, we can, by Exercise 19, write down a proposition $q$ which is logically equivalent to $p$ and uses only $\neg$, $\wedge$, and $\vee$. Now by DeMorgan's Law we can get rid of all the $\wedge$'s by replacing each occurrence of $p_1 \wedge p_2 \wedge \cdots \wedge p_n$ with the equivalent proposition $\neg(\neg p_1 \vee \neg p_2 \vee \cdots \vee \neg p_n)$.

**23.** The proposition $\neg(p \wedge q)$ is true when either $p$ or $q$, or both, are false, and is false when both $p$ and $q$ are true; since this was the definition of $p \mid q$, the two are logically equivalent.

**25.** The proposition $\neg(p \vee q)$ is true when both $p$ and $q$ are false, and is false otherwise; since this was the definition of $p \downarrow q$, the two are logically equivalent.

**27.** A straightforward approach, using the results of Exercise 26, parts (**a**) and (**b**), is as follows: $(p \rightarrow q)$ $\Longleftrightarrow (\neg p \vee q) \Longleftrightarrow ((p \downarrow p) \vee q) \Longleftrightarrow (((p \downarrow p) \downarrow q) \downarrow ((p \downarrow p) \downarrow q))$. If we allow the constant **F** in our expression, then a simpler answer is $\mathbf{F} \downarrow ((\mathbf{F} \downarrow p) \downarrow q)$.

**29.** This is clear from the definition, in which $p$ and $q$ play a symmetric role.

**31.** A truth table for a compound proposition involving $p$ and $q$ has four lines, one for each of the following combinations of truth values for $p$ and $q$: TT, TF, FT, and FF. Now each line of the truth table for the compound proposition can be either T or F. Thus there are two possibilities for the first line; for each of those there are two possibilities for the second line, giving $2 \cdot 2 = 4$ possibilities for the first two lines; for each of those there are two possibilities for the third line, giving $4 \cdot 2 = 8$ possibilities for the first three lines; and finally for each of those, there are two possibilities for the fourth line, giving $8 \cdot 2 = 16$ possibilities altogether.

⇒ **SECTION 1.3    Predicates and Quantifiers**

*The reader may find quantifiers hard to understand at first. Predicate logic (the study of propositions with quantifiers) is one level of abstraction above propositional logic (the study of propositions without quantifiers). Careful attention to this material will aid you in thinking more clearly, not only in mathematics but in other areas as well, from computer science to politics. Keep in mind exactly what the quantifiers mean: $\forall x$ means "for all $x$" or "for every $x$," and $\exists x$ means "there exists an $x$ such that" or "for some $x$." It is good practice to read every such sentence aloud, paying attention to English grammar as well as meaning. The reader should understand how the negations of quantified statements are formed (see the last few paragraphs of the section), and why this method is correct; it is just common sense, really.*

**1. a)** T, since $0 \leq 4$    **b)** T, since $4 \leq 4$    **c)** F, since $6 \nleq 4$

**3. a)** This is true.
**b)** This is false, since Lansing, not Detroit, is the capital.
**c)** This is false (but $Q(\text{Boston}, \text{Massachusetts})$ is true).
**d)** This is false, since Albany, not New York, is the capital.

**5.** The answers presented here are not the only ones possible; other answers can be obtained using different predicates and different variables.
**a)** $\forall x P(x)$, where $P(x)$ is "$x$ needs a course in discrete mathematics," and the universe of discourse is computer science students
**b)** $\exists x P(x)$, where $P(x)$ is "$x$ owns a personal computer," and the universe of discourse is students in this class
**c)** $\forall x \exists y P(x, y)$, where $P(x, y)$ is "$x$ has taken $y$"; $x$ ranges over students in this class, and $y$ ranges over computer science courses

**d)** $\exists x \exists y P(x, y)$, with the environment of part **(c)** (i.e., the same definition of $P$ and the same universes of discourse)

**e)** $\forall x \forall y P(x, y)$, where $P(x, y)$ is "$x$ has been in $y$"; $x$ ranges over students in this class, and $y$ ranges over buildings on campus

**f)** $\exists x \exists y \forall z (P(z, y) \rightarrow Q(x, z))$, where $P(z, y)$ is "$z$ is in $y$" and $Q(x, z)$ is "$x$ has been in $z$"; $x$ ranges over students in this class, $y$ ranges over buildings on campus, and $z$ ranges over rooms

**g)** $\forall x \forall y \exists z (P(z, y) \wedge Q(x, z))$, with the environment of part **(f)**

**7. a)** T, since $0 = 0^2$

   **b)** T, since $1 = 1^2$

   **c)** F, since $2 \neq 2^2$

   **d)** F, since $-1 \neq (-1)^2$

   **e)** T (let $x = 1$)

   **f)** F (let $x = 2$)

**9. a)** $P(1, 3) \vee P(2, 3) \vee P(3, 3)$

   **b)** $P(1, 1) \wedge P(1, 2) \wedge P(1, 3)$

   **c)** $P(1, 1) \wedge P(1, 2) \wedge P(1, 3) \wedge P(2, 1) \wedge P(2, 2) \wedge P(2, 3) \wedge P(3, 1) \wedge P(3, 2) \wedge P(3, 3)$

   **d)** $P(1, 1) \vee P(1, 2) \vee P(1, 3) \vee P(2, 1) \vee P(2, 2) \vee P(2, 3) \vee P(3, 1) \vee P(3, 2) \vee P(3, 3)$

   **e)** $(P(1, 1) \wedge P(1, 2) \wedge P(1, 3)) \vee (P(2, 1) \wedge P(2, 2) \wedge P(2, 3)) \vee (P(3, 1) \wedge P(3, 2) \wedge P(3, 3))$

   **f)** $(P(1, 1) \vee P(2, 1) \vee P(3, 1)) \wedge (P(1, 2) \vee P(2, 2) \vee P(3, 2)) \wedge (P(1, 3) \vee P(2, 3) \vee P(3, 3))$

Note the crucial difference between parts **(e)** and **(f)**.

**11.** We use the equivalences explained at the end of the section, twice:
$$\neg \exists x \forall y P(x, y) \Longleftrightarrow \forall x \neg \forall y P(x, y) \Longleftrightarrow \forall x \exists y \neg P(x, y).$$

**13.** Both are true precisely when at least one of $P(x)$ and $Q(x)$ is true for at least one value of $x$ in the universe of discourse.

**15. a)** This is certainly true: if there is a unique $x$ satisfying $P(x)$, then there certainly *is* an $x$ satisfying $P(x)$.

   **b)** Unless there is only one item in the universe of discourse, the truth of the hypothesis implies that there is more than one $x$ such that $P(x)$ holds. Therefore this proposition need not be true. (For example, let $P(x)$ be the proposition $x^2 \geq 0$ in the context of the real numbers. The hypothesis is true, but there is not a unique $x$ for which $x^2 \geq 0$.)

   **c)** This is true: if there is an $x$ (unique or not) such that $P(x)$ is false, then we can conclude that it is not the case that $P(x)$ holds for all $x$.

**17.** We simply want to say that there exists an $x$ such that $P(x)$ holds, and that any other $y$ such that $P(y)$ holds must be this same $x$. Thus we write $\exists x \big(P(x) \wedge \forall y (P(y) \rightarrow x = y)\big)$.

⇒ **SECTION 1.4    Sets**

*This exercise set (note that this is a "set" in the mathematical sense) reinforces the concepts introduced in this section—set description, subset and containment, cardinality, power set, and Cartesian product. A few of the exercises (mostly some of the even-numbered ones) are a bit subtle. Keep in mind the distinction between "is an element of" and "is a subset of." Similarly, there is a big difference between $\emptyset$ and $\{\emptyset\}$. In dealing with sets, as in most of mathematics, it is extremely important to say exactly what you mean.*

1. **a)** $\{1, -1\}$
   **b)** $\{1, 2, 3, 4, 5, 6, 7, 8, 9, 10, 11\}$
   **c)** $\{0, 1, 4, 9, 16, 25, 36, 49, 64, 81\}$
   **d)** $\emptyset$ ($\sqrt{2}$ is not an integer)

3. **a)** Yes; order and repetition do not matter.
   **b)** No; the first set has one element, and the second has two elements.
   **c)** No; the first set has no elements, and the second has one element (namely the empty set).

5. **a)** T (in fact it is the only element)
   **b)** T (every set is a subset of itself)
   **c)** F (the only element of $\{x\}$ is a letter, not a set)
   **d)** T (in fact, it is the only element)
   **e)** T (the empty set is a subset of every set)
   **f)** F (the only element of $\{x\}$ is a letter, not a set)

7. We need to show that every element of $A$ is also an element of $C$. Let $x \in A$. Then since $A \subseteq B$, we can conclude that $x \in B$. Furthermore, since $B \subseteq C$, the fact that $x \in B$ implies that $x \in C$, as we wished to show.

9. The cardinality of a set is the number of elements it has. The number of elements in its elements is irrelevant.
   **a)** 1    **b)** 1    **c)** 2    **d)** 3

11. **a)** $\{\emptyset, \{a\}\}$    **b)** $\{\emptyset, \{a\}, \{b\}, \{a, b\}\}$    **c)** $\{\emptyset, \{\emptyset\}, \{\{\emptyset\}\}, \{\emptyset, \{\emptyset\}\}\}$

13. **a)** Since the set we are working with has 3 elements, the power set has $2^3 = 8$ elements.
    **b)** Since the set we are working with has 4 elements, the power set has $2^4 = 16$ elements.
    **c)** The power set of the empty set has $2^0 = 1$ element. The power set of this set therefore has $2^1 = 2$ elements. In particular, it is $\{\emptyset, \{\emptyset\}\}$. (See Example 12.)

15. In each case we need to list all the ordered pairs, and there are $4 \times 2 = 8$ of them.
    **a)** $\{(a, y), (a, z), (b, y), (b, z), (c, y), (c, z), (d, y), (d, z)\}$
    **b)** $\{(y, a), (y, b), (y, c), (y, d), (z, a), (z, b), (z, c), (z, d)\}$

17. By definition, $\emptyset \times A$ consists of all pairs $(x, a)$ such that $x \in \emptyset$ and $a \in A$. Since there are no elements $x \in \emptyset$, there are no such pairs, so $\emptyset \times A = \emptyset$. Similar reasoning shows that $A \times \emptyset = \emptyset$.

**19.** The Cartesian product $A \times B$ has $mn$ elements. (This problem foreshadows the general discussion of counting in Chapter 4.) To see that this answer is correct, note that for each $a \in A$ there are $n$ different elements $b \in B$ with which to form the pair $(a, b)$. Since there are $m$ different elements of $A$, each leading to $n$ different pairs, there must be $mn$ pairs altogether.

**21.** First we prove the statement mentioned in the hint. The "if" part is immediate from the definition of equality. The "only if" part is rather subtle. We want to show that if $\{\{a\}, \{a, b\}\} = \{\{c\}, \{c, d\}\}$, then $a = c$ and $b = d$. First consider the case in which $a \neq b$. Then $\{\{a\}, \{a, b\}\}$ has exactly two elements, both of which are sets; exactly one of them contains one element, and exactly one of them contains two elements. Thus $\{\{c\}, \{c, d\}\}$ must have the same property; hence $c$ cannot equal $d$, and so $\{c\}$ is the element containing one element. Hence $\{a\} = \{c\}$, and so $a = c$. Also in this case the two-element elements $\{a, b\}$ and $\{c, d\}$ must be equal, and since $b \neq a = c$, we must have $b = d$. The other possibility is that $a = b$. Then $\{\{a\}, \{a, b\}\} = \{\{a\}\}$, a set with one element. Hence $\{\{c\}, \{c, d\}\}$ must also have only one element, which can only happen when $c = d$ and the set is $\{\{c\}\}$. It then follows that $a = c$, and hence $b = d$, as well.

Now there is really nothing else to prove. The property that we want ordered pairs to have is precisely the one that we just proved is satisfied by this definition. Furthermore, if we look at the proof, then it is clear how to "recover" both $a$ and $b$ from $\{\{a\}, \{a, b\}\}$. If this set has two elements, then $a$ is the unique element in the one-element element of this set, and $b$ is the unique member of the two-element element of this set other than $a$. If this set has only one element, then $a$ and $b$ are both equal to the unique element of the unique element of this set.

⇒ **SECTION 1.5    Set Operations**

*Most of the exercises involving operations on sets can be done fairly routinely by following the definitions. It is important to understand what it means for two sets to be equal and how to prove that two given sets are equal—using membership tables, using the definition to reduce the problem to logic, or showing that each is a subset of the other; see, for example, Exercise 9 through Exercise 14. It is often helpful when looking at operations on sets to draw the Venn diagram, even if you are not asked to do so. The* **symmetric difference** *is a fairly important set operation not discussed in the section; it is developed in Exercise 20 through Exercise 29. Two other new concepts,* **multisets** *and* **fuzzy sets**, *are also introduced in this set of exercises.*

**1. a)** the set of students who live within one mile of school and walk to class (only students who do both of these things are in the intersection)

**b)** the set of students who either live within one mile of school or walk to class (or, it goes without saying, both)

**c)** the set of students who live within one mile of school but do not walk to class

**d)** the set of students who live more than a mile from school but nevertheless walk to class

**3. a)** We include all numbers that are in one or both of the sets, obtaining $\{0, 1, 2, 3, 4, 5, 6\}$.

**b)** There is only one number in both of these sets, so the answer is $\{3\}$.

**c)** The set of numbers in $A$ but not in $B$ is $\{1, 2, 4, 5\}$.

**d)** The set of numbers in $B$ but not in $A$ is $\{0, 6\}$.

5. By definition $\overline{\overline{A}}$ is the set of elements of the universal set that are not in $\overline{A}$. Not being in $\overline{A}$ means being in $A$. Thus $\overline{\overline{A}}$ is the same set as $A$. We can give this proof in symbols as follows:
$$\overline{\overline{A}} = \{\, x \mid \neg x \in \overline{A} \,\} = \{\, x \mid \neg\neg x \in A \,\} = \{\, x \mid x \in A \,\} = A\,.$$

7. These follow directly from the corresponding properties for the logical operations $OR$ and $AND$.
   a) $A \cup B = \{\, x \mid x \in A \vee x \in B \,\} = \{\, x \mid x \in B \vee x \in A \,\} = B \cup A$
   b) $A \cap B = \{\, x \mid x \in A \wedge x \in B \,\} = \{\, x \mid x \in B \wedge x \in A \,\} = B \cap A$

9. This exercise asks for a proof of one of DeMorgan's Laws for sets. The primary way to show that two sets are equal is to show that each is a subset of the other. In other words, to show that $X = Y$, we must show that whenever $x \in X$, it follows that $x \in Y$, and that whenever $x \in Y$, it follows that $x \in X$. Exercise 5, Exercise 6, and Exercise 7 could also have been done this way, but it was easier in those cases to reduce the problems to the corresponding problems of logic. Here, too, we can reduce the problem to logic and invoke DeMorgan's Law for logic, but this problem requests specific proof techniques.

   a) This proof is similar to the proof of the dual property, given in Example 10. Suppose $x \in \overline{A \cup B}$. Then $x \notin A \cup B$, which means that $x$ is in neither $A$ nor $B$. In other words, $x \notin A$ and $x \notin B$. This is equivalent to saying that $x \in \overline{A}$ and $x \in \overline{B}$. Therefore $x \in \overline{A} \cap \overline{B}$, as desired. Conversely, if $x \in \overline{A} \cap \overline{B}$, then $x \in \overline{A}$ and $x \in \overline{B}$. This means $x \notin A$ and $x \notin B$, so $x$ cannot be in the union of $A$ and $B$. Since $x \notin A \cup B$, we conclude that $x \in \overline{A \cup B}$, as desired.

   b) The following membership table gives the desired equality, since columns four and seven are identical.

| $A$ | $B$ | $A \cup B$ | $\overline{A \cup B}$ | $\overline{A}$ | $\overline{B}$ | $\overline{A} \cap \overline{B}$ |
|-----|-----|------------|----------------------|----------------|----------------|----------------------------------|
| 1 | 1 | 1 | 0 | 0 | 0 | 0 |
| 1 | 0 | 1 | 0 | 0 | 1 | 0 |
| 0 | 1 | 1 | 0 | 1 | 0 | 0 |
| 0 | 0 | 0 | 1 | 1 | 1 | 1 |

11. This is clear, since both of these sets are precisely $\{\, x \mid x \in A \wedge x \notin B \,\}$.

13. There are many ways to prove these identities. One way is to reduce them to logical identities (some of the associative and distributive laws for $OR$ and $AND$). Alternately, we could argue in each case that the left-hand side is a subset of the right-hand side and vice versa. Another method would be to construct membership tables (they will have eight rows in order to cover all the possibilities). We will exhibit one of each method.

   a) $A \cup (B \cup C) = \{\, x \mid x \in A \vee x \in B \cup C \,\} = \{\, x \mid x \in A \vee (x \in B \vee x \in C) \,\} = \{\, x \mid (x \in A \vee x \in B) \vee x \in C \,\} = \{\, x \mid x \in A \cup B \vee x \in C \,\} = (A \cup B) \cup C$.

   b) First we show that any element of the left-hand side must be in the right-hand side as well. If $x \in A \cap (B \cap C)$, then $x$ must be in $A$ and also in $B \cap C$. Hence $x$ must be in $A$ and also in $B$ and in $C$. Since $x$ is in both $A$ and $B$, we conclude that $x \in A \cap B$. This, together with the fact that $x \in C$ tells us that $x \in (A \cap B) \cap C$, as desired. The argument in the other direction (if $x \in (A \cap B) \cap C$ then $x$ must be in $A \cap (B \cap C)$) is nearly identical.

   c) We construct the following membership table and note that the fifth and eighth columns are identical.

| $A$ | $B$ | $C$ | $B \cap C$ | $A \cup (B \cap C)$ | $A \cup B$ | $A \cup C$ | $(A \cup B) \cap (A \cup C)$ |
|---|---|---|---|---|---|---|---|
| 1 | 1 | 1 | 1 | 1 | 1 | 1 | 1 |
| 1 | 1 | 0 | 0 | 1 | 1 | 1 | 1 |
| 1 | 0 | 1 | 0 | 1 | 1 | 1 | 1 |
| 1 | 0 | 0 | 0 | 1 | 1 | 1 | 1 |
| 0 | 1 | 1 | 1 | 1 | 1 | 1 | 1 |
| 0 | 1 | 0 | 0 | 0 | 1 | 0 | 0 |
| 0 | 0 | 1 | 0 | 0 | 0 | 1 | 0 |
| 0 | 0 | 0 | 0 | 0 | 0 | 0 | 0 |

**15.** These are straightforward applications of the definitions.

  **a)** The set of elements common to all three sets is $\{4, 6\}$.

  **b)** The set of elements in at least one of the three sets is $\{0, 1, 2, 3, 4, 5, 6, 7, 8, 9, 10\}$.

  **c)** The set of elements in $C$ and at the same time in at least one of $A$ and $B$ is $\{4, 5, 6, 8, 10\}$.

  **d)** The set of elements either in $C$ or in both $A$ and $B$ (or in both of these) is $\{0, 2, 4, 5, 6, 7, 8, 9, 10\}$.

**17. a)** If $B$ adds nothing new to $A$, then we can conclude that all the elements of $B$ were already in $A$. In other words, $B \subseteq A$.

  **b)** In this case, all the elements of $A$ are forced to be in $B$ as well, so we conclude that $A \subseteq B$.

  **c)** This equality holds precisely when none of the elements of $A$ are in $B$ (if there were any such elements, then $A - B$ would not contain all the elements of $A$). Thus we conclude that $A$ and $B$ are disjoint ($A \cap B = \emptyset$).

  **d)** We can conclude nothing about $A$ and $B$ in this case, since this equality always holds.

  **e)** Every element in $A - B$ must be in $A$, and every element in $B - A$ must not be in $A$. Since no item can be in $A$ and not be in $A$ at the same time, there are no elements in both $A - B$ and $B - A$. Thus the only way for these two sets to be equal is if both if them are the empty set. This means that every element of $A$ must be in $B$, and every element of $B$ must be in $A$. Thus we conclude that $A = B$.

**19.** This is the set-theoretic version of the contrapositive law for logic, which says that $p \rightarrow q$ is logically equivalent to $\neg q \rightarrow \neg p$. We argue as follows.

$$A \subseteq B \iff \forall x (x \in A \rightarrow x \in B) \iff \forall x (x \notin B \rightarrow x \notin A) \iff \forall x (x \in \overline{B} \rightarrow x \in \overline{A}) \iff \overline{B} \subseteq \overline{A}.$$

**21.** Clearly this will be the set of students majoring in computer science or mathematics but not both.

**23.** There are precisely two ways that an item can be in either $A$ or $B$ but not both. It can be in $A$ but not $B$ (which is equivalent to saying that it is in $A - B$), or it can be in $B$ but not $A$ (which is equivalent to saying that it is in $B - A$). Thus an element is in $A \oplus B$ if and only if it is in $(A - B) \cup (B - A)$.

**25.** We will use the result of Exercise 23 as well as some obvious identities (some of which are in Exercise 6).

  **a)** $A \oplus A = (A - A) \cup (A - A) = \emptyset \cup \emptyset = \emptyset$

  **b)** $A \oplus \emptyset = (A - \emptyset) \cup (\emptyset - A) = A \cup \emptyset = A$

  **c)** $A \oplus U = (A - U) \cup (U - A) = \emptyset \cup \overline{A} = \overline{A}$

  **d)** $A \oplus \overline{A} = (A - \overline{A}) \cup (\overline{A} - A) = A \cup \overline{A} = U$

27. We can conclude that $B = \emptyset$. To see this, suppose that $B$ contains some element $b$. If $b \in A$, then $b$ is excluded from $A \oplus B$, so $A \oplus B$ cannot equal $A$. On the other hand, if $b \notin A$, then $b$ must be in $A \oplus B$, so again $A \oplus B$ cannot equal $A$. Thus in either case, $A \oplus B \neq A$. We conclude that $B$ cannot have any elements.

29. Yes. To show that $A = B$, we need to show that $x \in A$ implies $x \in B$ and conversely. By symmetry, it will be enough to show one direction of this. So assume that $A \oplus C = B \oplus C$, and let $x \in A$ be given. There are two cases to consider, depending on whether $x \in C$. If $x \in C$, then by definition we can conclude that $x \notin A \oplus C$. Therefore $x \notin B \oplus C$. Now if $x$ were *not* in $B$, then $x$ *would* be in $B \oplus C$ (since $x \in C$ by assumption). Since this is not true, we conclude that $x \in B$, as desired. For the other case, assume that $x \notin C$. Then $x \in A \oplus C$. Therefore $x \in B \oplus C$ as well. Again, if $x$ were *not* in $B$, then it could not be in $B \oplus C$ (since $x \notin C$ by assumption). Once again we conclude that $x \in B$, and the proof is complete.

31. a) The union of these sets is the set of elements that appear in at least one of them. In this case the sets are "increasing": $A_1 \subseteq A_2 \subseteq \cdots \subseteq A_n$. Therefore any element in any of the sets is in $A_n$, so the union is $A_n = \{1, 2, \ldots, n\}$.
    b) The intersection of these sets is the set of elements that appear in all of them. Since $A_1 = \{1\}$, only the number 1 has a chance to be in the intersection. In fact 1 is in the intersection, since it is in all of the sets. Therefore the intersection is $A_1 = \{1\}$.

33. The $i^{\text{th}}$ digit in the string indicates whether the $i^{\text{th}}$ number in the universal set (in this case the number $i$) is in the set in question.
    **a)** $\{1, 2, 3, 4, 7, 8, 9, 10\}$     **b)** $\{2, 4, 5, 6, 7\}$     **c)** $\{1, 10\}$

35. We are given two bit strings, representing two sets. We want to represent the set of elements that are in the first set but not the second. Thus the bit in the $i^{\text{th}}$ position of the bit string for the difference is 1 if the $i^{\text{th}}$ bit of the first string is 1 and the $i^{\text{th}}$ bit of the second string is 0, and is 0 otherwise.

37. We represent the sets by bit strings of length 26, using alphabetical order. Thus
    $A$ is represented by 1 11110 00000 00000 00000 00000,
    $B$ is represented by 0 11100 10000 00001 00010 10000,
    $C$ is represented by 0 01010 00100 00010 00001 00111, and
    $D$ is represented by 0 00110 01100 00110 00011 00110.
    To find the desired sets, we apply the indicated bitwise operations to these strings.
    **a)** 1 11110 00000 00000 00000 00000 $\vee$ 0 11100 10000 00001 00010 10000 =
    1 11110 10000 00001 00010 10000, which represents the set $\{a, b, c, d, e, g, p, t, v\}$
    **b)** 1 11110 00000 00000 00000 00000 $\wedge$ 0 11100 10000 00001 00010 10000 =
    0 11100 00000 00000 00000 00000, which represents the set $\{b, c, d\}$
    **c)** (1 11110 00000 00000 00000 00000 $\vee$ 0 00110 01100 00110 00011 00110) $\wedge$
    (0 11100 10000 00001 00010 10000 $\vee$ 0 01010 00100 00010 00001 00111) =
    1 11110 01100 00110 00011 00110 $\wedge$ 0 11110 10100 00011 00011 10111 =
    0 11110 00100 00010 00011 00110 which represents the set $\{b, c, d, e, i, o, t, u, x, y\}$
    **d)** 1 11110 00000 00000 00000 00000 $\vee$ 0 11100 10000 00001 00010 10000 $\vee$
    0 01010 00100 00010 00001 00111 $\vee$ 0 00110 01100 00110 00011 00110 =
    1 11110 11100 00111 00011 10111, which represents the set
    $\{a, b, c, d, e, g, h, i, n, o, p, t, u, v, x, y, z\}$

**39.** We simply add the set itself to the list of its elements.

    **a)** $\{1,2,3,\{1,2,3\}\}$    **b)** $\{\emptyset\}$    **c)** $\{\emptyset,\{\emptyset\}\}$    **d)** $\{\emptyset,\{\emptyset\},\{\emptyset,\{\emptyset\}\}\}$

**41. a)** The multiplicity of $a$ in the union is the maximum of 3 and 2, the multiplicities of $a$ in $A$ and $B$. Since the maximum is 3, we find that $a$ occurs with multiplicity 3 in the union. Working similarly with $b$, $c$ (which appears with multiplicity 0 in $B$), and $d$ (which appears with multiplicity 0 in $A$), we find that $A \cup B = \{3 \cdot a, 3 \cdot b, 1 \cdot c, 4 \cdot d\}$.

    **b)** This is similar to part **(a)**, with "maximum" replaced by "minimum." Thus $A \cap B = \{2 \cdot a, 2 \cdot b\}$. (In particular, $c$ and $d$ appear with multiplicity 0—i.e., do not appear—in the intersection.)

    **c)** In this case we subtract multiplicities, but never go below 0. Thus the answer is $\{1 \cdot a, 1 \cdot c\}$.

    **d)** Similar to part **(c)** (subtraction in the opposite order); the answer is $\{1 \cdot b, 4 \cdot d\}$.

    **e)** We add multiplicities here, to get $\{5 \cdot a, 5 \cdot b, 1 \cdot c, 4 \cdot d\}$.

**43.** Assume that the universal set contains just Alan, Brian, Fred, Oscar, and Ralph. We subtract the degrees of membership from 1 to obtain the complement. Thus $\overline{F}$ is $\{0.4 \text{ Alan}, 0.1 \text{ Brian}, 0.6 \text{ Fred}, 0.9 \text{ Oscar}, 0.5 \text{ Ralph}\}$, and $\overline{R}$ is $\{0.6 \text{ Alan}, 0.2 \text{ Brian}, 0.8 \text{ Fred}, 0.1 \text{ Oscar}, 0.3 \text{ Ralph}\}$.

**45.** Taking the minimums, we obtain $\{0.4 \text{ Alan}, 0.8 \text{ Brian}, 0.2 \text{ Fred}, 0.1 \text{ Oscar}, 0.5 \text{ Ralph}\}$ for $F \cap R$.

$\Rightarrow$ **SECTION 1.6**  **Functions**

*The importance of understanding what a function is cannot be overemphasized—functions permeate all of mathematics and computer science. This exercise set enables you to make sure you understand functions and their properties. Exercise 11 is a particularly good benchmark to test your full comprehension of the abstractions involved. The definitions play a crucial role in doing proofs about functions. To prove that a function $f : A \to B$ is one-to-one, you need to show that $x_1 \neq x_2 \to f(x_1) \neq f(x_2)$ for all $x_1, x_2 \in A$. To prove that such a function is onto, you need to show that $\forall y \in B \exists x \in A \, f(x) = y$.*

**1. a)** The expression $1/x$ is meaningless for $x = 0$, which is one of the elements in the domain; thus the "rule" is no rule at all. In other words, $f(0)$ is not defined.

    **b)** Things like $\sqrt{-3}$ are undefined (or, at best, are complex numbers).

    **c)** The "rule" for $f$ is ambiguous. We must have $f(x)$ defined uniquely, but here there are two values associated with every $x$, the positive square root and the negative square root of $x^2 + 1$.

**3.** The floor function rounds down and the ceiling function rounds up.

    **a)** 1    **b)** 0    **c)** 0    **d)** −1    **e)** 3    **f)** −1

**5.** We need to determine whether the range is all of $\{a, b, c, d\}$. It is for the function in part **(a)**, but not for the other two functions.

**7. a)** This function is onto, since every integer is 1 less than some integer. In particular, $f(x+1) = x$.

    **b)** This function is not onto. Since $n^2 + 1$ is always positive, the range cannot include any negative integers.

    **c)** This function is not onto, since the integer 2, for example, is not in the range. In other words, 2 is not the cube of any integer.

    **d)** This function is onto. If we want to obtain the value $x$, then we simply need to start with $2x$, since $f(2x) = \lceil 2x/2 \rceil = \lceil x \rceil = x$.

9. **a)** One way to determine whether a function is a bijection is to try to construct its inverse. This function is a bijection, since its inverse (obtained by solving $y = 2x + 1$ for $x$) is the function $g(y) = (y - 1)/2$. Alternately, we can argue directly. To show that the function is one-to-one, note that if $2x + 1 = 2x' + 1$, then $x = x'$. To show that the function is onto, note that $2((y-1)/2) + 1 = y$, so every number is in the range.

**b)** This function is not a bijection, since its range is the set of real numbers greater than or equal to 1 (which is sometimes written $[1, \infty)$), not all of **R**. (It is not injective either.)

**c)** This function is a bijection, since it has an inverse function, namely the function $f(y) = y^{1/3}$ (obtained by solving $y = x^3$ for $x$).

**d)** This function is not a bijection. It is easy to see that it is not injective, since $x$ and $-x$ have the same image, for all real numbers $x$. A little work shows that the range is only $\{ y \mid 0.5 \le y < 1 \} = [0.5, 1)$.

11. In both cases, we can argue directly from the definitions.

**a)** Assume that both $f$ and $g$ are one-to-one. We need to show that $f \circ g$ is one-to-one. This means that we need to show that if $x$ and $y$ are two distinct elements of $A$, then $f(g(x)) \ne f(g(y))$. First, since $g$ is one-to-one, the definition tells us that $g(x) \ne g(y)$. Second, since now $g(x)$ and $g(y)$ are distinct elements of $B$, and since $f$ is one-to-one, we conclude that $f(g(x)) \ne f(g(y))$, as desired.

**b)** Assume that both $f$ and $g$ are onto. We need to show that $f \circ g$ is onto. This means that we need to show that if $z$ is any element of $C$, then there is some element $x \in A$ such that $f(g(x)) = z$. First, since $f$ is onto, we can conclude that there is an element $y \in B$ such that $f(y) = z$. Second, since $g$ is onto and $y \in B$, we can conclude that there is an element $x \in A$ such that $g(x) = y$. Putting these together, we have $z = f(y) = f(g(x))$, as desired.

13. We just perform the indicated operations on the defining expressions. Thus $f + g$ is the function whose value at $x$ is $(x^2 + 1) + (x + 2)$, or, more simply, $(f + g)(x) = x^2 + x + 3$. Similarly $fg$ is the function whose value at $x$ is $(x^2 + 1)(x + 2)$; in other words, $(fg)(x) = x^3 + 2x^2 + x + 2$.

15. We simply solve the equation $y = ax + b$ for $x$. This gives $x = (y - b)/a$, which is well-defined since $a \ne 0$. Thus the inverse is $f^{-1}(y) = (y - b)/a$. To check that our work is correct, we must show that $f \circ f^{-1}(y) = y$ for all $y \in$ **R** and that $f^{-1} \circ f(x) = x$ for all $x \in$ **R**. Both of these are straightforward algebraic manipulations. For the first, we have $f \circ f^{-1}(y) = f(f^{-1}(y)) = f((y - b)/a) = a((y - b)/a) + b = y$. The second is similar.

17. Let us arrange for $S$ and $T$ to be nonempty sets that have empty intersection. Then the left-hand side will be $f(\emptyset)$, which is the empty set. If we can make the right-hand side nonempty, then we will be done. We can make the right-hand side nonempty by making the codomain consist of just one element, so that $f(S)$ and $f(T)$ will both be the set consisting of that one element. The simplest example is as follows. Let $A = \{1, 2\}$ and $B = \{3\}$. Let $f$ be the unique function from $A$ to $B$ (namely $f(1) = f(2) = 3$). Let $S = \{1\}$ and $T = \{2\}$. Then $f(S \cap T) = f(\emptyset) = \emptyset$, which is a proper subset of $f(S) \cap f(T) = \{3\} \cap \{3\} = \{3\}$.

19. **a)** We want to find the set of all numbers whose floor is 0. Since all numbers from 0 to 1 (including 0 but not 1) round down to 0, we conclude that $g^{-1}(\{0\}) = \{ x \mid 0 \le x < 1 \} = [0, 1)$.

**b)** This is similar to part (a). All numbers from $-1$ to 2 (including $-1$ but not 2) round down to $-1$, 0, or 1; we conclude that $g^{-1}(\{-1, 0, 1\}) = \{ x \mid -1 \le x < 2 \} = [-1, 2)$.

**c)** Since $g(x)$ is always an integer, there are no values of $x$ such that $g(x)$ is strictly between 0 and 1. Thus the inverse image in this case is the empty set.

21. There are two things to prove in order to show that these two sets are equal: that the left-hand side of the equation is a subset of the right-hand side, and that the right-hand side is a subset of the left-hand side. First let $x \in f^{-1}(\overline{S})$. This means that $f(x) \in \overline{S}$, or equivalently that $f(x) \notin S$. Therefore by definition of inverse image, $x \notin f^{-1}(S)$, so $x \in \overline{f^{-1}(S)}$. For the other direction, assume that $x \in \overline{f^{-1}(S)}$. Then $x \notin f^{-1}(S)$. By definition this means that $f(x) \notin S$, which means that $f(x) \in \overline{S}$. Therefore by definition, $x \in f^{-1}(\overline{S})$.

23. A straightforward way to do this problem is to consider the two cases determined by where in the interval between two consecutive integers the real number $x$ lies. Certainly any real number $x$ lies in the interval $[n, n+1)$ for some integer $n$; indeed, $n = \lfloor x \rfloor$. (Recall that $[s, t)$ is the notation for the set of real numbers greater than or equal to $s$ and less than $t$.) If $x \in [n, n+\frac{1}{2})$, then $2x$ lies in the interval $[2n, 2n+1)$, so $\lfloor 2x \rfloor = 2n$. Moreover in this case $x + \frac{1}{2}$ is still less than $n+1$, so $\lfloor x \rfloor + \lfloor x + \frac{1}{2} \rfloor = n + n = 2n$ as well. For the other case, we assume that $x \in [n+\frac{1}{2}, n+1)$. This time $2x \in [2n+1, 2n+2)$, so $\lfloor 2x \rfloor = 2n+1$. Moreover in this case $x + \frac{1}{2}$ is in $[n+1, n+\frac{3}{2})$, so $\lfloor x \rfloor + \lfloor x + \frac{1}{2} \rfloor = n + (n+1) = 2n+1$ as well.

25. The graph will look exactly like the graph of the function $f(x) = \lfloor x \rfloor$, shown in Figure 10a, except that the picture will be compressed by a factor of 2 in the horizontal direction, since $x$ has been replaced by $2x$.

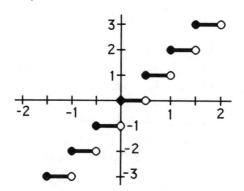

27. We simply need to solve the equation $y = x^3 + 1$ for $x$. This is easily done by algebra: $x = (y-1)^{1/3}$. Therefore the inverse function is given by the rule $f^{-1}(y) = (y-1)^{1/3}$ (or, equivalently, by the rule $f^{-1}(x) = (x-1)^{1/3}$, since the variable in the definition is just a dummy variable).

29. We can prove all of these identities by showing that the left-hand side is equal to the right-hand side for all possible values of $x$. In each instance (except part **(c)**, in which there are only two cases), there are four cases to consider, depending on whether $x$ is in $A$ and/or $B$.
   **a)** If $x$ is in both $A$ and $B$, then $f_{A \cap B}(x) = 1$; and the right-hand side is $1 \cdot 1 = 1$ as well. Otherwise $x \notin A \cap B$, so the left-hand side is 0, and the right-hand side is either $0 \cdot 1$ or $1 \cdot 0$ or $0 \cdot 0$, all of which are also 0.
   **b)** If $x$ is in both $A$ and $B$, then $f_{A \cup B}(x) = 1$; and the right-hand side is $1 + 1 - 1 \cdot 1 = 1$ as well. If $x$ is in $A$ but not $B$, then $x \in A \cup B$, so the left-hand side is still 1, and the right-hand side is

$1 + 0 - 1 \cdot 0 = 1$, as desired. The case in which $x$ is in $B$ but not $A$ is similar. Finally, if $x$ is in neither $A$ nor $B$, then the left-hand side is $0$, and the right-hand side is $0 + 0 - 0 \cdot 0 = 0$ as well.

c) If $x \in A$, then $x \notin \overline{A}$, so $f_{\overline{A}}(x) = 0$. The right-hand side equals $1 - 1 = 0$ in this case, as well. On the other hand, if $x \notin A$, then $x \in \overline{A}$, so the left-hand side is $1$, and the right-hand side is $1 - 0 = 1$ as well.

d) If $x$ is in both $A$ and $B$, then $x \notin A \oplus B$, so $f_{A \oplus B}(x) = 0$. The right-hand side is $1 + 1 - 2 \cdot 1 \cdot 1 = 0$ as well. Next, if $x \in A$ but $x \notin B$, then $x \in A \oplus B$, so the left-hand side is $1$. The right-hand side is $1 + 0 - 2 \cdot 1 \cdot 0 = 1$ as well. The case $x \in B \land x \notin A$ is similar. Finally, if $x$ is in neither $A$ nor $B$, then $x \notin A \oplus B$, so the left-hand side is $0$; and the right-hand side is also $0 + 0 - 2 \cdot 0 \cdot 0 = 0$.

⇒ **SECTION 1.7    Sequences and Summations**

*The first half of this exercise set contains routine practice with the concept of and notation for sequences. It also introduces the **product notation**, corresponding to the summation notation discussed in the section, as well as the **factorial function**, which occurs repeatedly in subsequent chapters. The last part of the exercise set has some fairly challenging exercises involving infinite sets. Do not be surprised if you find this very strange and hard to comprehend at first going; mathematicians did not understand it at all until the late nineteenth century, three hundred years after calculus was well understood. To show that an infinite set is countable, you need to find a one-to-one correspondence between the set and the set of natural numbers. One way to do this directly is to provide a listing of the elements of the set. (There is no listing, for instance, of the set of real numbers.) Various indirect means are also available, such as showing that the set is a subset of a countable set, or showing that it is the union of a countable collection of countable sets.*

1. **a)** $a_0 = 2 \cdot (-3)^0 + 5^0 = 2 \cdot 1 + 1 = 3$

   **b)** $a_1 = 2 \cdot (-3)^1 + 5^1 = 2 \cdot (-3) + 5 = -1$

   **c)** $a_4 = 2 \cdot (-3)^4 + 5^4 = 2 \cdot 81 + 625 = 787$

   **d)** $a_5 = 2 \cdot (-3)^5 + 5^5 = 2 \cdot (-243) + 3125 = 2639$

3. **a)** $2 + 3 + 4 + 5 + 6 = 20$

   **b)** $1 - 2 + 4 - 8 + 16 = 11$

   **c)** $3 + 3 + \cdots + 3 = 10 \cdot 3 = 30$

   **d)** This series "telescopes": each term cancels part of the term before it. The sum is $(2 - 1) + (4 - 2) + (8 - 4) + \cdots + (512 - 256) = -1 + 512 = 511$.

5. **a)** $0$, since anything times $0$ is $0$.

   **b)** $5 \cdot 6 \cdot 7 \cdot 8 = 1680$

   **c)** Each factor is either $1$ or $-1$, so the product is either $1$ or $-1$. To see which it is, we need to determine how many of the factors are $-1$. Clearly there are $50$ such factors, namely when $i = 1$, $3$, $5$, ..., $99$. Since $(-1)^{50} = 1$, the product is $1$.

   **d)** $2 \cdot 2 \cdots 2 = 2^{10} = 1024$

7. $0! + 1! + 2! + 3! + 4! = 1 + 1 + 1 \cdot 2 + 1 \cdot 2 \cdot 3 + 1 \cdot 2 \cdot 3 \cdot 4 = 1 + 1 + 2 + 6 + 24 = 34$

9.  **a)** The negative integers are countable. Each negative integer can be paired with its absolute value to give the desired one-to-one correspondence: $1 \leftrightarrow -1$, $2 \leftrightarrow -2$, $3 \leftrightarrow -3$, etc.

    **b)** The even integers are countable. We can list the set of even integers in the order $0, 2, -2, 4, -4, 6, -6, \ldots$, and pair them with the natural numbers listed in their natural order. Thus $1 \leftrightarrow 0$, $2 \leftrightarrow 2$, $3 \leftrightarrow -2$, $4 \leftrightarrow 4$, etc. There is no need to give a formula for this correspondence—the discussion given is quite sufficient; but it is not hard to see that we are pairing the natural number $n$ with the even integer $f(n)$, where $f(n) = n$ if $n$ is even and $f(n) = 1 - n$ if $n$ is odd.

    **c)** The proof that the set of real numbers between 0 and 1 is not countable (Example 10) can easily be modified to show that the set of real numbers between 0 and 1/2 is not countable. We need to let the digit $d_i$ be something like 2 if $d_{ii} \neq 2$ and 3 otherwise. The number thus constructed will be a real number between 0 and 1/2 that is not in the list.

    **d)** This set is countable, exactly as in part **(b)**; the only difference is that there we are looking at the multiples of 2 and here we are looking at the multiples of 7. The correspondence is given by pairing the natural number $n$ with $7n/2$ if $n$ is even and $-7(n-1)/2$ if $n$ is odd.

11. This is just the contrapositive of Exercise 10 and so follows directly from it. In more detail, suppose that $B$ were countable, say with elements $b_1, b_2, \ldots$. Then since $A \subseteq B$, we can list the elements of $A$ using the order in which they appear in this listing of $B$. Therefore $A$ is countable, contradicting the hypothesis. Thus $B$ is not countable.

13. Since empty sets do not contribute any elements to unions, we can assume that none of the sets in our given countable collection of countable sets is the empty set. If there are no sets in the collection, then the union is empty and therefore countable. Otherwise let the countable sets be $A_1$, $A_2$, $\ldots$. (If there are only a finite number $k$ of them, then we can still assume that they form an infinite sequence by taking $A_{k+1} = A_{k+2} = \cdots = A_1$.) Since each set $A_i$ is countable and nonempty, we can list its elements in a sequence as $a_{i1}$, $a_{i2}$, $\ldots$; again, if the set is finite we can list its elements and then list $a_{i1}$ repeatedly to assure an infinite sequence. Now we just need a systematic way to put all the elements $a_{ij}$ into a sequence. We do this by listing first all the elements in which $i + j = 2$ (there is only one such pair, $(1,1)$), then all the elements in which $i + j = 3$ (there are only two such pairs, $(1,2)$ and $(2,1)$), and so on; except that we do not list any element which we have already listed. The result of this process will be either an infinite sequence or a finite sequence containing all the elements of the union of the sets $A_i$. Thus that union is countable.

15. There are only a finite number of bit strings of each finite length, so we can list all the bit strings by listing first those of length 0, then those of length 1, etc. The listing might be $\lambda, 0, 1, 00, 01, 10, 11,$ $000, 001, \ldots$. (Recall that $\lambda$ denotes the empty string.) Actually this is a special case of Exercise 13: the set of all bit strings is the union of a countable number of countable (actually finite) sets, namely the sets of bit strings of length $n$ for $n = 0, 1, 2, \ldots$.

⇒  **SECTION 1.8    The Growth of Functions**

*The big-O notation is used extensively in computer science and other areas. Think of it as a crude ruler for measuring functions in terms of how fast they grow. The idea is to treat all functions that are more or less the same as one function—one mark on this ruler. Thus, for example, all linear functions are simply thought of as $O(n)$. Although technically the big-O notation gives an upper bound on the growth of a function, in practice we choose the smallest big-O estimate that applies. (This can be made more rigorous with the **theta notation**, discussed in Exercise 10 and Exercise 11.) In practice, one finds best big-O estimates by discarding lower order terms and multiplicative constants. A related concept, used in combinatorics and applied mathematics, is the **little-o notation**, dealt with in Exercise 17 through Exercise 23.*

1. **a)** Yes, since $|10| \leq |x|$ for all $x > 10$.

   **b)** Yes, since $|3x + 7| \leq |4x| = 4|x|$ for all $x > 7$.

   **c)** No. There is no *constant* $C$ such that $|x^2 + x + 1| \leq C|x|$ for all sufficiently large $x$. To see this, suppose this inequality held for all sufficiently large positive values of $x$. Then we would have $x^2 \leq Cx$, which would imply that $x \leq C$ for *all* sufficiently large $x$, an obvious impossibility.

   **d)** Yes. This follows from the fact that $\log x < x$ for all $x > 1$ (which in turn follows from the fact that $x < 2^x$, which can be formally proved by mathematical induction—see Section 3.2). Therefore $|5 \log x| \leq 5|x|$ for all $x > 1$.

   **e)** Yes. This follows from the fact that $\lfloor x \rfloor \leq x$. Thus $|\lfloor x \rfloor| \leq |x|$ for all $x > 0$.

   **f)** Yes. This follows from the fact that $\lceil x/2 \rceil \leq x/2 + 1$. Thus $|\lceil x/2 \rceil| \leq |x/2 + 1| \leq |x|$ for all $x > 2$.

3. For the first part we have $3x^4 + 1 \leq 4x^4 = 8|x^4/2|$ for all $x > 1$. For the second part we have $x^4/2 \leq 3x^4 \leq 1 \cdot |3x^4 + 1|$ for all $x$.

5. A function $f$ is $O(1)$ if $|f(x)| \leq C$ for all sufficiently large $x$. In other words, $f$ is $O(1)$ if its absolute value is **bounded** for all $x > k$ (where $k$ is some constant).

7. Let $C_1$, $C_2$, $k_1$, and $k_2$ be numbers such that $|f(x)| \leq C_1|g(x)|$ for all $x > k_1$ and $|g(x)| \leq C_2|h(x)|$ for all $x > k_2$. Let $C = C_1 C_2$ and let $k$ be the larger of $k_1$ and $k_2$. Then for all $x > k$ we have $|f(x)| \leq C_1|g(x)| \leq C_1 C_2|h(x)| = C|h(x)|$, which is precisely what we needed to show.

9. **a)** The significant terms here are the $n^2$ being multiplied by the $n$; thus this function is $O(n^3)$.

   **b)** Since $\log n$ is smaller than $n$, the significant term in the first factor is $n^2$. Therefore the entire function is $O(n^5)$.

   **c)** For the first factor we note that $2^n < n!$ for $n \geq 4$, so the significant term is $n!$. For the second factor, the significant term is $n^3$. Therefore this function is $O(n^3 n!)$.

11. If $f(x) = \Theta(g(x))$, then $|f(x)| \leq C_2|g(x)|$ and $|g(x)| \leq C_1^{-1}|f(x)|$ for all $x > k$. Thus $f(x) = O(g(x))$ and $g(x) = O(f(x))$. Conversely, suppose that $f(x) = O(g(x))$ and $g(x) = O(f(x))$. Then (with appropriate choice of variable names) we may assume that $|f(x)| \leq C_2|g(x)|$ and $|g(x)| \leq C|f(x)|$ for all $x > k$. (The $k$ here will be the larger of the two $k$'s involved in the hypotheses.) If $C > 0$ then we can take $C_1 = C^{-1}$ to obtain the desired inequalities in $f(x) = \Theta(g(x))$. If $C = 0$, then $g(x) = 0$ for all $x > k$, and hence by the first inequality $f(x) = 0$ for all $x > k$; thus we have $f(x) = g(x)$ for all $x > k$, and we can take $C_1 = C_2 = 1$.

**13.** We are given that $|f(x)| \le C|g(x)|$ for all $x > b$ (we cannot use the variable name $k$ here since we need it later). Hence $|f^k(x)| = |f(x)|^k \le C^k|g^k(x)|$ for all $x > b$, so $f^k(x) = O(g^k(x))$ (take the constants in the definition to be $C^k$ and $b$).

**15.** Since the functions are given to be increasing and unbounded, we may assume that they both take on values greater than 1 for all sufficiently large $x$. The hypothesis can then be written as $f(x) \le Cg(x)$ for all $x > k$. If we take the logarithm of both sides then we obtain $\log f(x) \le \log C + \log g(x)$. Finally, this latter expression is less than $2\log g(x)$ for large enough $x$, since $\log g(x)$ is growing without bound.

**17.** All that we need to do is determine if the ratio of the two functions approaches 0 as $x$ approaches infinity.

**a)** $\displaystyle \lim_{x \to \infty} \frac{x^2}{x^3} = \lim_{x \to \infty} \frac{1}{x} = 0$

**b)** $\displaystyle \lim_{x \to \infty} \frac{x \log x}{x^2} = \lim_{x \to \infty} \frac{\log x}{x} = \lim_{x \to \infty} \frac{1}{x \ln 2} = 0$ (using L'Hôpital's rule for the second equality)

**c)** $\displaystyle \lim_{x \to \infty} \frac{x^2}{2^x} = \lim_{x \to \infty} \frac{2x}{2^x \ln 2} = \lim_{x \to \infty} \frac{2}{2^x (\ln 2)^2} = 0$ (with two applications of L'Hôpital's rule)

**d)** $\displaystyle \lim_{x \to \infty} \frac{x^2 + x + 1}{x^2} = \lim_{x \to \infty} \left(1 + \frac{1}{x} + \frac{1}{x^2}\right) = 1 \ne 0$

**19.** No. As one example, take $f(x) = x^{-2}$ and $g(x) = x^{-1}$. Then $f(x) = o(g(x))$, since $\displaystyle \lim_{x \to \infty} \frac{x^{-2}}{x^{-1}} = \lim_{x \to \infty} \frac{1}{x} = 0$. On the other hand $\displaystyle \lim_{x \to \infty} (2^{x^{-2}}/2^{x^{-1}}) = \lim_{x \to \infty} 2^{x^{-2} - x^{-1}} = 2^0 = 1 \ne 0$.

**21. a)** Since the limit of $f(x)/g(x)$ is 0 (as $x \to \infty$), so too is the limit of $|f(x)|/|g(x)|$. In particular, for $x$ large enough, this ratio is certainly less than 1. In other words $|f(x)| \le |g(x)|$ for sufficiently large $x$, which meets the definition of $f(x) = O(g(x))$.

**b)** We can simply let $f(x) = g(x)$ be any function with positive values. Then the limit of their ratio is 1, not 0, so $f(x) \ne o(g(x))$, but certainly $f(x) = O(g(x))$.

**23.** This follows immediately from Exercise 21a (whereby we can conclude that $f_2(x) = O(g(x))$ and Corollary 1 to Theorem 1.

**25.** What we want to show is equivalent to the statement that $\log(n^n)$ is at most a constant times $\log(n!)$, which in turn is equivalent to the statement that $n^n$ is at most a constant power of $n!$ (because of the fact that $C \log A = \log(A^C)$—see Appendix 1). We will show that in fact $n^n \le (n!)^2$ for all $n > 1$. To do this, let us write $(n!)^2$ as $(n \cdot 1) \cdot ((n-1) \cdot 2) \cdot ((n-2) \cdot 3) \cdots (2 \cdot (n-1)) \cdot (1 \cdot n)$. Now clearly each product pair $(i+1) \cdot (n-i)$ is at least as big as $n$ (indeed, the ones near the middle are significantly bigger than $n$). Therefore the entire product is at least as big as $n^n$, as desired.

⇒ **SUPPLEMENTARY EXERCISES FOR CHAPTER 1**

1. **a)** $q \rightarrow p$ (note that "only if" does not mean "if")

   **b)** $q \wedge p$

   **c)** $\neg q \vee \neg p$ (assuming inclusive use of the English word "or" is intended by the speaker)

   **d)** $q \leftrightarrow p$ (this is another way to say "if and only if" in English words

3. We could use truth tables, but we can also argue as follows.

   **a)** Since $q$ is false but the implication $p \rightarrow q$ is true, we must conclude that $p$ is also false.

   **b)** The disjunction says that either $p$ or $q$ is true. Since $p$ is given to be false, it follows that $q$ must be true.

5. The straightforward approach is to use disjunctive normal form. There are four cases in which exactly three of the variables are true. The desired proposition is $(p \wedge q \wedge r \wedge \neg s) \vee (p \wedge q \wedge \neg r \wedge s) \vee (p \wedge \neg q \wedge r \wedge s) \vee (\neg p \wedge q \wedge r \wedge s)$.

7. **a)** F, since 4 does not divide 5

   **b)** T, since 2 divides 4

   **c)** F, by the counterexample in part **(a)**

   **d)** T, since 1 divides every positive integer

   **e)** F, since no number is a multiple of all positive integers (No matter what positive integer $n$ one chooses, if we take $m = n + 1$, then $P(m, n)$ is false, since $n + 1$ does not divide $n$.)

   **f)** T, since 1 divides every positive integer

9. Suppose that $\exists x(P(x) \rightarrow Q(x))$ is true. Then for some $x$, either $Q(x)$ is true or $P(x)$ is false. If $Q(x)$ is true for some $x$, then the implication $\forall x P(x) \rightarrow \exists x Q(x)$ is true (having true conclusion). If $P(x)$ is false for some $x$, then again the implication $\forall x P(x) \rightarrow \exists x Q(x)$ is true (having false hypothesis). Conversely, suppose that $\exists x(P(x) \rightarrow Q(x))$ is false. That means that for every $x$, the implication $P(x) \rightarrow Q(x)$ is false, or, in other words, $P(x)$ is true and $Q(x)$ is false. The latter statement implies that $\exists x Q(x)$ is false. Thus $\forall x P(x) \rightarrow \exists x Q(x)$ has a true hypothesis and a false conclusion and is therefore false.

11. **a)** $\overline{A}$ = the set of words that are not in $A$

    **b)** $A \cap B$ = the set of words that are in both $A$ and $B$

    **c)** $A - B$ = the set of words that are in $A$ but not $B$

    **d)** $\overline{A} \cap \overline{B} = \overline{(A \cup B)}$ = the set of words that are in neither $A$ nor $B$

    **e)** $A \oplus B$ = the set of words that are in $A$ or $B$ but not both (can also be written as $(A - B) \cup (B - A)$ or as $(A \cup B) - (A \cap B)$)

13. **a)** We must show that no element is in $A \cap \overline{A}$. This is clear, since $A \cap \overline{A}$ consists of elements that are in $A$ and not in $A$ at the same time, obviously an impossibility.

    **b)** We must show that every element (of the universal set) is in $A \cup \overline{A}$. This is clear, since every element is either in $A$ (and hence in that union) or else not in $A$ (and hence in that union).

15. We will show that each side is a subset of the other. First suppose $x \in A - (A - B)$. Then $x \in A$ and $x \notin A - B$. Now the only way for $x$ not to be in $A - B$, given that it is in $A$, is for it to be in $B$. Thus we have that $x$ is in both $A$ and $B$, so $x \in A \cap B$. For the other direction, let $x \in A \cap B$. Then $x \in A$ and $x \in B$. It follows that $x \notin A - B$, and so $x$ is in $A - (A - B)$.

**17.** We need only provide a counterexample to show that $(A-B)-C$ is not necessarily equal to $A-(B-C)$. Let $A = C = \{1\}$, and let $B = \emptyset$. Then $(A - B) - C = (\{1\} - \emptyset) - \{1\} = \{1\} - \{1\} = \emptyset$, whereas $A - (B - C) = \{1\} - (\emptyset - \{1\}) = \{1\} - \emptyset = \{1\}$.

**19. a)** Since $\emptyset \subseteq A \cap B \subseteq A \subseteq A \cup B \subseteq U$, we have the order $|\emptyset| \leq |A \cap B| \leq |A| \leq |A \cup B| \leq |U|$.

**b)** Note that $A - B \subseteq A \oplus B \subseteq A \cup B$. Also recall that $|A \cup B| = |A| + |B| - |A \cap B|$, so that $|A \cup B|$ is always less than or equal to $|A| + |B|$. Putting this all together, we have $|\emptyset| \leq |A - B| \leq |A \oplus B| \leq |A \cup B| \leq |A| + |B|$.

**21. a)** Yes, $f$ is one-to-one, since each element of the domain $\{1, 2, 3, 4\}$ is sent by $f$ to a different element of the codomain. No, $g$ is not one-to-one, since $g$ sends the two different elements $a$ and $d$ of the domain to the same element, 2.

**b)** Yes, $f$ is onto, since every element in the codomain $\{a, b, c, d\}$ is the image under $f$ of some element in the domain $\{1, 2, 3, 4\}$. In other words, the range of $f$ is the entire codomain. No, $g$ is not onto, since the element 4 in the codomain is not in the range of $g$ (is not the image under $g$ of any element of the domain $\{a, b, c, d\}$).

**c)** Certainly $f$ has an inverse, since it is one-to-one and onto. Its inverse is the function from $\{a, b, c, d\}$ which sends $a$ to 3, sends $b$ to 4, sends $c$ to 2, and sends $d$ to 1. (Each element in $\{a, b, c, d\}$ gets sent by $f^{-1}$ to the element in $\{1, 2, 3, 4\}$ which gets sent to it by $f$.) Since $g$ is not one-to-one and onto, it has no inverse.

**23.** We need to look at an example in which $f$ is not one-to-one. Suppose we let $A$ be a set with two elements, say 1 and 2, and let $B$ be a set with just one element, say 3. Of course $f$ will be the unique function from $A$ to $B$. If we let $S = \{1\}$ and $T = \{2\}$, then $f(S \cap T) = f(\emptyset) = \emptyset$, but $f(S) \cap f(T) = \{3\} \cap \{3\} = \{3\}$.

**25.** We need to perform the inner operation first, for each value of the outer variable.

**a)** If we just calculate from the definition, then we obtain $(0 \cdot 0 + 0 \cdot 1 + 0 \cdot 2 + 0 \cdot 3 + 0 \cdot 4) + (1 \cdot 0 + 1 \cdot 1 + 1 \cdot 2 + 1 \cdot 3 + 1 \cdot 4) + (2 \cdot 0 + 2 \cdot 1 + 2 \cdot 2 + 2 \cdot 3 + 2 \cdot 4) + (3 \cdot 0 + 3 \cdot 1 + 3 \cdot 2 + 3 \cdot 3 + 3 \cdot 4) = (0+0+0+0+0) + (0+1+2+3+4) + (0+2+4+6+8) + (0+3+6+9+12) = 0 + 10 + 20 + 30 = 60$. A somewhat more sophisticated approach would be to note that $\sum_{j=0}^{4} ij = i \cdot \sum_{j=0}^{4} j = i \cdot (0 + 1 + 2 + 3 + 4) = 10i$, and then $\sum_{i=0}^{3} 10i = 10 \cdot \sum_{i=0}^{3} i = 10 \cdot (0 + 1 + 2 + 3) = 10 \cdot 6 = 60$.

**b)** The inner summation is $j + j + j + j = 4j$ (since there are four values through which $i$ passes). Thus we are looking at $\prod_{j=1}^{4} 4j = (4 \cdot 1) \cdot (4 \cdot 2) \cdot (4 \cdot 3) \cdot (4 \cdot 4) = 4 \cdot 8 \cdot 12 \cdot 16 = 6144$.

**c)** The inner sum is $i + 1$, since there are $i + 1$ terms, each of them equal to 1. Thus the sum is $2 + 3 + 4 + 5 + 6 = 20$.

**d)** This is a product containing the factor 0 (since $j$ starts at 0). Thus the product must be 0, regardless of what the other terms are.

**27.** In the first factor the $x^2$ term dominates the other term, since $(\log x)^3 = O(x)$. Therefore by Theorem 1 in Section 1.8, this term is $O(x^2)$. Similarly, in the second factor, the $2^x$ term dominates. Thus by Theorem 2 of Section 1.8, the product is $O(x^2 2^x)$.

# CHAPTER 2
# The Fundamentals: Algorithms, the Integers, and Matrices

⇒ **SECTION 2.1    Algorithms**

*Many of the exercises here are actually miniature programming assignments. Since this is not a book on programming, we have glossed over some of the finer points. For example, there are (at least) two ways to pass variables to procedures—by value and by reference. In the former case the original values of the arguments are not changed. In the latter case they are. In most cases we will assume that arguments are passed by reference. None of these exercises are tricky; they just give the reader a chance to become familiar with algorithms written in pseudocode.*

1. Initially $max$ is set equal to the first element of the list, namely 1. The **for** loop then begins, with $i$ set equal to 2. Immediately $i$ (namely 2) is compared to $n$, which equals 10 for this sequence (the entire input is known to the computer, including the value of $n$). Since $2 < 10$, the statement in the loop is executed. This is an **if**...**then** statement, so first the comparison in the **if** part is made: $max$ (which equals 1) is compared to $a_i = a_2 = 8$. Since the condition is true, namely $1 < 8$, the **then** part of the statement is executed, so $max$ is assigned the value 8.

   The only statement in the **for** loop has now been executed, so the loop variable $i$ is incremented (from 2 to 3), and we repeat the process. First we check again to verify that $i$ is still less than $n$ (namely $3 < 10$), and then we execute the **if**...**then** statement in the body of the loop. This time, too, the condition is satisfied, since $max = 8$ is less than $a_3 = 12$. Therefore the assignment statement $max := a_i$ is executed, and $max$ receives the value 12.

   Next the loop variable is incremented again, so that now $i = 4$. After a comparison to determine that $4 < 10$, the **if**...**then** statement is executed. This time the condition fails, since $max = 12$ is not less than $a_4 = 9$. Therefore the **then** part of the statement is not executed. Having finished with this pass through the loop, we increment $i$ again, to 5. This pass through the loop, as well as the next pass through, behave exactly as the previous pass, since the condition $max < a_i$ continues to fail. On the sixth pass through the loop, however, with $i = 7$, we find again that $max < a_i$, namely $12 < 14$. Therefore $max$ is assigned the value 14.

   After three more uneventful passes through the loop (with $i = 8$, 9, and 10), we finally increment $i$ to 11. At this point, when the comparison of $i$ with $n$ is made, we find that $i$ is no longer less than or equal to $n$, so no further passes through the loop are made. Instead, control passes beyond the loop. In this case there are no statements beyond the loop, so execution halts. Note that when execution halts, $max$ has the value 14 (which is the correct maximum of the list), and $i$ has the value 11. (Actually in many programming languages, the value of $i$ after the loop has terminated in this way is undefined.)

3. We will call the procedure $sum$. Its input is a list of integers, just as was the case for Algorithm 1. Indeed, we can just mimic the structure of Algorithm 1. We assume that the list is not empty (an assumption made in Algorithm 1 as well).

> **procedure** $sum(a_1, a_2, \ldots, a_n : integers)$
> $sum := a_1$
> **for** $i := 2$ **to** $n$
>         $sum := sum + a_i$
> { $sum$ is the sum of all the elements in the list }

5. We cannot simply write $x := y$ followed by $y := x$, because then the two variables will have the same value, and the original value of $x$ will be lost. Thus there is no way to accomplish this task with just two assignment statements. Three are necessary, and sufficient, as the following code shows. The idea is that we need to save temporarily the original value of $x$.

> $temp := x$
> $x := y$
> $y := temp$

7. We will not give these answers in quite the detail we used in Exercise 1.

   **a)** Note that $n = 8$ and $x = 9$. Initially $i$ is set equal to 1. The **while** loop is executed as long as $i \leq 8$ and the $i^{\text{th}}$ element of the list is not equal to 9. Thus on the first pass we check that $1 \leq 8$ and that $9 \neq 1$ (since $a_1 = 1$), and therefore perform the statement $i := i + 1$. At this point $i = 2$. We check that $2 \leq 8$ and $9 \neq 3$, and therefore again increment $i$, this time to 3. This process continues until $i = 7$. At that point the condition "$i \leq 8$ and $9 \neq a_i$" is false, since $a_7 = 9$. Therefore the body of the loop is not executed (so $i$ is still equal to 7), and control passes beyond the loop.

   The next statement is the **if**...**then** statement. The condition is satisfied, since $7 \leq 8$, so the statement $location := i$ is executed, and $location$ receives the value 7. The **else** clause is not executed. This completes the procedure, so $location$ has the correct value, namely 7, which indicates the location of the element $x$ (namely 9) in the list: 9 is the seventh element.

   **b)** Initially $i$ is set equal to 1 and $j$ is set equal to 8. Since $i < j$ at this point, the steps of the **while** loop are executed. First $m$ is set equal to $\lfloor (1+8)/2 \rfloor = 4$. Then since $x$ (which equals 9) is greater than $a_4$ (which equals 5), the statement $i := m + 1$ is executed, so $i$ now has the value 5. At this point the first iteration through the loop is finished, and the search has been narrowed to the sequence $a_5, \ldots, a_8$.

   In the next pass through the loop (there is another pass since $i < j$ is still true), $m$ becomes $\lfloor (5+8)/2 \rfloor = 6$. Since again $x > a_m$, we reset $i$ to be $m + 1$, which is 7. The loop is now repeated with $i = 7$ and $j = 8$. This time $m$ becomes 7, so the test $x > a_m$ (i.e., $9 > 9$) fails; thus $j := m$ is executed, so now $j = 7$.

   At this point $i \not< j$, so there are no more iterations of the loop. Instead control passes to the statement beyond the loop. Since the condition $x = a_i$ is true, $location$ is set to 7, as it should be, and the algorithm is finished.

9. We need to find where $x$ goes, then slide the rest of the list down to make room for $x$, then put $x$ into the space created. In the procedure that follows, we employ the trick of temporarily tacking $x + 1$ onto the end of the list, so that the **while** loop will always terminate. Also note that the indexing in the **for** loop is slightly tricky since we need to work from the end of the list toward the front.

> **procedure** $insert(x, a_1, a_2, \ldots, a_n : integers)$
> { the list is in order: $a_1 \leq a_2 \leq \cdots \leq a_n$ }
> $a_{n+1} := x + 1$
> $i := 1$

**while** $x > a_i$
    $i := i + 1$ {the loop ends when $i$ is the index for $x$ }
**for** $j := 0$ **to** $n - i$ {shove the rest of the list to the right}
    $a_{n-j+1} := a_{n-j}$
$a_i := x$
{ $x$ has been inserted into the correct spot in the list, now of length $n + 1$ }

11. This algorithm is similar to *max*, except that we need to keep track of the location of the maximum value, as well as the maximum value itself. Note that we need a strict inequality in the test $max < a_i$, since we do not want to change *location* if we find another occurrence of the maximum value. As usual we assume that the list is not empty.

    **procedure** *first largest*$(a_1, a_2, \ldots, a_n : $ integers$)$
    $max := a_1$
    $location := 1$
    **for** $i := 2$ **to** $n$
        **if** $max < a_i$ **then**
        **begin**
            $max := a_i$
            $location := i$
        **end**
    { *location* is the location of the first occurrence of the largest element in the list}

13. We need to handle the six possible orderings in which the three integers might occur. (Actually there are more than six possibilities, because some of the numbers might be equal to others—we get around this problem by using $\leq$ rather than $<$ for our comparisons.) We will use the **if**...**then**...**else if**...**then**...**else if**... construction. A condition such as $a \leq b \leq c$ is really the conjunction of two conditions: $a \leq b$ and $b \leq c$. (Alternately, we could have handled the cases in a nested fashion.) Note that the mean is computed first, independent of the ordering.

    **procedure** *mean median max min*$(a, b, c : $ integers$)$
    $mean := (a + b + c)/3$
    **if** $a \leq b \leq c$ **then**
    **begin**
        $min := a$
        $median := b$
        $max := c$
    **end**
    **else if** $a \leq c \leq b$ **then**
    **begin**
        $min := a$
        $median := c$
        $max := b$
    **end**
    **else if** $b \leq a \leq c$ **then**
    **begin**
        $min := b$
        $median := a$
        $max := c$
    **end**
    **else if** $b \leq c \leq a$ **then**
    **begin**
        $min := b$

$$median := c$$
$$max := a$$
**end**
**else if** $c \le a \le b$ **then**
**begin**
$$min := c$$
$$median := a$$
$$max := b$$
**end**
**else if** $c \le b \le a$ **then**
**begin**
$$min := c$$
$$median := b$$
$$max := a$$
**end**
{the correct values of *mean*, *median*, *max*, and *min* have been assigned}

15. We must assume that the sequence has at least three terms. This is a special case of a sorting algorithm. Our approach is to interchange numbers in the list when they are out of order. It is not hard to see that this needs to be done only three times in order to guarantee that the elements are finally in correct order: test and interchange (if necessary) the first two elements, then test and interchange (if necessary) the second and third elements (insuring that the largest of the three is now third), then test and interchange (if necessary) the first and second elements again (insuring that the smallest is now first).

**procedure** *first three*$(a_1, a_2, \ldots, a_n : \text{integers})$
**if** $a_1 > a_2$ **then** interchange $a_1$ and $a_2$
**if** $a_2 > a_3$ **then** interchange $a_2$ and $a_3$
**if** $a_1 > a_2$ **then** interchange $a_1$ and $a_2$
{the first three elements are now in nondecreasing order}

17. For notation, assume that $f : A \to B$, where $A$ is the set consisting of the distinct elements $a_1$, $a_2$, $\ldots$, $a_n$, and $B$ is the set consisting of the distinct elements $b_1$, $b_2$, $\ldots$, $b_m$. Without loss of generality we will assume that these elements are integers. All $n + m + 1$ of these entities (the elements of $A$, the elements of $B$, and the function $f$) are the input to the algorithm. We set up an array called *hit* (indexed by the integers from 1 to $m$) to keep track of which elements of $B$ are the images of elements of $A$; thus $hit(i)$ equals 0 until we find an $a_j$ such that $f(a_j) = b_i$, at which time we set $hit(i)$ equal to 1. Simultaneously we keep track of how many hits we have made (i.e., how many times we changed some $hit(i)$ from 0 to 1). If at the end we have made $m$ hits, then $f$ is onto; otherwise it is not. Note that we record the output as a logical value assigned to the variable which has the name of the procedure. This is a common practice in some programming languages.

**procedure** *onto*$(f : \text{function}, a_1, a_2, \ldots, a_n, b_1, b_2, \ldots, b_m : \text{integers})$
**for** $i := 1$ **to** $m$
$\quad$ $hit(i) := 0$ {no one has been hit yet}
$count := 0$ {there have been no hits yet}
**for** $j := 1$ **to** $n$
$\quad$ **if** $hit(f(a_j)) = 0$ **then** {a new hit!}
$\quad$ **begin**
$\qquad$ $hit(f(a_j)) := 1$
$\qquad$ $count := count + 1$
$\quad$ **end**

      **if** $count = m$ **then** $onto :=$ **true**
      **else** $onto :=$ **false**
      { $f$ is onto if and only if there have been $m$ hits }

19. This algorithm is straightforward.

      **procedure** *count ones*$(a_1 a_2 \ldots a_n :$ bit string)
      $count := 0$ {no 1's yet}
      **for** $i := 1$ **to** $n$
           **if** $a_i = 1$ **then** $count := count + 1$
      { $count$ contains the number of 1's }

$\Rightarrow$ **SECTION 2.2    Complexity of Algorithms**

*Some of these exercises involve analysis of algorithms, as was done in the examples in this section. These are a matter of carefully counting the operations of interest, usually in the worst case. Some of the others are algebra exercises that display the results of the analysis in real terms—the number of years of computer time, for example, required to solve a large problem.* **Horner's method** *for evaluating a polynomial, given in Exercise 8, is a nice trick to know. It is extremely handy for polynomial evaluation on a pocket calculator (especially if the calculator is so cheap that it does not use the usual precedence rules).*

1. Assuming that the algorithm given to find the smallest element of a list is identical to Algorithm 1 in Section 2.1, except that the inequality is reversed (and the name *max* replaced by the name *min*), the analysis will be identical to the analysis given in Example 1 in the current section. In particular, there will be $2n - 1$ comparisons needed, counting the bookkeeping for the loop.

3. The linear search would find this element after at most 9 comparisons (4 to determine that we have not yet finished with the **while** loop, 4 more to determine if we have located the desired element yet, and 1 to set the value of *location*). Binary search, according to Example 3, will take $2 \log 32 + 2 = 2 \cdot 5 + 2 = 12$ comparisons. Since $9 < 12$, the linear search will be faster, in terms of comparisons.

5. The algorithm simply scans the bits one at a time. Thus clearly $O(n)$ comparisons are required (perhaps one for bookkeeping and one for looking at the $i^{\text{th}}$ bit, for each $i$ from 1 to $n$).

7. **a)** Here we have $n = 2$, $a_0 = 1$, $a_1 = 1$, $a_2 = 3$, and $c = 2$. Initially, then we set *power* equal to 1 and $y$ equal to 1. The first time through the **for** loop (with $i = 1$), *power* becomes 2 and so $y$ becomes $1 + 1 \cdot 2 = 3$. The second and final time through the loop, *power* becomes $2 \cdot 2 = 4$ and $y$ becomes $3 + 3 \cdot 4 = 15$. Thus the value of the polynomial at $x = 2$ is 15.
**b)** Each pass through the loop requires two multiplications and one addition. Therefore there are a total of $2n$ multiplications and $n$ additions.

9. This is an exercise in algebra, numerical analysis (for some of the parts), and using a calculator. Since each bit operation requires $10^{-9}$ seconds, we want to know for what value of $n$ there will be at most $10^9$ bit operations required. Thus we need to set the expression equal to $10^9$, solve for $n$, and round down if necessary.

a) Solving $\log n = 10^9$, we get (recalling that "log" means logarithm base 2) $n = 2^{10^9}$. By taking $\log_{10}$ of both sides, we find that this number is approximately equal to $10^{300,000,000}$.

b) Clearly $n = 10^9$.

c) Solving $n \log n = 10^9$ is not trivial. There is no good formula for solving such **transcendental** equations. An algorithm that works well with a calculator is to rewrite the equation as $n = 10^9 / \log n$, enter a random starting value, say $n = 2$, and repeatedly calculating a new value of $n$. Thus we would obtain, in succession, $n = 10^9 / \log 2 = 10^9$, $n = 10^9 / \log(10^9) \approx 33,447,777.3$, $n = 10^9 / \log(33,447, 777.3) \approx 40,007,350.14$, $n = 10^9 / \log(40,007,350.14) \approx 39,598,061.08$, and so on. After a few more iterations, the numbers stabilize at approximately $39,620,077.73$, so the answer is $39,620,077$.

d) Solving $n^2 = 10^9$ gives $n = 10^{4.5}$ which is $31,622$ when rounded down.

e) Solving $2^n = 10^9$ gives $n = \log(10^9) \approx 29.9$. Rounding down gives the answer, $29$.

f) The quickest way to find the largest value of $n$ such that $n! \le 10^9$ is simply to try a few values of $n$. We find that $12! \approx 4.8 \times 10^8$ while $13! \approx 6.2 \times 10^9$, so the answer is $12$.

11. In each case, we just multiply the number of seconds per operation by the number of operations (namely $2^{50}$). To convert seconds to minutes, we divide by $60$; to convert minutes to hours, we divide by $60$ again. To convert hours to days, we divide by $24$; to convert days to years, we divide by $365\frac{1}{4}$.

a) $2^{50} \times 10^{-6} = 1,125,899,907$ seconds $\approx 36$ years

b) $2^{50} \times 10^{-9} = 1,125,899.907$ seconds $\approx 13$ days

c) $2^{50} \times 10^{-12} = 1,125.899907$ seconds $\approx 19$ minutes

13. If the element is not in the list, then $2n + 2$ comparisons are needed: two for each pass through the loop, one more to get out of the loop, and one more for the statement just after the loop. If the element is in the list, say as the $i^{\text{th}}$ element, then we need to enter the loop $i$ times, each time costing two comparisons, and use one comparison for the final assignment of *location*. Thus $2i + 1$ comparisons are needed. We need to average the numbers $2i + 1$ (for $i$ from 1 to $n$), to find the average number of comparisons needed for a successful search. This is $(3 + 5 + \cdots + (2n + 1))/n = (n + (2 + 4 + \cdots + 2n))/n = (n + 2(1 + 2 + \cdots + n))/n = (n + 2(n(n + 1)/2))/n = n + 2$. Finally, we average the $2n + 2$ comparisons for the unsuccessful search with this average $n + 2$ comparisons for a successful search to obtain a grand average of $(2n + 2 + n + 2)/2 = (3n + 4)/2$ comparisons.

⇒ **SECTION 2.3   The Integers and Division**

*Number theory is playing an increasingly important role in computer science. This section and these exercises just scratch the surface of what is relevant. Many of these exercises are simply a matter of applying definitions. It is sometimes hard for a beginning student to remember that in order to prove something about a concept (such as modular arithmetic), it is usually necessary to invoke the definition. Exercise 26 through Exercise 31 hint at the rich structure that modular arithmetic has (sometimes resembling real number arithmetic more than integer arithmetic). In many contexts in mathematics and computer science, modular arithmetic is more relevant and convenient than ordinary integer arithmetic.*

1. **a)** Yes, since $68 = 17 \cdot 4$    **b)** No, remainder $= 16$    **c)** Yes, since $357 = 17 \cdot 21$
   **d)** No, remainder $= 15$

3. If $a \mid b$, then we know that $b = at$ for some integer $t$. Therefore $bc = a(tc)$, so by definition $a \mid bc$.

5. The given conditions imply that there are integers $s$ and $t$ such that $a = bs$ and $b = at$. Combining these, we obtain $a = ats$; since $a \neq 0$, we conclude that $st = 1$. Now the only way for this to happen is for $s = t = 1$ or $s = t = -1$. Therefore either $a = b$ or $a = -b$.

7. The given condition means that $bc = (ac)t$ for some integer $t$, and it implies that $ac \neq 0$. In particular $c \neq 0$, so we can divide both sides by $c$ to obtain $b = at$. This is the definition of $a \mid b$, as desired.

9. In each case we need to find (the unique integers) $q$ and $r$ such that $a = dq + r$ and $0 \leq r < d$, where $a$ and $d$ are the given integers. In each case $q = \lfloor a/d \rfloor$.
   **a)** $19 = 7 \cdot 2 + 5$, so $q = 2$ and $r = 5$
   **b)** $-111 = 11 \cdot (-11) + 10$, so $q = -11$ and $r = 10$
   **c)** $789 = 23 \cdot 34 + 7$, so $q = 34$ and $r = 7$
   **d)** $1001 = 13 \cdot 77 + 0$, so $q = 77$ and $r = 0$
   **e)** $0 = 19 \cdot 0 + 0$, so $q = 0$ and $r = 0$
   **f)** $3 = 5 \cdot 0 + 3$, so $q = 0$ and $r = 3$
   **g)** $-1 = 3 \cdot (-1) + 2$, so $q = -1$ and $r = 2$
   **h)** $4 = 1 \cdot 4 + 0$, so $q = 4$ and $r = 0$

11. $10! = 2 \cdot 3 \cdot 4 \cdot 5 \cdot 6 \cdot 7 \cdot 8 \cdot 9 \cdot 10 = 2 \cdot 3 \cdot (2 \cdot 2) \cdot 5 \cdot (2 \cdot 3) \cdot 7 \cdot 2^3 \cdot 3^2 \cdot (2 \cdot 5) = 2^8 \cdot 3^4 \cdot 5^2 \cdot 7$

13. We give a proof by contradiction. Suppose that in fact $\log_2 3$ is the rational number $p/q$, where $p$ and $q$ are integers. Since $\log_2 3 > 0$, we can assume that $p$ and $q$ are positive. Translating the equation $\log_2 3 = p/q$ into its exponential equivalent, we obtain $3 = 2^{p/q}$. Raising both sides to the $q^{\text{th}}$ power yields $3^q = 2^p$. Now this is a violation of the Fundamental Theorem of Arithmetic, since it gives two different prime factorizations of the same number. Hence our assumption (that $\log_2 3$ is rational) must be wrong, and we conclude that $\log_2 3$ is irrational.

15. We compute $\phi(n)$ here by enumerating the set of positive integers less than $n$ that are relatively prime to $n$.
   **a)** $\phi(4) = |\{1, 3\}| = 2$
   **b)** $\phi(10) = |\{1, 3, 7, 9\}| = 4$
   **c)** $\phi(13) = |\{1, 2, 3, 4, 5, 6, 7, 8, 9, 10, 11, 12\}| = 12$

17. All the positive integers less than or equal to $p^k$ (and there are clearly $p^k$ of them) are less than $p^k$ and relatively prime to $p^k$ unless they are a multiple of $p$. Since the fraction $1/p$ of them are multiples of $p$, we have $\phi(p^k) = p^k(1 - 1/p) = p^k - p^{k-1}$.

19. The quotient $n/k$ lies between two consecutive integers, say $b - 1$ and $b$, possibly equal to $b$. In symbols, there exists a positive integer $b$ such that $(b-1) < n/k \leq b$. In particular, $\lceil n/k \rceil = b$. Also, since $n/k > (b-1)$, we have $n > k(b-1)$, and so (since everything is an integer) $n - 1 \geq k(b-1)$. This means that $(n-1)/k \geq (b-1)$, so $\lfloor (n-1)/k \rfloor \geq b - 1$. On the other hand, $\lfloor (n-1)/k \rfloor \leq (n-1)/k < (n/k)$, so $\lfloor (n-1)/k \rfloor < b$. Therefore $\lfloor (n-1)/k \rfloor = b - 1$. The desired conclusion follows.

21. For these problems, we need to perform the division (as in Exercise 9) and report the remainder.
    a) $13 = 3 \cdot 4 + 1$, so $13 \bmod 3 = 1$
    b) $-97 = 11 \cdot (-9) + 2$, so $-97 \bmod 11 = 2$
    c) $155 = 19 \cdot 8 + 3$, so $155 \bmod 19 = 3$
    d) $-221 = 23 \cdot (-10) + 9$, so $-221 \bmod 23 = 9$

23. For these problems, we need to divide by 17 and see if the remainder equals 5. Remember that the quotient can be negative, but the remainder $r$ must satisfy $0 \le r < 17$.
    a) $80 = 17 \cdot 4 + 12$, so $80 \not\equiv 5 \pmod{17}$
    b) $103 = 17 \cdot 6 + 1$, so $103 \not\equiv 5 \pmod{17}$
    c) $-29 = 17 \cdot (-2) + 5$, so $80 \equiv 5 \pmod{17}$
    d) $-122 = 17 \cdot (-8) + 14$, so $80 \not\equiv 5 \pmod{17}$

25. The important observation to make here is that the smaller of any two numbers plus the larger of the two numbers is always equal to the sum of the two numbers. Since the exponent of the prime $p$ in $gcd(a, b)$ is the smaller of the exponents of $p$ in $a$ and in $b$, and since the exponent of the prime $p$ in $lcm(a, b)$ is the larger of the exponents of $p$ in $a$ and in $b$, the exponent of $p$ in $gcd(a, b)lcm(a, b)$ is the sum of the smaller and the larger of these two values. Therefore by the observation, it equals the sum of the two values themselves, which is clearly equal to the exponent of $p$ in $ab$. Since this is true for every prime $p$, we conclude that $gcd(a, b)lcm(a, b)$ and $ab$ have the same prime factorizations and are therefore equal.

27. The hypothesis $a \equiv b \pmod{m}$ means that $m \,|\, (a - b)$. Since we are given that $n \,|\, m$, Theorem 1 (part 3) implies that $n \,|\, (a - b)$. Therefore $a \equiv b \pmod{n}$, as desired.

29. To show that this implication does not necessarily hold, we need to find an example in which $ac \equiv bc \pmod{m}$, but $a \not\equiv b \pmod{m}$. Let $m = 4$ and $c = 2$ (what is important in constructing this example is that $gcd(m, c) > 1$). Let $a = 0$ and $b = 2$. Then $ac = 0$ and $bc = 4$, so $ac \equiv bc \pmod{4}$, but $0 \not\equiv 2 \pmod{4}$.

31. There are at least two ways to prove this. One way is to invoke Theorem 7 repeatedly. Since $a \equiv b \pmod{m}$, Theorem 7 implies that $a \cdot a \equiv b \cdot b \pmod{m}$, i.e., $a^2 \equiv b^2 \pmod{m}$. Invoking Theorem 7 again, since $a \equiv b \pmod{m}$ and $a^2 \equiv b^2 \pmod{m}$, we obtain $a^3 \equiv b^3 \pmod{m}$. After $k - 1$ applications of this process, we obtain $a^k \equiv b^k \pmod{m}$, as desired.

    Alternately, we can argue directly, using the algebraic identity $a^k - b^k = (a - b)(a^{k-1} + a^{k-2}b + \cdots + ab^{k-2} + b^{k-1})$. Specifically, the hypothesis that $a \equiv b \pmod{m}$ means that $m \,|\, (a - b)$. Therefore by Theorem 1 (part 2), $m$ divides the right-hand side of this identity, so $m \,|\, (a^k - b^k)$. This means precisely that $a^k \equiv b^k \pmod{m}$.

⇒ **SECTION 2.4   Integers and Algorithms**

*In addition to calculation exercises on the Euclidean algorithm, the base conversion algorithm, and algorithms for the basic arithmetic operations, this exercise set introduces other forms of representing integers. These are **balanced ternary expansion**, **Cantor expansion**, **binary coded decimal** (or **BCD**) representation, and **one's complement** representation. Each has a practical and/or theoretical importance in mathematics or computer science. If all else fails, one can carry out an algorithm by "playing computer" and mechanically following the pseudocode step by step.*

1. **a)** By Lemma 1, $gcd(12, 18)$ is the same as the $gcd$ of the smaller of these two numbers (12) and the remainder when the larger (18) is divided by the smaller. In this case the remainder is 6, so $gcd(12, 18) = gcd(12, 6)$. Now $gcd(12, 6)$ is the same as the $gcd$ of the smaller of *these* two numbers (6) and the remainder when the larger (12) is divided by the smaller, namely 0. This gives $gcd(12, 6) = gcd(6, 0)$. But $gcd(x, 0) = x$ for all positive integers, so $gcd(6, 0) = 6$. Thus the answer is 6. In brief (the form we will use for the remaining parts), $gcd(12, 18) = gcd(12, 6) = gcd(6, 0) = 6$.
   **b)** $gcd(111, 201) = gcd(111, 90) = gcd(90, 21) = gcd(21, 6) = gcd(6, 3) = gcd(3, 0) = 3$
   **c)** $gcd(1001, 1331) = gcd(1001, 330) = gcd(330, 11) = gcd(11, 0) = 11$
   **d)** $gcd(12345, 54321) = gcd(12345, 4941) = gcd(4941, 2463) = gcd(2463, 15) = gcd(15, 3) = gcd(3, 0)$
   $= 3$

3. We divide repeatedly by 2, noting the remainders. The remainders are then arranged from right to left to obtain the binary representation of the given number.
   **a)** We begin by dividing 231 by 2, obtaining a quotient of 115 and a remainder of 1. Therefore $a_0 = 1$. Next $115/2 = 57$, remainder 1. Therefore $a_1 = 1$. Similarly $57/2 = 28$, remainder 1. Therefore $a_2 = 1$. Then $28/2 = 14$, remainder 0, so $a_3 = 0$. Similarly $a_4 = 0$, after we divide 14 by 2, obtaining 7 with remainder 0. Three more divisions yield quotients of 3, 1, and 0, with remainders of 1, 1, and 1, respectively, so $a_5 = a_6 = a_7 = 1$. Putting all this together, we see that the binary representation is $(a_7 a_6 a_5 a_4 a_3 a_2 a_1 a_0)_2 = (111\ 00111)_2$.
   **b)** Following the same procedure as in part **(a)**, we obtain successive remainders 0, 0, 1, 0, 1, 1, 0, 1, 1, 0, 0, 0, 1. Therefore $4532 = (100\ 01101\ 10100)_2$.
   **c)** By the same method we obtain $97644 = (10\ 11111\ 01011\ 01100)_2$.

5. The method is to convert each hexadecimal digit to its 4-bit binary equivalent $(1 \to 0001, 2 \to 0010, 3 \to 0011, \ldots, 9 \to 1001, A \to 1010, B \to 1011, \ldots, F \to 1111)$. For example, $(E54)_{16} = (1110\ 0101\ 0100)_2 = (11\ 10010\ 10100)_2$. The reason that this method works is that $2^4 = 16$.

7. We follow the method given in Exercise 5.
   **a)** $(80E)_{16} = (1000\ 0000\ 1110)_2 = (10\ 00000\ 01110)_2$
   **b)** $(135AB)_{16} = (0001\ 0011\ 0101\ 1010\ 1011)_2 = (10\ 01101\ 01101\ 01011)_2$
   **c)** $(ABBA)_{16} = (1010\ 1011\ 1011\ 1010)_2 = (1\ 01010\ 11101\ 11010)_2$
   **d)** $(DEFACED)_{16} = (1101\ 1110\ 1111\ 1010\ 1100\ 1110\ 1101)_2$
   $= (110\ 11110\ 11111\ 01011\ 00111\ 01101)_2$

9. The binary expansion of an integer represents the integer as a sum of distinct powers of two. For example, since $21 = (10101)_2$, we have $21 = 2^4 + 2^2 + 2^0$. Since binary expansions are unique, each integer can be so represented uniquely.

11. Let the decimal expansion of the integer $a$ be given by $a = (a_{n-1}a_{n-2} \ldots a_1 a_0)_{10}$. Thus $a = 10^{n-1}a_{n-1} + 10^{n-2}a_{n-2} + \cdots + 10a_1 + a_0$. Since $10 \equiv 1 \pmod 3$, we have $a \equiv a_{n-1} + a_{n-2} + \cdots + a_1 + a_0 \pmod 3$. Therefore $a \equiv 0 \pmod 3$ if and only if the sum of the digits is congruent to $0 \pmod 3$. Since being divisible by 3 is the same as being congruent to $0 \pmod 3$, we have proved that a positive integer is divisible by 3 if and only if the sum of its decimal digits is divisible by 3.

13. **a)** Since the leading bit is a 1, this represents a negative number. The binary expansion of the absolute value of this number is the complement of the rest of the expansion, namely the complement of 1001, or 0110. Since $(0110)_2 = 6$, the answer is $-6$.

    **b)** Since the leading bit is a 0, this represents a positive number, namely the number whose binary expansion is the rest of this string, 1101. Since $(1101)_2 = 13$, the answer is 13.

    **c)** The answer is the negative of the complement of 0001, namely $-(1110)_2 = -14$.

    **d)** $-(0000)_2 = 0$

15. We must assume that the sum actually represents a number in the appropriate range. Assume that $n + 1$ bits are being used, so that numbers strictly between $-2^n$ and $2^n$ can be represented. The answer is almost, but not quite, that to obtain the one's complement representation of the sum of two numbers, we simply add the two strings representing these numbers using Algorithm 3. Instead, after performing this operation, there may be a carry out of the left-most column; in such a case, we then add 1 more to the answer. For example, suppose $n = 3$, so that numbers from $-7$ to 7 can be represented. To add $-5$ and 3, we add 1010 and 0011, obtaining 1101; there was no carry out of the left-most column. Since 1101 is the one's complement representation of $-2$, we have the correct answer. On the other hand, to add $-4$ and $-3$, we add 1011 and 1100, obtaining 1 0111. The 1 that was carried out of the left-most column is instead added to 0111, yielding 1000, which is the one's complement representation of $-7$. A proof that this method works entails considering the various cases determined by the signs and magnitudes of the addends.

17. Clearly we need $4n$ digits, 4 for each digit of the decimal representation.

19. To find the Cantor expansion, we will work from left to right. Thus the first step will be to find the largest number $n$ whose factorial is still less than or equal to the given positive integer $x$. Then we determine the digits in the expansion, starting with $a_n$ and ending with $a_1$.

> **procedure** $Cantor(x : \text{positive integer})$
> $n := 1$; $factorial := 1$
> **while** $(n + 1) \cdot factorial \le x$
> **begin**
>     $n := n + 1$
>     $factorial := factorial \cdot n$
> **end** {at this point we know that there are $n$ digits in the expansion}
> $y := x$ {this is just so we do not destroy the original input}
> **while** $n > 0$
> **begin**
>     $a_n := \lfloor y/factorial \rfloor$
>     $y := y - a_n \cdot factorial$
>     $factorial := factorial/n$
>     $n := n - 1$
> **end**
> {we are done: $x = a_n n! + a_{n-1}(n-1)! + \cdots + a_2 2! + a_1 1!$}

**21.** Note that $n = 5$. Initially the carry $c = 0$, and we start the **for** loop with $j = 0$. Since $a_0 = 1$ and $b_0 = 0$, we set $d$ to be $\lfloor (1 + 0 + 0)/2 \rfloor = 0$; then $s_0 = 1 + 0 + 0 - 2 \cdot 0$, which equals 1, and finally $c = 0$. At the end of the first pass, then, the right-most digit of the answer has been determined (it's a 1), and there is a carry of 0 into the next column.

Now $j = 1$, and we compute $d$ to be $\lfloor (a_1 + b_1 + c)/2 \rfloor = \lfloor (1 + 1 + 0)/2 \rfloor = 1$; whereupon $s_1$ becomes $1 + 1 + 0 - 2 \cdot 1 = 0$, and $c$ is set to 1. Thus far we have determined that the last two bits of the answer are 01 (from left to right), and there is a carry of 1 into the next column.

The next three passes through the loop are similar. As a result of the pass when $j = 2$ we set $d = 1$, $s_2 = 0$, and then $c = 1$. When $j = 3$, we obtain $d = 1$, $s_3 = 0$, and then $c = 1$. Finally, when $j = 4$, we obtain $d = 1$, $s_4 = 1$, and then $c = 1$. At this point the loop is terminated, and when we execute the final step, $s_5 = 1$. Thus the answer is 1 10001.

**23.** We will assume that the answer is not negative, since otherwise we would need something like the one's complement representation. The algorithm is similar to the algorithm for addition, except that we need to borrow instead of carry. Rather than trying to incorporate the two cases (borrow or no borrow) into one, as was done in the algorithm for addition, we will use an **if...then** statement to treat the cases separately. The notation is the usual one: $a = (a_{n-1} \ldots a_1 a_0)_2$ and $b = (b_{n-1} \ldots b_1 b_0)_2$

     **procedure** *subtract*$(a, b :$ nonnegative integers$)$
     *borrow* $:= 0$
     **for** $j := 0$ **to** $n - 1$
         **if** $a_j - borrow \geq b_j$ **then**
         **begin**
             $s_j := a_j - borrow - b_j$
             *borrow* $:= 0$
         **end**
         **else**
         **begin**
             $s_j := a_j + 2 - borrow - b_j$
             *borrow* $:= 1$
         **end**
     {assuming $a \geq b$, we have $a - b = (s_{n-1}s_{n-2} \ldots s_1 s_0)_2$ }

**25.** To determine which of two integers (we assume they are nonnegative), given in binary as $a = (a_{n-1} \ldots a_1 a_0)_2$ and $b = (b_{n-1} \ldots b_1 b_0)_2$, is larger, we need to compare digits from the most significant end ($i = n - 1$) to the least ($i = 0$), stopping if and when we find a difference. For variety here we record the answer as a character string; in most applications it would probably be better to set *compare* to one of three code values (such as $-1$, 1, and 0) to indicate which of the three possibilities held.

     **procedure** *compare*$(a, b :$ nonnegative integers$)$
     $i := n - 1$
     **while** $i > 0$ **and** $a_i = b_i$
         $i := i - 1$
     **if** $a_i > b_i$ **then** *answer* $:=$ "$a > b$"
     **else if** $a_i < b_i$ **then** *answer* $:=$ "$a < b$"
     **else** *answer* $:=$ "$a = b$"
     {the answer is recorded in *answer* }

**27.** There is one division for each pass through the **while** loop. Also, each pass generates one digit in the base $b$ expansion. Thus the number of divisions equals the number of digits in the base $b$

expansion of $n$. This is just $\lfloor \log_b n \rfloor + 1$ (for example, numbers from 10 to 99, inclusive, have common logarithms in the interval $[1, 2)$). Therefore exactly $\lfloor \log_b n \rfloor + 1 = O(\log n)$ divisions are required. (We are counting only the actual division operation in the statement $q := \lfloor q/b \rfloor$. If we also count the implied division in the statement $a_k := q \bmod b$, then there are twice as many as we computed here. The big-$O$ estimate is the same, of course.)

⇒ **SECTION 2.5    Matrices**

*In addition to routine exercises with matrix calculations, there are several exercises here asking for proofs of various properties of matrix operations. In most cases the proofs follow immediately from the definitions of the matrix operations and the properties of the corresponding operations on the set from which the entries in the matrices are drawn. Also, the important notion of the (multiplicative)* **inverse** *of a matrix is examined in Exercise 14 to Exercise 17. Keep in mind that some matrix operations are performed "entrywise," whereas others operate on whole rows or columns at a time. The general problem of efficient calculation of multiple matrix products, suggested by Exercise 19 to Exercise 21, is interesting and nontrivial. Exercise 25 foreshadows material in Section 6.4.*

1.  **a)** Since $A$ has 3 rows and 4 columns, its size is $3 \times 4$.

    **b)** The third column of $A$ is the $3 \times 1$ matrix $\begin{bmatrix} 1 \\ 4 \\ 3 \end{bmatrix}$.

    **c)** The second row of $A$ is the $1 \times 4$ matrix $[2\ 0\ 4\ 6]$.

    **d)** This is the element in the third row, second column, namely 1.

    **e)** The transpose of $A$ is the $4 \times 3$ matrix $\begin{bmatrix} 1 & 2 & 1 \\ 1 & 0 & 1 \\ 1 & 4 & 3 \\ 3 & 6 & 7 \end{bmatrix}$.

3.  Since the $(i, j)$th entry of $\mathbf{0} + \mathbf{A}$ is the sum of the $(i, j)$th entry of $\mathbf{0}$ (namely 0) and the $(i, j)$th entry of $\mathbf{A}$, this entry is the same as the $(i, j)$th entry of $\mathbf{A}$. Therefore by the definition of matrix equality, $\mathbf{0} + \mathbf{A} = \mathbf{A}$. A similar argument shows that $\mathbf{A} + \mathbf{0} = \mathbf{A}$.

5.  We simply look at the $(i, j)$th entries of each side. The $(i, j)$th entry of the left-hand side is $a_{ij} + (b_{ij} + c_{ij})$. The $(i, j)$th entry of the right-hand side is $(a_{ij} + b_{ij}) + c_{ij}$. By the associativity law for real number addition, these are equal. The conclusion follows.

7.  In order for $\mathbf{AB}$ to be defined, the number of columns of $\mathbf{A}$ must equal the number of rows of $\mathbf{B}$. In order for $\mathbf{BA}$ to be defined, the number of columns of $\mathbf{B}$ must equal the number of rows of $\mathbf{A}$. Thus for some positive integers $m$ and $n$, it must be the case that $\mathbf{A}$ is an $m \times n$ matrix and $\mathbf{B}$ is an $n \times m$ matrix. Another way to say this is to say that $\mathbf{A}$ must have the same size as $\mathbf{B}^t$ and vice versa.

9. Let us begin with the left-hand side and find its $(i,j)$th entry. First we need to find the entries of $\mathbf{BC}$. By definition, the $(q,j)$th entry of $\mathbf{BC}$ is $\sum_{r=1}^{k} b_{qr} c_{rj}$. Therefore the $(i,j)$th entry of $\mathbf{A(BC)}$ is $\sum_{q=1}^{p} a_{iq} \big( \sum_{r=1}^{k} b_{qr} c_{rj} \big)$. By distributing multiplication over addition (for real numbers), we can move the term $a_{iq}$ inside the inner summation, to obtain $\sum_{q=1}^{p} \sum_{r=1}^{k} a_{iq} b_{qr} c_{rj}$. (We are also implicitly using associativity of multiplication of real numbers here, to avoid putting parentheses in the product $a_{iq} b_{qr} c_{rj}$.)

A similar analysis with the right-hand side shows that the $(i,j)$th entry there is equal to $\sum_{r=1}^{k} \big( \sum_{q=1}^{p} a_{iq} b_{qr} \big) c_{rj} = \sum_{r=1}^{k} \sum_{q=1}^{p} a_{iq} b_{qr} c_{rj}$. Now by the commutativity of addition, the order of summation (whether we sum over $r$ first and then $q$, or over $q$ first and then $r$) does not matter, so these two expressions are equal, and the proof is complete.

11. Let us begin by computing $\mathbf{A}^n$ for the first few values of $n$.

$$\mathbf{A}^1 = \begin{bmatrix} 1 & 1 \\ 0 & 1 \end{bmatrix}, \quad \mathbf{A}^2 = \begin{bmatrix} 1 & 2 \\ 0 & 1 \end{bmatrix}, \quad \mathbf{A}^3 = \begin{bmatrix} 1 & 3 \\ 0 & 1 \end{bmatrix}, \quad \mathbf{A}^4 = \begin{bmatrix} 1 & 4 \\ 0 & 1 \end{bmatrix}, \quad \mathbf{A}^5 = \begin{bmatrix} 1 & 5 \\ 0 & 1 \end{bmatrix}.$$

It seems clear from this pattern, then, that $\mathbf{A}^n = \begin{bmatrix} 1 & n \\ 0 & 1 \end{bmatrix}$. (A proof of this fact could be given using mathematical induction, discussed in Section 3.2.)

13. a) The $(i,j)$th entry of $(\mathbf{A+B})^t$ is the $(j,i)$th entry of $\mathbf{A+B}$, namely $a_{ji} + b_{ji}$. On the other hand, the $(i,j)$th entry of $\mathbf{A}^t + \mathbf{B}^t$ is the sum of the $(i,j)$th entries of $\mathbf{A}^t$ and $\mathbf{B}^t$, which are the $(j,i)$th entries of $\mathbf{A}$ and $\mathbf{B}$, again $a_{ji} + b_{ji}$. Hence $(\mathbf{A+B})^t = \mathbf{A}^t + \mathbf{B}^t$.

b) The $(i,j)$th entry of $(\mathbf{AB})^t$ is the $(j,i)$th entry of $\mathbf{AB}$, namely $\sum_{k=1}^{n} a_{jk} b_{ki}$. On the other hand, the $(i,j)$th entry of $\mathbf{B}^t \mathbf{A}^t$ is $\sum_{k=1}^{n} b_{ki} a_{jk}$ (since the $(i,k)$th entry of $\mathbf{B}^t$ is $b_{ki}$ and the $(k,j)$th entry of $\mathbf{A}^t$ is $a_{jk}$). By the commutativity of multiplication of real numbers, these two values are the same, so the matrices are equal.

15. All we have to do is form the products $\mathbf{AA}^{-1}$ and $\mathbf{A}^{-1}\mathbf{A}$, using the purported $\mathbf{A}^{-1}$, and see that both of them are the $2 \times 2$ identity matrix. It is easy to see that the upper left and lower right entries in each case are $(ad - bc)/(ad - bc) = 1$, and the upper right and lower left entries are all $0$.

17. Since matrix multiplication is associative, we can write the given product as

$$\mathbf{A}^n \big( (\mathbf{A}^{-1})^n \big) = \mathbf{A}(\mathbf{A} \dots (\mathbf{A}(\mathbf{AA}^{-1})\mathbf{A}^{-1}) \dots \mathbf{A}^{-1})\mathbf{A}^{-1}.$$

By dropping each $\mathbf{AA}^{-1} = \mathbf{I}$ from the center as it is obtained, this product reduces to $\mathbf{I}$. Similarly $\big( (\mathbf{A}^{-1})^n \big) \mathbf{A}^n = \mathbf{I}$. Therefore by definition $(\mathbf{A}^n)^{-1} = (\mathbf{A}^{-1})^n$. (A more formal proof requires mathematical induction; see Section 3.2.)

19. In order to compute the $(i,j)$th entry of the product $\mathbf{AB}$, we need to compute the product $a_{ik} b_{kj}$ for each $k$ from 1 to $m_2$, requiring $m_2$ multiplications. Since there are $m_1 m_3$ such pairs $(i,j)$, we need a total of $m_1 m_2 m_3$ multiplications.

**21.** There are five different ways to perform this multiplication:

$$(A_1 A_2)(A_3 A_4), \quad ((A_1 A_2)A_3)A_4, \quad A_1(A_2(A_3 A_4)), \quad (A_1(A_2 A_3))A_4, \quad A_1((A_2 A_3)A_4).$$

Using the result of Exercise 19, we find that the numbers of multiplications needed in these five cases are $4.5 \times 10^6$, $6 \times 10^7$, $5.4 \times 10^5$, $4.8 \times 10^7$, and $1.44 \times 10^6$, respectively. The winner is therefore $A_1(A_2(A_3 A_4))$, requiring $5.4 \times 10^5$ multiplications. Note that the worst arrangement requires $6 \times 10^7$ multiplications; it will take over 100 times as long!

**23.** These routine exercises simply require application of the appropriate definitions. Parts **(a)** and **(b)** are entry-wise operations, whereas the operation $\odot$ in part **(c)** is similar to matrix multiplication (the $(i,j)$th entry of $A \odot B$ depends on the $i^{\text{th}}$ row of $A$ and the $j^{\text{th}}$ column of $B$).

**a)** $A \vee B = \begin{bmatrix} 1 & 1 & 1 \\ 1 & 1 & 0 \\ 1 & 0 & 1 \end{bmatrix}$     **b)** $A \wedge B = \begin{bmatrix} 0 & 0 & 1 \\ 1 & 0 & 0 \\ 0 & 0 & 1 \end{bmatrix}$     **c)** $A \odot B = \begin{bmatrix} 1 & 1 & 1 \\ 1 & 1 & 1 \\ 1 & 0 & 1 \end{bmatrix}$

**25.** Note that $A^{[2]}$ means $A \odot A$, and $A^{[3]}$ means $A \odot A \odot A$.

**a)** $A^{[2]} = \begin{bmatrix} 1 & 0 & 0 \\ 1 & 1 & 0 \\ 1 & 0 & 1 \end{bmatrix}$     **b)** $A^{[3]} = \begin{bmatrix} 1 & 0 & 0 \\ 1 & 0 & 1 \\ 1 & 1 & 0 \end{bmatrix}$     **c)** $A \vee A^{[2]} \vee A^{[3]} = \begin{bmatrix} 1 & 0 & 0 \\ 1 & 1 & 1 \\ 1 & 1 & 1 \end{bmatrix}$

**27.** These are immediate from the commutativity of the corresponding logical operations on variables.
    **a)** $A \vee B = [a_{ij} \vee b_{ij}] = [b_{ij} \vee a_{ij}] = B \vee A$
    **b)** $B \wedge A = [b_{ij} \wedge a_{ij}] = [a_{ij} \wedge b_{ij}] = A \wedge B$

**29.** These are immediate from the distributivity of the corresponding logical operations on variables.
    **a)** $A \vee (B \wedge C) = [a_{ij} \vee (b_{ij} \wedge c_{ij})] = [(a_{ij} \vee b_{ij}) \wedge (a_{ij} \vee c_{ij})] = (A \vee B) \wedge (A \vee C)$
    **b)** $A \wedge (B \vee C) = [a_{ij} \wedge (b_{ij} \vee c_{ij})] = [(a_{ij} \wedge b_{ij}) \vee (a_{ij} \wedge c_{ij})] = (A \wedge B) \vee (A \wedge C)$

**31.** The proof is identical to the proof in Exercise 9, except that real number multiplication is replaced by $\wedge$, and real number addition is replaced by $\vee$. Briefly, in symbols, $A \odot (B \odot C) = [\bigvee\limits_{q=1}^{p} a_{iq} \wedge (\bigvee\limits_{r=1}^{k} (b_{qr} \wedge c_{rj}))] = [\bigvee\limits_{q=1}^{p} \bigvee\limits_{r=1}^{k} a_{iq} \wedge b_{qr} \wedge c_{rj}] = [\bigvee\limits_{r=1}^{k} \bigvee\limits_{q=1}^{p} a_{iq} \wedge b_{qr} \wedge c_{rj}] = [\bigvee\limits_{r=1}^{k} (\bigvee\limits_{q=1}^{p} a_{iq} \wedge b_{qr}) \wedge c_{rj}] = (A \odot B) \odot C.$

⇒ **SUPPLEMENTARY EXERCISES FOR CHAPTER 2**

1. **a)** This algorithm will be identical to the algorithm *first largest* for Exercise 11 of Section 2.1, except that we want to change the value of *location* each time we find another element in the list that is equal to the current value of *max*. Therefore we simply change the strict less than ($<$) in the comparison $max < a_i$ to a less than or equal to, rendering the fifth line of that procedure "**if** $max \leq a_i$ **then**."
   **b)** The number of comparisons used by this algorithm can be computed as follows. There are $n - 1$ passes through the **for** loop, each one requiring a comparison of *max* with $a_i$. In addition, $n$ comparisons are needed for bookkeeping for the loop (comparison of $i$ with $n$, as $i$ assumes the values $2, 3, \ldots, n + 1$). Therefore $2n - 1 = O(n)$ comparisons are needed altogether.

3. **a)** We will try to write an algorithm sophisticated enough to avoid unnecessary checking. The answer— **true** or **false**—will be placed in a variable called *zeros*, the name of the procedure.

> **procedure** *zeros*($a_1 a_2 \ldots a_n$ : bit string)
> $i := 1$
> *zeros* := **false** {no pair of zeros found yet}
> **while** $i < n$ and $\neg zeros$
>     **if** $a_i = 1$ **then** $i := i + 1$
>     **else if** $a_{i+1} = 1$ **then** $i := i + 2$
>     **else** *zeros* := **true**
> { *zeros* was set to **true** if and only if there were a pair of consecutive zeros}

   **b)** The number of comparisons depends on whether a pair of zeros is found and also depends on the pattern of increments of the looping variable $i$. Without getting into the intricate details of exactly which is the worst case, we note that at worst there are approximately $n$ passes through the loop, each requiring one comparison of $a_i$ with 1 (there may be two comparisons on some passes, but then there will be fewer passes). In addition, $n$ bookkeeping comparisons of $i$ with $n$ are needed (we are ignoring the testing of the logical variable *zeros*). Thus a total of approximately $2n = O(n)$ comparisons are used.

5. Obviously there are an infinite number of possible answers. The numbers congruent to 5 modulo 17 include $5, 22, 39, 56, \ldots$, as well as $-12, -29, -46, \ldots$.

7. From the hypothesis $ac \equiv bc \pmod{m}$ we know that $ac - bc = km$ for some integer $k$. Divide both sides by $c$ to obtain the equation $a - b = (km)/c$. Now the left-hand side is an integer, and so the right-hand side must be an integer as well. In other words, $c \mid km$. Letting $d = gcd(m, c)$, we write $c = de$. Then the way that $c$ divides $km$ is that $d \mid m$ and $e \mid k$ (since no factor of $e$ divides $m/d$). Thus our equation reduces to $a - b = (k/e)(m/d)$, where both factors on the right are integers. By definition, this means that $a \equiv b \pmod{m/d}$.

9. $gcd(10223, 33341) = gcd(10223, 2672) = gcd(2672, 2207) = gcd(2207, 465) = gcd(465, 347) = gcd(347, 118) = gcd(118, 111) = gcd(111, 7) = gcd(7, 6) = gcd(6, 1) = gcd(1, 0) = 1$

11. By Lemma 1 in Section 2.4, $gcd(2n + 1, 3n + 2) = gcd(2n + 1, n + 1)$, since $2n + 1$ goes once into $3n + 2$ with a remainder of $n + 1$. Now if we divide $n + 1$ into $2n + 1$, we get a remainder of $n$, so the answer must equal $gcd(n + 1, n)$. At this point, the remainder when dividing $n$ into $n + 1$ is 1, so the answer must equal $gcd(n, 1)$, which is clearly 1. Thus the answer is 1.

13. This problem is similar to Exercise 11 in Section 2.4. Without loss of generality, we may assume that the given integer is positive (since $n \mid a$ if and only if $n \mid (-a)$, and the case $a = 0$ is trivial). Let the decimal expansion of the integer $a$ be given by $a = (a_{n-1}a_{n-2}\ldots a_1 a_0)_{10}$. Thus $a = 10^{n-1}a_{n-1} + 10^{n-2}a_{n-2} + \cdots + 10a_1 + a_0$. Since $10 \equiv 1 \pmod 9$, we have $a \equiv a_{n-1} + a_{n-2} + \cdots + a_1 + a_0 \pmod 9$. Therefore $a \equiv 0 \pmod 9$ if and only if the sum of the digits is congruent to $0 \pmod 9$. Since being divisible by 9 is the same as being congruent to $0 \pmod 9$, we have proved that an integer is divisible by 9 if and only if the sum of its decimal digits is divisible by 9.

15. Let us begin by computing $\mathbf{A}^n$ for the first few values of $n$.

$$\mathbf{A}^1 = \begin{bmatrix} 0 & 1 \\ -1 & 0 \end{bmatrix}, \quad \mathbf{A}^2 = \begin{bmatrix} -1 & 0 \\ 0 & -1 \end{bmatrix}, \quad \mathbf{A}^3 = \begin{bmatrix} 0 & -1 \\ 1 & 0 \end{bmatrix}, \quad \mathbf{A}^4 = \begin{bmatrix} 1 & 0 \\ 0 & 1 \end{bmatrix}.$$

Since $\mathbf{A}^4 = \mathbf{I}$, the pattern will repeat from here: $\mathbf{A}^5 = \mathbf{A}^4\mathbf{A} = \mathbf{I}\mathbf{A} = \mathbf{A}$, $\mathbf{A}^6 = \mathbf{A}^2$, $\mathbf{A}^7 = \mathbf{A}^3$, and so on. Thus for all $n \geq 0$ we have

$$\mathbf{A}^{4n+1} = \begin{bmatrix} 0 & 1 \\ -1 & 0 \end{bmatrix}, \quad \mathbf{A}^{4n+2} = \begin{bmatrix} -1 & 0 \\ 0 & -1 \end{bmatrix}, \quad \mathbf{A}^{4n+3} = \begin{bmatrix} 0 & -1 \\ 1 & 0 \end{bmatrix}, \quad \mathbf{A}^{4n+4} = \begin{bmatrix} 1 & 0 \\ 0 & 1 \end{bmatrix}.$$

17. (The notation $c\mathbf{I}$ means the identity matrix $\mathbf{I}$ with each entry multiplied by the real number $c$; thus this matrix consists of $c$'s along the main diagonal and $0$'s elsewhere.) Let $\mathbf{A} = \begin{bmatrix} a & b \\ c & d \end{bmatrix}$. We will determine what these entries have to be by using the fact that $\mathbf{AB} = \mathbf{BA}$ for a few judiciously chosen matrices $\mathbf{B}$. First let $\mathbf{B} = \begin{bmatrix} 0 & 1 \\ 0 & 0 \end{bmatrix}$. Then $\mathbf{AB} = \begin{bmatrix} 0 & a \\ 0 & c \end{bmatrix}$, and $\mathbf{BA} = \begin{bmatrix} c & d \\ 0 & 0 \end{bmatrix}$. Since these two must be equal, we know that $0 = c$ and $a = d$. Next choose $\mathbf{B} = \begin{bmatrix} 0 & 0 \\ 1 & 0 \end{bmatrix}$. Then we get $\begin{bmatrix} b & 0 \\ d & 0 \end{bmatrix} = \begin{bmatrix} 0 & 0 \\ a & b \end{bmatrix}$, whence $b = 0$. Therefore the matrix $\mathbf{A}$ must be in the form $\begin{bmatrix} a & 0 \\ 0 & a \end{bmatrix}$, which is just $a$ times the identity matrix, as desired.

19. In an $n \times n$ upper-triangular matrix, all entries $a_{ij}$ are zero unless $i \leq j$. Therefore we can store such matrices in about half the space that would be required to store an ordinary $n \times n$ matrix. In implementing something like Algorithm 1 in Section 2.5, then, we need only do the computations for those values of the indices which can produce nonzero entries. The following algorithm does this. We follow the usual notation: $\mathbf{A} = [a_{ij}]$ and $\mathbf{B} = [b_{ij}]$.

> **procedure** *triangular matrix multiplication*$(\mathbf{A}, \mathbf{B}$ : upper-triangular matrices)
> **for** $i := 1$ **to** $n$
>     **for** $j := i$ **to** $n$ {since we want $j \geq i$}
>     **begin**
>         $c_{ij} := 0$
>         **for** $k := i$ **to** $j$ {the only relevant part}
>             $c_{ij} := c_{ij} + a_{ik}b_{kj}$
>     **end**
> {the upper-triangular matrix $\mathbf{C} = [c_{ij}]$ is the product of $\mathbf{A}$ and $\mathbf{B}$}

21. We simply need to show that the alleged inverse of $\mathbf{AB}$ has the correct defining property—that its product with $\mathbf{AB}$ (on either side) is the identity. Thus we compute

$$(\mathbf{AB})(\mathbf{B}^{-1}\mathbf{A}^{-1}) = \mathbf{A}(\mathbf{BB}^{-1})\mathbf{A}^{-1} = \mathbf{AIA}^{-1} = \mathbf{AA}^{-1} = \mathbf{I},$$

and similarly $(\mathbf{B}^{-1}\mathbf{A}^{-1})(\mathbf{AB}) = \mathbf{I}$. Therefore $(\mathbf{AB})^{-1} = \mathbf{B}^{-1}\mathbf{A}^{-1}$. (Note that the indicated matrix multiplications were all defined, since the hypotheses implied that both $\mathbf{A}$ and $\mathbf{B}$ were $n \times n$ matrices for some (and the same) $n$.)

23. **a)** The $(i,j)$th entry of $\mathbf{A} \odot \mathbf{0}$ is by definition the Boolean sum ($\vee$) of some Boolean products ($\wedge$) of the form $a_{ik} \wedge 0$. Since the latter always equals $0$, every entry is $0$, so $\mathbf{A} \odot \mathbf{0} = \mathbf{0}$. Similarly $\mathbf{0} \odot \mathbf{A}$ consists of entries which are all $0$, so it, too, equals $\mathbf{0}$.

**b)** Since $\vee$ operates entrywise, the statements that $\mathbf{A} \vee \mathbf{0} = \mathbf{A}$ and $\mathbf{0} \vee \mathbf{A} = \mathbf{A}$ follow from the facts that $a_{ij} \vee 0 = a_{ij}$ and $0 \vee a_{ij} = a_{ij}$.

**c)** Since $\wedge$ operates entrywise, the statements that $\mathbf{A} \wedge \mathbf{0} = \mathbf{0}$ and $\mathbf{0} \wedge \mathbf{A} = \mathbf{0}$ follow from the facts that $a_{ij} \wedge 0 = 0$ and $0 \wedge a_{ij} = 0$.

# CHAPTER 3
## Mathematical Reasoning

⇒ **SECTION 3.1   Methods of Proof**

*Learning to construct good mathematical proofs takes years. There is no algorithm for constructing the proof of a true proposition (there is actually a deep theorem in mathematical logic that says this). Instead, the construction of a valid proof is an art, honed after much practice. There are two problems for the beginning student—figuring out the key ideas in a problem (what is it that really makes the proposition true?) and writing down the proof in acceptable mathematical language.*

*Here are some general things to keep in mind in constructing proofs. First, of course, you need to find out exactly what is going on—why the proposition is true. This can take anywhere from ten seconds (for a really simple proposition) to a lifetime (some mathematicians have spent their entire lives trying to prove certain conjectures). For a typical student at this level, tackling a typical problem, the median might be somewhere around twenty minutes. This time should be spent looking at examples, making tentative assumptions, breaking the problem down into cases, perhaps looking at analogous but simpler problems, and in general bringing all of your mathematical intuition and training to bear.*

*It is often easiest to give a proof by contradiction, since you get to assume the most (all the hypotheses as well as the negation of the conclusion), and all you have to do is to derive a contradiction. Another thing to try early in attacking a problem is to separate the proposition into several cases; proof by cases is a valid technique, if you make sure to include all the possibilities. In proving propositions, all the rules of inference are at your disposal, as well as axioms and previously proved results. Ask yourself what definitions, axioms, or other theorems might be relevant to the problem at hand.*

*Once you think you see what is involved, you need to write down the proof. In doing so, pay attention both to content (does each statement follow logically? are you making any fallacious arguments? are you leaving out any cases or using hidden assumptions?) and to style. There are certain conventions in mathematical proofs, and you need to follow them. For example, you must use complete sentences and say exactly what you mean. (A formula is a complete sentence, with "equals" usually being the verb; however, a good proof will usually have more English words than mathematical symbols in it.) The point of a proof is to convince the reader that your line of argument is sound, and that therefore the proposition under discussion is true; put yourself in the reader's shoes, and ask yourself whether you are convinced.*

*Most of the proofs called for in this exercise set are not extremely difficult. Nevertheless, expect to have a fairly rough time constructing proofs that look like those presented in this solutions manual, the textbook, or other mathematics textbooks. The more proofs you write, utilizing the different methods discussed in this section, the better you will become at it. As a bonus, your ability to construct and respond to nonmathematical arguments (politics, religion, or whatever) will be enhanced. Good luck!*

1.  **a)** This is the addition rule. We are concluding from $p$ that $p \vee q$ must be true, where $p$ is "Alice is a mathematics major" and $q$ is "Alice is a computer science major."

    **b)** This is the simplification rule. We are concluding from $p \wedge q$ that $p$ must be true, where $p$ is "Jerry is a mathematics major" and $q$ is "Jerry is a computer science major.".

    **c)** This is modus ponens. We are concluding from $p \to q$ and $p$ that $q$ must be true, where $p$ is "it will be rainy" and $q$ is "the pool will be closed."

    **d)** This is modus tollens. We are concluding from $p \to q$ and $\neg q$ that $\neg p$ must be true, where $p$ is "it will snow today" and $q$ is "the university will close today."

    **e)** This is hypothetical syllogism. We are concluding from $p \to q$ and $q \to r'$ that $p \to r$ must be true, where $p$ is "I will go swimming," $q$ is "I will stay in the sun too long," and $r$ is "I will sunburn."

3.  The proposition we are trying to prove is "If 0 is a positive integer greater than 1, then $0^2 > 0$." Our proof is a vacuous one, exactly as in Example 11. Since the hypothesis is false, the implication is automatically true.

5.  The proposition we are trying to prove is "If $a$ and $b$ are positive real numbers, then $(a+b)^1 \geq a^1 + b^1$." Our proof is a direct one. By the definition of exponentiation, any real number to the power 1 is itself. Hence $(a+b)^1 = a+b = a^1 + b^1$. Finally, by the addition rule, we can conclude from $(a+b)^1 = a^1 + b^1$ that $(a+b)^1 \geq a^1 + b^1$ (the latter being the disjunction of $(a+b)^1 = a^1 + b^1$ and $(a+b)^1 > a^1 + b^1$). One might also say that this is a trivial proof, since we did not use the hypothesis that $a$ and $b$ are positive (although of course we used the hypothesis that they are numbers).

7.  We give a direct proof. Suppose $a$ and $b$ are two odd numbers. Then there exist integers $s$ and $t$ such that $a = 2s + 1$ and $b = 2t + 1$. Adding, we obtain $a + b = (2s + 1) + (2t + 1) = 2(s + t + 1)$. Since this represents $a + b$ as 2 times the integer $s + t + 1$, we conclude that $a + b$ is even, as desired.

9.  We give a proof by contradiction. Let $r$ be a rational number and $i$ an irrational number. We want to show that $s = r + i$ is irrational. Suppose instead that $s$ is rational. Then by Exercise 8, the sum of the rational numbers $s$ and $-r$ must be rational. (Indeed, if $s = a/b$ and $r = c/d$, where $a$, $b$, $c$, and $d$ are integers, with $b \neq 0$ and $d \neq 0$, then by algebra we see that $s + (-r) = (ad - bc)/(bd)$, so that patently $s + (-r)$ is a rational number.) But $s + (-r) = r + i - r = i$, forcing us to the conclusion that $i$ is rational. This contradicts our hypothesis that $i$ is irrational. Therefore the assumption that $s$ was irrational was incorrect, and we conclude, as desired, that $s$ is rational.

11. The proof is similar to the proof that $\sqrt{2}$ is irrational, given in Example 15. It is a proof by contradiction. Suppose that $3^{1/3}$ (or $\sqrt[3]{3}$, which is the same thing) is the rational number $p/q$, where $p$ and $q$ are positive integers with no common factors (the fraction is in lowest terms). Cubing, we see that $3 = p^3/q^3$, or, equivalently, $p^3 = 3q^3$. Thus 3 is a divisor of $p^3$. Now if 3 were not a divisor of $p$, then by the Fundamental Theorem of Arithmetic, there is no way that 3 could be a divisor of $p^3$. Therefore $3 \mid p$ (recall the notation from Section 2.3), so we can write $p = 3s$ for some integer $s$. Substituting into the equation $p^3 = 3q^3$, we obtain $27s^3 = 3q^3$, which simplifies to $9s^3 = q^3$.

    Now we play the same game with $q$. Since 3 divides $9s^3$, and $9s^3 = q^3$, we know that $3 \mid q^3$. Therefore, as above, $3 \mid q$. We have now concluded that 3 is a common divisor of $p$ and $q$. This contradicts the choice of $p/q$ to be in lowest terms. Therefore our original assumption—that $\sqrt[3]{3}$ is rational—is in error, so we have proved that $\sqrt[3]{3}$ is irrational.

13. Following the hint, we consider the two cases determined by the relative sizes of $x$ and $y$. First suppose that $x \geq y$. Then by definition $\max(x, y) = x$ and $\min(x, y) = y$. Therefore in this case $\max(x, y) + \min(x, y) = x + y$, exactly as desired. For the second (and final) case, suppose that $x < y$. Then $\max(x, y) = y$ and $\min(x, y) = x$. Therefore in this case $\max(x, y) + \min(x, y) = y + x = x + y$, again the desired conclusion. Hence in all cases, the equality holds.

15. There are several cases to consider. If $x$ and $y$ are both nonnegative, then $|x| + |y| = x + y = |x + y|$. Similarly, if both are negative, then $|x| + |y| = (-x) + (-y) = -(x + y) = |x + y|$, since $x + y$ is negative in this case. The complication (and strict inequality) comes if one of the variables is nonnegative and the other is negative. By the symmetry of the roles of $x$ and $y$ here (strictly speaking, by the commutativity of addition), we can assume without loss of generality that it is $x$ that is nonnegative and $y$ that is negative. So we have $x \geq 0$ and $y < 0$.

  Now there are two subcases to consider within this case, depending on the relative sizes of the nonnegative numbers $x$ and $-y$. First suppose that $x \geq -y$. Then $|x + y| = x + y$ is a nonnegative number smaller than $x$ (since $y$ is negative). On the other hand $|x| + |y| = x + |y|$ is a positive number bigger than $x$. Therefore we have $|x + y| < x < |x| + |y|$, as desired.

  Finally, consider the possibility that $x < -y$. Then $|x + y| = -(x + y) = (-x) + (-y)$ is a positive number less than or equal to $(-y)$ (since $-x$ is nonpositive). On the other hand $|x| + |y| = |x| + (-y)$ is a positive number greater than or equal to $-y$. Therefore we have $|x + y| \leq -y \leq |x| + |y|$, as desired.

17. By definition, $a^2 \equiv b^2 \pmod{p}$ means that $p \,|\, (a^2 - b^2)$. Note that $a^2 - b^2 = (a + b)(a - b)$. Since $p$ is prime, knowing that $p$ divides the product $(a + b)(a - b)$ allows us to conclude that $p$ divides one of the factors (this is a consequence of the Fundamental Theorem of Arithmetic). Therefore either $p \,|\, (a + b)$ or $p \,|\, (a - b)$. The first assertion is by definition equivalent to saying that $a \equiv -b \pmod{p}$, and the second is equivalent to saying that $a \equiv b \pmod{p}$, so our proof is complete.

19. We need only find a prime number $n$ such that $n + 2$ is not prime. The smallest examples are $n = 2$ and $n = 7$.

21. This statement is true for $n \leq 5$; in other words, all of the numbers $2 + 1 = 3$, $2 \cdot 3 + 1 = 7$, $2 \cdot 3 \cdot 5 + 1 = 31$, $2 \cdot 3 \cdot 5 \cdot 7 + 1 = 211$, and $2 \cdot 3 \cdot 5 \cdot 7 \cdot 11 + 1 = 2311$ are prime. However, $2 \cdot 3 \cdot 5 \cdot 7 \cdot 11 \cdot 13 + 1 = 30031 = 59 \cdot 509$ is not prime. (There was no way to anticipate this answer—you simply had to keep trying until you found an example.)

⇒ **SECTION 3.2**    **Mathematical Induction**

*Understanding and constructing proofs by mathematical induction are extremely difficult tasks for most students. Do not be discouraged, and do not give up, because, without doubt, this proof technique is the most important one there is in mathematics and computer science. Pay careful attention to the conventions to be observed in writing down a proof by induction. As with all proofs, remember that a proof by mathematical induction is like an essay—it must have a beginning, a middle, and an end; it must consist of complete sentences, logically and aesthetically arranged; and it must convince the reader. Be sure that your basis step is correct (that you have verified the proposition in question for the smallest value or values of $n$), and be sure that your inductive step is correct and complete (that you have derived the proposition for $n + 1$, assuming the inductive hypothesis that the proposition is true for $n$).*

*Some, but not all, proofs by induction are like Exercise 1 through Exercise 8 and Exercise 13 through Exercise 15. In each of these, you are asked to prove that a certain summation has a "closed form" representation given by a certain expression. Here the proofs are usually straightforward algebra. For the inductive step you start with the summation for $P(n + 1)$, find the summation for $P(n)$ as its first $n$ terms, replace that much by the closed form given by the inductive hypothesis, and do the algebra to get the resulting expression into the desired form. When doing proofs like this, however, remember to include all the words surrounding your algebra—the algebra alone is not the proof. Also keep in mind that $P(n)$ is the proposition that the sum equals the closed-form expression, not just the sum and not just the expression.*

*Many inequalities can be proved by induction; see Exercise 9, Exercise 10, Exercise 11, Exercise 12, and Exercise 16. The method also extends to such things as set operations—see Exercise 21 through Exercise 25. The more interesting proofs by induction, however, are not of any of these forms; a sampling of them is given in other exercises in this set. Some are quite complicated.*

1. We can obtain a formula for the sum of the first $n$ even positive integers from the formula for the sum of the first $n$ positive integers, since $2 + 4 + 6 + \cdots + 2n = 2(1 + 2 + 3 + \cdots + n)$. Therefore, using the result of Example 9, the sum of the first $n$ even positive integers is $2(n(n + 1)/2) = n(n + 1)$.

   We can also prove our formula directly by induction. We want to prove the proposition $P(n)$ : $2 + 4 + 6 + \cdots + 2n = n(n + 1)$. The base case, $n = 1$, says that $2 = 1 \cdot (1 + 1)$, which is certainly true. For the inductive step, we assume that $P(n)$ is true, namely that

   $$2 + 4 + 6 + \cdots + 2n = n(n + 1),$$

   and try to prove from this assumption that $P(n + 1)$ is true, namely that

   $$2 + 4 + 6 + \cdots + 2n + 2(n + 1) = (n + 1)(n + 2).$$

   (Note that the left-hand side consists of the sum of the first $n + 1$ even positive integers.) We have

   $$2 + 4 + 6 + \cdots + 2n + 2(n + 1) = (2 + 4 + 6 + \cdots + 2n) + 2(n + 1)$$
   $$= n(n + 1) + 2(n + 1) \quad \text{(by the inductive hypothesis)}$$
   $$= (n + 1)(n + 2),$$

   as desired, and our proof by mathematical induction is complete.

3. Let $P(n)$ be the proposition $3 + 3 \cdot 5 + 3 \cdot 5^2 + \cdots + 3 \cdot 5^n = 3(5^{n+1} - 1)/4$. To prove that this is true for all nonnegative integers $n$, we proceed by mathematical induction. First we verify $P(0)$, namely

that $3 = 3(5-1)/4$, which is certainly true. Next we assume that $P(n)$ is true and try to derive $P(n+1)$. Now $P(n+1)$ is the formula

$$3 + 3 \cdot 5 + 3 \cdot 5^2 + \cdots + 3 \cdot 5^n + 3 \cdot 5^{n+1} = \frac{3(5^{n+2} - 1)}{4}.$$

All but the last term of the left-hand side of this equation is exactly the left-hand side of $P(n)$, so by the inductive hypothesis, it equals $3(5^{n+1} - 1)/4$. Thus we have

$$3 + 3 \cdot 5 + 3 \cdot 5^2 + \cdots + 3 \cdot 5^n + 3 \cdot 5^{n+1} = \frac{3(5^{n+1} - 1)}{4} + 3 \cdot 5^{n+1}$$

$$= 5^{n+1}\left(\frac{3}{4} + 3\right) - \frac{3}{4} = 5^{n+1} \cdot \frac{15}{4} - \frac{3}{4}$$

$$= 5^{n+2} \cdot \frac{3}{4} - \frac{3}{4} = \frac{3(5^{n+2} - 1)}{4}.$$

5. We proceed by induction. The base case, $n = 1$, is true, since $1^2 = 1 \cdot 2 \cdot 3/6$. Assume the inductive hypothesis that

$$1^2 + 2^2 + \cdots + n^2 = \frac{n(n+1)(2n+1)}{6}.$$

We want to show that

$$1^2 + 2^2 + \cdots + n^2 + (n+1)^2 = \frac{(n+1)(n+2)(2n+3)}{6}$$

(the right-hand side is the same formula with $n+1$ plugged in for $n$). Now the left-hand side equals, by the inductive hypothesis, $n(n+1)(2n+1)/6 + (n+1)^2$. We need only do a bit of algebraic manipulation to get this expression into the desired form: factor out $(n+1)/6$ and then factor the rest. In detail,

$$\left(1^2 + 2^2 + \cdots + n^2\right) + (n+1)^2 = \frac{n(n+1)(2n+1)}{6} + (n+1)^2$$

$$\text{(by the inductive hypothesis)}$$

$$= \frac{n+1}{6}\left(n(2n+1) + 6(n+1)\right) = \frac{n+1}{6}(2n^2 + 7n + 6)$$

$$= \frac{n+1}{6}(n+2)(2n+3) = \frac{(n+1)(n+2)(2n+3)}{6}.$$

7. We proceed by induction. The base case, $n = 0$, is true, since $1^2 = 1 \cdot 1 \cdot 3/3$. Assume the inductive hypothesis that

$$1^2 + 3^2 + 5^2 + \cdots + (2n+1)^2 = \frac{(n+1)(2n+1)(2n+3)}{3}.$$

We want to show that

$$1^2 + 3^2 + 5^2 + \cdots + (2n+1)^2 + (2n+3)^2 = \frac{(n+2)(2n+3)(2n+5)}{3}$$

(the right-hand side is the same formula with $n+1$ plugged in for $n$). Now the left-hand side equals, by the inductive hypothesis, $(n+1)(2n+1)(2n+3)/3 + (2n+3)^2$. We need only do a bit of algebraic manipulation to get this expression into the desired form: factor out $(2n+3)/3$ and then factor the rest. In detail,

$$\left(1^2 + 3^2 + 5^2 + \cdots + (2n+1)^2\right) + (2n+3)^2$$
$$= \frac{(n+1)(2n+1)(2n+3)}{3} + (2n+3)^2 \quad \text{(by the inductive hypothesis)}$$
$$= \frac{2n+3}{3}\left((n+1)(2n+1) + 3(2n+3)\right) = \frac{2n+3}{3}(2n^2 + 9n + 10)$$
$$= \frac{2n+3}{3}\left((n+2)(2n+5)\right) = \frac{(n+2)(2n+3)(2n+5)}{3}.$$

9. We can assume that $h > -1$ is fixed, and prove the proposition by induction on $n$. Let $P(n)$ be the proposition $1 + nh \le (1+h)^n$. The base case is $n = 0$, in which case $P(0)$ is simply $1 \le 1$, certainly true. Now we assume the inductive hypothesis, that $1 + nh \le (1+h)^n$; we want to show that $1 + (n+1)h \le (1+h)^{n+1}$. Since $h > -1$, it follows that $1 + h > 0$, so we can multiply both sides of the inductive hypothesis by $1 + h$ to obtain $(1+h)(1+nh) \le (1+h)^{n+1}$. Thus to complete the proof it is enough to show that $1 + (n+1)h \le (1+h)(1+nh)$. But the right-hand side of this inequality is the same as $1 + h + nh + nh^2 = 1 + (n+1)h + nh^2$, which is greater than or equal to $1 + (n+1)h$ because $nh^2 \ge 0$.

11. Let $P(n)$ be the proposition $2^n > n^2$. We want to show that $P(n)$ is true for all $n > 4$. The base case is therefore $n = 5$, and we check that $2^5 = 32 > 25 = 5^2$. Now we assume the inductive hypothesis that $2^n > n^2$ and want to derive the statement that $2^{n+1} > (n+1)^2$. Working from the right-hand side, we have $(n+1)^2 = n^2 + 2n + 1 < n^2 + 2n + n = n^2 + 3n < n^2 + n^2$ (since $n > 3$). Thus we have $(n+1)^2 < 2n^2 < 2 \cdot 2^n$ (by the inductive hypothesis), which in turn equals $2^{n+1}$, as desired.

13. The base case of the statement $P(n) : 1 \cdot 2 + 2 \cdot 3 + \cdots + n(n+1) = n(n+1)(n+2)/3$, when $n = 1$, is $1 \cdot 2 = 1 \cdot 2 \cdot 3/3$, which is certainly true. We assume the inductive hypothesis $P(n)$, and try to derive $P(n+1)$:

$$1 \cdot 2 + 2 \cdot 3 + \cdots + n(n+1) + (n+1)(n+2) = \frac{(n+1)(n+2)(n+3)}{3}.$$

Starting with the left-hand side of $P(n+1)$, we have

$$\left(1 \cdot 2 + 2 \cdot 3 + \cdots + n(n+1)\right) + (n+1)(n+2)$$
$$= \frac{n(n+1)(n+2)}{3} + (n+1)(n+2) \quad \text{(by the inductive hypothesis)}$$
$$= (n+1)(n+2)\left(\frac{n}{3} + 1\right) = \frac{(n+1)(n+2)(n+3)}{3},$$

the right-hand side of $P(n+1)$.

15. The base case of the statement $P(n) : 1^2 - 2^2 + 3^2 - \cdots + (-1)^{n-1}n^2 = (-1)^{n-1}n(n+1)/2$, when $n = 1$, is $1^2 = (-1)^0 \cdot 1 \cdot 2/2$, which is certainly true. Assume the inductive hypothesis $P(n)$, and try to derive $P(n+1)$:

$$1^2 - 2^2 + 3^2 - \cdots + (-1)^{n-1}n^2 + (-1)^n(n+1)^2 = (-1)^n \frac{(n+1)(n+2)}{2}.$$

Starting with the left-hand side of $P(n+1)$, we have

$$\left(1^2 - 2^2 + 3^2 - \cdots + (-1)^{n-1}n^2\right) + (-1)^n(n+1)^2$$

$$= (-1)^{n-1}\frac{n(n+1)}{2} + (-1)^n(n+1)^2 \quad \text{(by the inductive hypothesis)}$$

$$= (-1)^n(n+1)\big((-n/2) + n + 1\big)$$

$$= (-1)^n(n+1)\left(\frac{n}{2}+1\right) = (-1)^n\frac{(n+1)(n+2)}{2},$$

the right-hand side of $P(n+1)$.

17. There are several ways to prove this proposition. One method, using the first principle of mathematical induction, is indicated in the answer section of the textbook. Below we give two proofs—a proof using the second principle of induction, and a direct proof not using induction at all. Incidentally, some mathematical theorems have a dozen or more proofs, often strikingly different from one another.

We first prove this proposition by the second principle of mathematical induction, with three base cases. The proposition we wish to prove is that for $n > 7$ we can find nonnegative integers $a$ and $b$ such that $3a + 5b = 7$. The base cases are for postages of $n = 8$, 9, and 10. These can be achieved with one 3-cent stamp and one 5-cent stamp ($a = 1$ and $b = 1$), three 3-cent stamps ($a = 3$ and $b = 0$), and two 5-cent stamps ($a = 0$ and $b = 2$), respectively. Now assume that the statement is true for all $k$ such that $7 < k < n$, namely that for each such $k$ there exist nonnegative integers $a'$ and $b'$ such that $k = 3a' + 5b'$. We want to show that there exist nonnegative integers $a$ and $b$ such that $n = 3a + 5b$. Since we have already looked at the cases $n \leq 10$, we may assume that $n > 10$, which means that $n - 3 > 7$. Therefore by the inductive hypothesis (with $k = n - 3$) we can find nonnegative integers $a'$ and $b'$ such that $n - 3 = 3a' + 5b'$. Adding 3 to both sides we obtain $n = 3(a' + 1) + 5b'$, which is precisely what we wanted—we take $a = a' + 1$ and $b = b'$.

Next we give a direct proof, arguing as follows. Any positive integer $n$ (the amount of postage, in cents, that we wish to form with our stamps) can be written as $n = 3q + r$, with $q \geq 0$ and $0 \leq r \leq 2$ (this is the division algorithm, Section 2.3). If $r = 0$, then clearly we can form the postage $n$ by using only 3-cent stamps. If $r = 1$, then, since $n > 7$, we know that $q > 2$. Thus we can write $n = \big(3(q-3)+9\big)+1 = 3(q-3)+10$, and we can achieve the desired postage by using $(q-3)$ 3-cent stamps and two 5-cent stamps. Finally, if $r = 2$, then we write $n = 3(q-1)+5$, and use $(q-1)$ 3-cent stamps and one 5-cent stamp.

19. Before we begin, we should point out that using mathematical induction is not the only way to prove this proposition; it can also be proved by considering the five cases determined by the value of $n \bmod 5$. The reader is encouraged to write down such a proof.

To prove that $P(n) : 5 \mid (n^5 - n)$ holds for all nonnegative integers $n$, we first check that $P(0)$ is true; indeed $5 \mid 0$. Next assume that $5 \mid (n^5 - n)$, so that we can write $n^5 - n = 5t$ for some integer $t$. Then we want to prove $P(n+1)$, namely that $5 \mid \big((n+1)^5 - (n+1)\big)$. We expand and then factor the right-hand side to obtain

$$(n+1)^5 - (n+1) = n^5 + 5n^4 + 10n^3 + 10n^2 + 5n + 1 - n - 1$$

$$= (n^5 - n) + 5(n^4 + 2n^3 + 2n^2 + n)$$

$$= 5t + 5(n^4 + 2n^3 + 2n^2 + n) \quad \text{(by the inductive hypothesis)}$$

$$= 5(t + n^4 + 2n^3 + 2n^2 + n).$$

Thus we have shown that $(n+1)^5 - (n+1)$ is also a multiple of 5, and our proof by induction is complete.

**21.** In order to prove this statement, we need to use one of the distributive laws from set theory: $(X \cup Y) \cap Z = (X \cap Z) \cup (Y \cap Z)$ (see Section 1.5). Indeed, the proposition at hand is the generalization of this distributive law, from 2 sets in the union to $n$ sets in the union. We will also be using implicitly the associative law for set union.

The base case, $n = 1$, is the statement $A_1 \cap B = A_1 \cap B$, which is obviously true. Therefore we assume the inductive hypothesis that

$$(A_1 \cup A_2 \cup \cdots \cup A_n) \cap B = (A_1 \cap B) \cup (A_2 \cap B) \cup \cdots \cup (A_n \cap B).$$

We wish to prove the similar statement for $n + 1$, namely

$$(A_1 \cup A_2 \cup \cdots \cup A_n \cup A_{n+1}) \cap B = (A_1 \cap B) \cup (A_2 \cap B) \cup \cdots \cup (A_n \cap B) \cup (A_{n+1} \cap B).$$

Starting with the left-hand side, we apply the distributive law for two sets:

$$\begin{aligned}
((A_1 \cup A_2 \cup \cdots \cup A_n) \cup A_{n+1}) \cap B &= ((A_1 \cup A_2 \cup \cdots \cup A_n) \cap B) \cup (A_{n+1} \cap B) \\
&= ((A_1 \cap B) \cup (A_2 \cap B) \cup \cdots \cup (A_n \cap B)) \cup (A_{n+1} \cap B) \\
&\qquad \text{(by the inductive hypothesis)} \\
&= (A_1 \cap B) \cup (A_2 \cap B) \cup \cdots \cup (A_n \cap B) \cup (A_{n+1} \cap B),
\end{aligned}$$

as desired.

**23.** In order to prove this statement, we need to use one of DeMorgan's laws from set theory: $\overline{(A \cup B)} = \overline{A} \cap \overline{B}$ (see Section 1.5). Indeed, the proposition at hand is the generalization of this law, from 2 sets in the union to $n$ sets in the union. We will also be using implicitly the associative laws for set union and intersection.

The base case, $n = 1$, is the statement $\overline{A_1} = \overline{A_1}$ (since the union or intersection of just one set is the set itself), and this proposition is obviously true. Therefore we assume the inductive hypothesis that

$$\overline{\bigcup_{k=1}^{n} A_k} = \bigcap_{k=1}^{n} \overline{A_k}.$$

We wish to prove the similar statement for $n + 1$, namely

$$\overline{\bigcup_{k=1}^{n+1} A_k} = \bigcap_{k=1}^{n+1} \overline{A_k}.$$

Starting with the left-hand side, we group, apply DeMorgan's law for two sets, and then the inductive hypothesis:

$$\begin{aligned}
\overline{\bigcup_{k=1}^{n+1} A_k} &= \overline{\left(\bigcup_{k=1}^{n} A_k\right) \cup A_{n+1}} \\
&= \overline{\bigcup_{k=1}^{n} A_k} \cap \overline{A_{n+1}} \quad \text{(by DeMorgan's law)} \\
&= \left(\bigcap_{k=1}^{n} \overline{A_k}\right) \cap \overline{A_{n+1}} \quad \text{(by the inductive hypothesis)} \\
&= \bigcap_{k=1}^{n+1} \overline{A_k}.
\end{aligned}$$

**25.** Let $P(n)$ be the proposition

$$[(p_1 \to p_2) \wedge (p_2 \to p_3) \wedge \cdots \wedge (p_{n-1} \to p_n)] \to [(p_1 \wedge p_2 \wedge \cdots \wedge p_{n-1}) \to p_n].$$

We want to prove this proposition for all $n \geq 2$. The base case, $(p_1 \to p_2) \to (p_1 \to p_2)$, is clearly true (a tautology), since any proposition implies itself. Now we assume $P(n)$ and want to show $P(n+1)$, namely

$$[(p_1 \to p_2) \wedge (p_2 \to p_3) \wedge \cdots \wedge (p_{n-1} \to p_n) \wedge (p_n \to p_{n+1})] \to$$
$$[(p_1 \wedge p_2 \wedge \cdots \wedge p_{n-1} \wedge p_n) \to p_{n+1}].$$

To show this, we will assume that the hypothesis (everything in the first square brackets) is true and show that the conclusion (the implication in the second square brackets) is also true.

So we assume $(p_1 \to p_2) \wedge (p_2 \to p_3) \wedge \cdots \wedge (p_{n-1} \to p_n) \wedge (p_n \to p_{n+1})$. By the associativity of $\wedge$, we can group this as $\big((p_1 \to p_2) \wedge (p_2 \to p_3) \wedge \cdots \wedge (p_{n-1} \to p_n)\big) \wedge (p_n \to p_{n+1})$. By the simplification rule, we can conclude that the first group, $(p_1 \to p_2) \wedge (p_2 \to p_3) \wedge \cdots \wedge (p_{n-1} \to p_n)$, must be true. Now the inductive hypothesis allows us to conclude that $(p_1 \wedge p_2 \wedge \cdots \wedge p_{n-1}) \to p_n$. This together with the rest of the assumption, namely $p_n \to p_{n+1}$, yields, by the hypothetical syllogism rule, $(p_1 \wedge p_2 \wedge \cdots \wedge p_{n-1}) \to p_{n+1}$.

That is almost what we wanted to prove, but not quite. We wanted to prove that $(p_1 \wedge p_2 \wedge \cdots \wedge p_{n-1} \wedge p_n) \to p_{n+1}$. In order to prove this, let us assume its hypothesis, $p_1 \wedge p_2 \wedge \cdots \wedge p_{n-1} \wedge p_n$. Again using the simplification rule we obtain $p_1 \wedge p_2 \wedge \cdots \wedge p_{n-1}$. Now by modus ponens with the proposition $(p_1 \wedge p_2 \wedge \cdots \wedge p_{n-1}) \to p_{n+1}$, which we proved above, we obtain $p_{n+1}$. Thus we have proved $(p_1 \wedge p_2 \wedge \cdots \wedge p_{n-1} \wedge p_n) \to p_{n+1}$, as desired.

**27.** The one and only flaw in this proof is in this statement, which is part of the inductive step: "the set of the first $n$ horses and the set of the last $n$ horses [in the collection of $n+1$ horses being considered] overlap." The only assumption made about the number $n$ in this argument is that $n$ is a positive integer. When $n = 1$, so that $n + 1 = 2$, the statement quoted is obviously nonsense: the set of the first horse and the set of the last horse, in this set of two horses, are disjoint.

**29.** To show that the second form of mathematical induction is valid, let us suppose that we have a proposition $\forall n P(n)$ which has been proved using it. We must show that in fact $\forall n P(n)$ is true (to say that a principle of proof is valid means that it proves only true propositions). Let $S$ be the set of counterexamples, i.e., $S = \{ n \mid \neg P(n) \}$. We want to show that $S = \varnothing$. We argue by contradiction. Assume that $S \neq \varnothing$. Then by the well-ordering property, $S$ has a smallest element $n$. Since part of the method of the second form of mathematical induction is to show that $P(1)$ is true, it cannot be the case that $n = 1$. Furthermore, since $n$ is the smallest element of $S$, it must be the case that $P(1) \wedge P(2) \wedge \cdots \wedge P(n-1)$ is true. But the rest of the proof using the second form of mathematical induction involved showing that $P(1) \wedge P(2) \wedge \cdots \wedge P(n-1)$ implied $P(n)$; therefore since the hypothesis is true, the conclusion must be true as well, i.e., $P(n)$ is true. This contradicts our assumption that $n \in S$. Therefore we conclude that $S = \varnothing$, so $\forall n P(n)$ is true.

**31.** Recall that $H_k = 1/1 + 1/2 + \cdots + 1/k$. We want to prove that $H_{2^n} \leq 1 + n$ for all $n$. We proceed by induction, noting that the base case $n = 0$ is the trivial statement $H_1 = 1 \leq 1 + 0$. Therefore we assume that $H_{2^n} \leq 1 + n$; we want to show that $H_{2^{n+1}} \leq 1 + (n+1)$. We have

$$H_{2^{n+1}} = H_{2^n} + \frac{1}{2^n+1} + \frac{1}{2^n+2} + \cdots + \frac{1}{2^{n+1}} \quad \text{(by definition; there are } 2^n \text{ fractions here)}$$

$$\leq (1+n) + \frac{1}{2^n+1} + \frac{1}{2^n+2} + \cdots + \frac{1}{2^{n+1}} \quad \text{(by the inductive hypothesis)}$$

$$\leq (1+n) + \frac{1}{2^n+1} + \frac{1}{2^n+1} + \cdots + \frac{1}{2^n+1} \quad \text{(we made the denominators smaller)}$$

$$= 1 + n + \frac{2^n}{2^n+1} < 1 + n + 1 = 1 + (n+1).$$

33. This exercise involves some messy algebra, but the logic is the usual logic for proofs by induction. We prove the given statement by induction. The base case ($n = 1$) is true, since 1 is greater than $2(\sqrt{2} - 1) \approx 0.83$. We assume that

$$1 + \frac{1}{\sqrt{2}} + \cdots + \frac{1}{\sqrt{n}} > 2(\sqrt{n+1} - 1)$$

and try to derive the corresponding statement for $n + 1$:

$$1 + \frac{1}{\sqrt{2}} + \cdots + \frac{1}{\sqrt{n}} + \frac{1}{\sqrt{n+1}} > 2(\sqrt{n+2} - 1).$$

Since by the inductive hypothesis we know that

$$1 + \frac{1}{\sqrt{2}} + \cdots + \frac{1}{\sqrt{n}} + \frac{1}{\sqrt{n+1}} > 2(\sqrt{n+1} - 1) + \frac{1}{\sqrt{n+1}},$$

we will be finished if we can show that the inequality

$$2(\sqrt{n+1} - 1) + \frac{1}{\sqrt{n+1}} > 2(\sqrt{n+2} - 1)$$

holds. By cancelling the $-2$ from both sides and rearranging, we obtain the equivalent inequality

$$2(\sqrt{n+2} - \sqrt{n+1}) < \frac{1}{\sqrt{n+1}},$$

which in turn is equivalent to

$$2(\sqrt{n+2} - \sqrt{n+1})(\sqrt{n+2} + \sqrt{n+1}) < \frac{\sqrt{n+1}}{\sqrt{n+1}} + \frac{\sqrt{n+2}}{\sqrt{n+1}}.$$

This last inequality simplifies to

$$2 < 1 + \frac{\sqrt{n+2}}{\sqrt{n+1}},$$

which is clearly true. Therefore the original inequality is true, and our proof is complete.

35. This exercise, as the double star indicates, is quite hard. The trick is to induct not on $n$ itself, but rather on $\log n$. In other words, we write $n = 2^k$ and prove the statement by induction on $k$. This will prove the statement for all $n$ which are a power of 2; a separate argument is needed to extend to the general case.

We take the base case to be $k = 1$ (the case $k = 0$ is trivially true, as well), so that $n = 2^1 = 2$. In this case the trick is to start with the true inequality $(\sqrt{a_1} - \sqrt{a_2})^2 \geq 0$. Expanding, we have $a_1 - 2\sqrt{a_1 a_2} + a_2 \geq 0$, whence $(a_1 + a_2)/2 \geq (a_1 a_2)^{1/2}$, as desired. For the inductive step, we assume that the inequality holds for $n = 2^k$ and prove that it also holds for $2n = 2^{k+1}$. What we need to show, then, is that

$$\frac{a_1 + a_2 + \cdots + a_{2n}}{2n} \geq (a_1 a_2 \cdots a_{2n})^{1/(2n)}.$$

First we observe that

$$\frac{a_1 + a_2 + \cdots + a_{2n}}{2n} = \left( \frac{a_1 + a_2 + \cdots + a_n}{n} + \frac{a_{n+1} + a_{n+2} + \cdots + a_{2n}}{n} \right) \bigg/ 2$$

and

$$(a_1 a_2 \cdots a_{2n})^{1/(2n)} = \left( (a_1 a_2 \cdots a_n)^{1/n} (a_{n+1} a_{n+2} \cdots a_{2n})^{1/n} \right)^{1/2}.$$

Now to simplify notation, let $A(x, y, \ldots)$ denote the arithmetic mean and $G(x, y, \ldots)$ denote the geometric mean of the numbers $x, y, \ldots$. It is clear that if $x \leq x'$, $y \leq y'$, and so on, then $A(x, y, \ldots) \leq A(x', y', \ldots)$ and $G(x, y, \ldots) \leq G(x', y', \ldots)$. Now we have

$$
\begin{aligned}
A(a_1, \ldots, a_{2n}) &= A\big(A(a_1, \ldots, a_n), A(a_{n+1}, \ldots, a_{2n})\big) &&\text{(by the first observation above)} \\
&\geq A\big(G(a_1, \ldots, a_n), G(a_{n+1}, \ldots, a_{2n})\big) &&\text{(by the inductive hypothesis)} \\
&\geq G\big(G(a_1, \ldots, a_n), G(a_{n+1}, \ldots, a_{2n})\big) &&\text{(this was the case } n = 2) \\
&= G(a_1, \ldots, a_{2n}) &&\text{(by the second observation above)}.
\end{aligned}
$$

Having proved the inequality in the case in which $n$ is a power of 2, we now turn to the case of $n$ which is not a power of 2. Let $m$ be the smallest power of 2 bigger than $m$. (For instance, if $n = 25$, then $m = 32$.) Denote the arithmetic mean $A(a_1, \ldots, a_n)$ by $a$, and set $a_{n+1} = a_{n+2} = \cdots = a_m$ all equal to $a$. One effect of this is that then $A(a_1, \ldots, a_m) = a$. Now we have

$$\left( \big(\prod_{i=1}^{n} a_i\big) a^{m-n} \right)^{1/m} \leq A(a_1, \ldots, a_m)$$

by the case we have already proved, since $m$ is a power of 2. Using algebra on the left-hand side and the observation that $A(a_1, \ldots, a_m) = a$ on the right, we obtain

$$\big(\prod_{i=1}^{n} a_i\big)^{1/m} a^{1-n/m} \leq a$$

or

$$\big(\prod_{i=1}^{n} a_i\big)^{1/m} \leq a^{n/m}.$$

Finally we raise both sides to the power $m/n$ to give

$$\big(\prod_{i=1}^{n} a_i\big)^{1/n} \leq a,$$

as desired.

37. The proof in Example 12 guides us to one solution (it is certainly not unique). We begin by placing an L-shaped piece in the center, with its gap in the same quadrant as the missing square in the upper left corner of the board (this piece is distinctively shaded in our solution below). This reduces the problem to four problems on $4 \times 4$ boards. Then we place L-shaped pieces in the centers of these four

quadrants, using the same principle (shaded somewhat differently below). Finally, we place pieces in the remaining squares to fill up each quadrant.

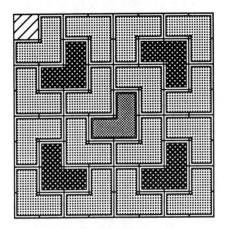

39. Suppose we have two such pairs, say $(q, r)$ and $(q', r')$, so that $a = dq+r = dq'+r'$, with $0 \leq r, r' < d$. We will show that the pairs are really the same, that is, that $q = q'$ and $r = r'$. From $dq+r = dq'+r'$ we obtain $d(q-q') = r'-r$. Therefore $d \,|\, (r'-r)$. But $|r'-r| < d$ (since both $r'$ and $r$ are nonnegative integers less than $d$). The only multiple of $d$ in that range is $0$, so we are forced to conclude that $r' = r$. Then it easily follows that $q = q'$ as well, since $q = (a - r)/d = (a - r')/d = q'$.

$\Rightarrow$ **SECTION 3.3    Recursive Definitions**

*The best way to approach a recursive definition is first to compute several instances. For example, if you are given a recursive definition of a function $f$, then compute $f(0)$ through $f(8)$ to get a feeling for what is happening. Most of the time it is necessary to prove statements about recursively defined objects using induction, and the induction practically takes care of itself, mimicking the recursive definition.*

1. In each case, we compute $f(1)$ by using the recursive part of the definition with $n = 0$, together with the given fact that $f(0) = 1$. Then we compute $f(2)$ by using the recursive part of the definition with $n = 1$, together with the given value of $f(1)$. We continue in this way to obtain $f(3)$ and $f(4)$.

   **a)** $f(1) = f(0) + 2 = 1 + 2 = 3$; $f(2) = f(1) + 2 = 3 + 2 = 5$; $f(3) = f(2) + 2 = 5 + 2 = 7$; $f(4) = f(3) + 2 = 7 + 2 = 9$.

   **b)** $f(1) = 3f(0) = 3 \cdot 1 = 3$; $f(2) = 3f(1) = 3 \cdot 3 = 9$; $f(3) = 3f(2) = 3 \cdot 9 = 27$; $f(4) = 3f(3) = 3 \cdot 27 = 81$.

   **c)** $f(1) = 2^{f(0)} = 2^1 = 2$; $f(2) = 2^{f(1)} = 2^2 = 4$; $f(3) = 2^{f(2)} = 2^4 = 16$; $f(4) = 2^{f(3)} = 2^{16} = 65{,}536$.

   **d)** $f(1) = f(0)^2 + f(0) + 1 = 1^2 + 1 + 1 = 3$; $f(2) = f(1)^2 + f(1) + 1 = 3^2 + 3 + 1 = 13$; $f(3) = f(2)^2 + f(2) + 1 = 13^2 + 13 + 1 = 183$; $f(4) = f(3)^2 + f(3) + 1 = 183^2 + 183 + 1 = 33{,}673$.

3. We need to write $F(n+1)$ in terms of $F(n)$. Since $F(n)$ is the sum of the first $n$ positive integers (namely 1 through $n$), and $F(n+1)$ is the sum of the first $n+1$ positive integers (namely 1 through $n+1$), we can obtain $F(n+1)$ from $F(n)$ by adding $n+1$. Therefore the recursive part of the definition is $F(n+1) = F(n) + n + 1$. The initial condition is a specification of the value of $F(0)$; the sum of no positive integers is clearly 0, so we set $F(0) = 0$. (Alternately, if we assume that the argument for $F$ is intended to be strictly positive, then we set $F(1) = 1$, since the sum of the first one positive integer is 1.)

5. We need to see how $P_m(n+1)$ relates to $P_m(n)$. Now $P_m(n+1) = m(n+1) = mn + m = P_m(n) + m$. Thus the recursive part of our definition is just $P_m(n+1) = P_m(n) + m$. The base case is $P_m(0) = 0$, since $m \cdot 0 = 0$, no matter what value $m$ has.

7. We prove this by induction. The base case is $n = 1$, and in that case the statement to be proved is just $f_1 = f_2$; this is true since both values are 1. Next we assume the inductive hypothesis, that

$$f_1 + f_3 + \cdots + f_{2n-1} = f_{2n},$$

and try to prove the corresponding statement for $n+1$, namely,

$$f_1 + f_3 + \cdots + f_{2n-1} + f_{2n+1} = f_{2n+2}.$$

We have

$$f_1 + f_3 + \cdots + f_{2n-1} + f_{2n+1} = f_{2n} + f_{2n+1} \quad \text{(by the inductive hypothesis)}$$
$$= f_{2n+2} \quad \text{(by the definition of the Fibonacci numbers)}.$$

9. Let $d_n$ be the number of divisions used by Algorithm 1 in Section 2.4 (the Euclidean algorithm) to find $gcd(f_{n+1}, f_n)$. We write the calculation in this order, since $f_{n+1} \geq f_n$. We begin by finding the values of $d_n$ for the first few values of $n$, in order to find a pattern and make a conjecture as to what the answer is. For $n = 0$ we are computing $gcd(f_1, f_0) = gcd(1, 0)$. Without performing any divisions, we know immediately that the answer is 1, so $d_0 = 0$. For $n = 1$ we are computing $gcd(f_2, f_1) = gcd(1, 1)$. One division is used to show that $gcd(1, 1) = gcd(1, 0)$, so $d_1 = 1$. For $n = 2$ we are computing $gcd(f_3, f_2) = gcd(2, 1)$. One division is used to show that $gcd(2, 1) = gcd(1, 0)$, so $d_2 = 1$. For $n = 3$, the computation gives successively $gcd(f_4, f_3) = gcd(3, 2) = gcd(2, 1) = gcd(1, 0)$, for a total of 2 divisions; thus $d_3 = 2$. For $n = 4$, we have $gcd(f_5, f_4) = gcd(5, 3) = gcd(3, 2) = gcd(2, 1) = gcd(1, 0)$, for a total of 3 divisions; thus $d_4 = 3$. At this point we see that each increase of 1 in $n$ seems to add one more division, in order to reduce $gcd(f_{n+1}, f_n)$ to $gcd(f_n, f_{n-1})$. Perhaps, then, for $n \geq 2$, we have $d_n = n - 1$. Let us make that conjecture. We have already verified the base case when we computed that $d_2 = 1$. Now assume the inductive hypothesis, that $d_n = n - 1$. We must show that $d_{n+1} = n$. Now $d_{n+1}$ is the number of divisions used in computing $gcd(f_{n+2}, f_{n+1})$. The first step in the algorithm is to divide $f_{n+1}$ into $f_{n+2}$. Since $f_{n+2} = f_{n+1} + f_n$ (this is the key point) and $f_n < f_{n+1}$, we get a quotient of 1 and a remainder of $f_n$. Thus we have, after one division, $gcd(f_{n+2}, f_{n+1}) = gcd(f_{n+1}, f_n)$. Now by the inductive hypothesis we need exactly $d_n$ divisions, since the algorithm proceeds from this point exactly as it proceeded given the inputs for the case of $n$. Therefore there are a total of $1 + d_n = 1 + (n-1) = n$ divisions used, and our proof is complete. The answer, then, is that $d_0 = 0$, $d_1 = 1$, and $d_n = n - 1$ for $n \geq 2$. (If we interpreted the problem as insisting that we compute $gcd(f_n, f_{n+1})$, with that order of the arguments, then the analysis and the answer are slightly different: $d_0 = 1$, and $d_n = n$ for $n \geq 1$.)

**11.** The determinant of the matrix $\mathbf{A} = \begin{bmatrix} a & b \\ c & d \end{bmatrix}$, written $|\mathbf{A}|$, is by definition $ad-bc$; and the determinant has the multiplicative property that $|\mathbf{AB}| = |\mathbf{A}||\mathbf{B}|$. Therefore the determinant of the matrix $\mathbf{A} = \begin{bmatrix} 1 & 1 \\ 1 & 0 \end{bmatrix}$ in Exercise 10 is $1 \cdot 0 - 1 \cdot 1 = -1$, and $|\mathbf{A}^n| = |\mathbf{A}|^n = (-1)^n$. On the other hand, the determinant of the matrix $\begin{bmatrix} f_{n+1} & f_n \\ f_n & f_{n-1} \end{bmatrix}$ is by definition $f_{n+1}f_{n-1} - f_n^2$. In Exercise 10 we showed that $\mathbf{A}^n$ is this latter matrix. The identity in Exercise 8 follows.

**13.** Assume the definitions given in Exercise 12 were as follows: the max or min of one number is itself; $\max(a_1, a_2) = a_1$ if $a_1 \geq a_2$ and $a_2$ if $a_1 < a_2$, whereas $\min(a_1, a_2) = a_2$ if $a_1 \geq a_2$ and $a_1$ if $a_1 < a_2$; and for $n \geq 2$,

$$\max(a_1, a_2, \ldots, a_{n+1}) = \max(\max(a_1, a_2, \ldots, a_n), a_{n+1})$$

and

$$\min(a_1, a_2, \ldots, a_{n+1}) = \min(\min(a_1, a_2, \ldots, a_n), a_{n+1}).$$

We can then prove the three statements here by induction on $n$.

**a)** For $n = 1$, both sides of the equation equal $-a_1$. For $n = 2$, we must show that $\max(-a_1, -a_2) = -\min(a_1, a_2)$. There are two cases, depending on the relationship between $a_1$ and $a_2$. If $a_1 \leq a_2$, then $-a_1 \geq -a_2$, so by our definition, $\max(-a_1, -a_2) = -a_1$. On the other hand our definition implies that $\min(a_1, a_2) = a_1$. Therefore $\max(-a_1, -a_2) = -a_1 = -\min(a_1, a_2)$. The other case, $a_1 > a_2$, is similar: $\max(-a_1, -a_2) = -a_2 = -\min(a_1, a_2)$. Now we are ready for the inductive step. Assume the inductive hypothesis, that

$$\max(-a_1, -a_2, \ldots, -a_n) = -\min(a_1, a_2, \ldots, a_n).$$

We need to show the corresponding equality for $n + 1$. We have

$$\max(-a_1, -a_2, \ldots, -a_n, -a_{n+1})$$
$$= \max(\max(-a_1, -a_2, \ldots, -a_n), -a_{n+1}) \quad \text{(by definition)}$$
$$= \max(-\min(a_1, a_2, \ldots, a_n), -a_{n+1}) \quad \text{(by the inductive hypothesis)}$$
$$= -\min(\min(a_1, a_2, \ldots, a_n), a_{n+1}) \quad \text{(by the inductive hypothesis for } n = 2)$$
$$= -\min(a_1, a_2, \ldots, a_n, a_{n+1}) \quad \text{(by definition)}.$$

**b)** For $n = 1$, the equation is simply the identity $a_1 + b_1 = a_1 + b_1$. For $n = 2$, the situation is a little messy. Let us consider first the case that $a_1 + b_1 \geq a_2 + b_2$. Then $\max(a_1 + b_1, a_2 + b_2) = a_1 + b_1$. Also note that $a_1 \leq \max(a_1, b_1)$, and $b_1 \leq \max(b_1, b_2)$, so that $a_1 + b_1 \leq \max(a_1, a_2) + \max(b_1, b_2)$. Therefore we have $\max(a_1 + b_1, a_2 + b_2) = a_1 + b_1 \leq \max(a_1, a_2) + \max(b_1, b_2)$. The other case, in which $a_1 + b_1 < a_2 + b_2$, is similar. Now for the inductive step, we first need a lemma: if $u \leq v$, then $\max(u, w) \leq \max(v, w)$; this is easy to prove by looking at the three cases determined by the size of $w$ relative to the sizes of $u$ and $v$. Now assuming the inductive hypothesis, we have

$$\max(a_1 + b_1, a_2 + b_2, \ldots, a_n + b_n, a_{n+1} + b_{n+1})$$
$$= \max(\max(a_1 + b_1, a_2 + b_2, \ldots, a_n + b_n), a_{n+1} + b_{n+1}) \quad \text{(by definition)}$$
$$\leq \max(\max(a_1, a_2, \ldots, a_n) + \max(b_1, b_2, \ldots, b_n), a_{n+1} + b_{n+1})$$
$$\quad \text{(by the inductive hypothesis and the lemma)}$$
$$\leq \max(\max(a_1, a_2, \ldots, a_n), a_{n+1}) + \max(\max(b_1, b_2, \ldots, b_n), b_{n+1})$$
$$\quad \text{(by the inductive hypothesis for } n = 2)$$
$$= \max(a_1, a_2, \ldots, a_n, a_{n+1}) + \max(b_1, b_2, \ldots, b_n, b_{n+1}) \quad \text{(by definition)}.$$

**c)** The proof here is exactly dual to the proof in part **(b)**. We replace every occurrence of "max" by "min," and invert each inequality. The proof then reads as follows. For $n = 1$, the equation is simply the identity $a_1 + b_1 = a_1 + b_1$. For $n = 2$, the situation is a little messy. Let us consider first the case that $a_1 + b_1 \leq a_2 + b_2$. Then $\min(a_1 + b_1, a_2 + b_2) = a_1 + b_1$. Also note that $a_1 \geq \min(a_1, a_2)$, and $b_1 \geq \min(b_1, b_2)$, so that $a_1 + b_1 \geq \min(a_1, a_2) + \min(b_1, b_2)$. Therefore we have $\min(a_1 + b_1, a_2 + b_2) = a_1 + b_1 \geq \min(a_1, a_2) + \min(b_1, b_2)$. The other case, in which $a_1 + b_1 > a_2 + b_2$, is similar. Now for the inductive step, we first need a lemma: if $u \geq v$, then $\min(u, w) \geq \min(v, w)$; this is easy to prove by looking at the three cases determined by the size of $w$ relative to the sizes of $u$ and $v$. Now assuming the inductive hypothesis, we have

$$\min(a_1 + b_1, a_2 + b_2, \ldots, a_n + b_n, a_{n+1} + b_{n+1})$$

$$= \min(\min(a_1 + b_1, a_2 + b_2, \ldots, a_n + b_n), a_{n+1} + b_{n+1}) \quad \text{(by definition)}$$

$$\geq \min(\min(a_1, a_2, \ldots, a_n) + \min(b_1, b_2, \ldots, b_n), a_{n+1} + b_{n+1})$$

$$\text{(by the inductive hypothesis and the lemma)}$$

$$\geq \min(\min(a_1, a_2, \ldots, a_n), a_{n+1}) + \min(\min(b_1, b_2, \ldots, b_n), b_{n+1})$$

$$\text{(by the inductive hypothesis for } n = 2\text{)}$$

$$= \min(a_1, a_2, \ldots, a_n, a_{n+1}) + \min(b_1, b_2, \ldots, b_n, b_{n+1}) \quad \text{(by definition)}.$$

**15.** We can define the set $S = \{ x \mid x \text{ is a positive integer and } x \text{ is a multiple of } 5 \}$ by the base case requirement that $5 \in S$ and the recursive requirement that if $n \in S$, then $n + 5 \in S$. Alternately we can mimic Example 7, making the recursive part of the definition that $x + y \in S$ whenever $x$ and $y$ are in $S$.

**17.** The answer depends on whether we require fully parenthesized expressions. Assuming that we do not, then the following definition is the most straightforward. Let $F$ be the required collection of formulae. The base case is that all specific sets and all variables representing sets are to be in $F$. The recursive part of the definition is that if $\alpha$ and $\beta$ are in $F$, then so are $\overline{\alpha}$, $(\alpha)$, $\alpha \cup \beta$, $\alpha \cap \beta$, and $\alpha - \beta$.

**19.** The string of length 0, namely the empty string, is its own reversal, so we define $\lambda^R = \lambda$. A string $w$ of length $n + 1$ can always be written as $vy$, where $v$ is a string of length $n$ (the first $n$ symbols of $w$), and $y$ is a symbol (the last symbol of $w$). To reverse $w$, we need to start with $y$, and then follow it by the first part of $w$ (namely $v$), reversed. Thus we define $w^R = y(v^R)$.

**21.** We set $w^0 = \lambda$ (the concatenation of no copies of $w$ should be defined to be the empty string). For $i \geq 0$, we define $w^{i+1} = ww^i$, where this notation means that we first write down $w$ and then follow it with $w^i$.

**23.** The recursive part of this definition tells us that the only way to modify a string in $A$ to obtain another string in $A$ is to tack a 0 onto the front and a 1 onto the end. Starting with the empty string, then, the only strings we get are $\lambda$, 01, 0011, 000111, $\ldots$. In other words, $A = \{ 0^n 1^n \mid n \geq 0 \}$.

**25.** The base case is $i = 0$, where we need to show that the length of $w^0$ is 0 times the length of $w$. This is true, no matter what $w$ is, since $l(w^0) = l(\lambda) = 0$. Assume the inductive hypothesis that $l(w^i) = i \cdot l(w)$. Then $l(w^{i+1}) = l(ww^i) = l(w) + l(w^i)$, this latter equality having been shown in Example 12. Now by the inductive hypothesis we have $l(w) + l(w^i) = l(w) + i \cdot l(w) = (i + 1) \cdot l(w)$, as desired.

**27.** **a)** It is clear that $P_{mm} = P_m$, since a number exceeding $m$ can never be used in a partition of $m$.

**b)** We need to verify all five lines of this definition, show that the recursive references are to a smaller value of $m$ or $n$, and check that they take care of all the cases and are mutually compatible. Let us do the last of these first. The first two lines take care of the case in which either $m$ or $n$ is equal to 1. They are consistent with each other in case $m = n = 1$. The last three lines are mutually exclusive and take care of all the possibilities for $m$ and $n$ if neither is equal to 1, since, given any two numbers, either they are equal or one is greater than the other. Note finally that the third line allows $m = 1$; in that case the value is defined to be $P_{11}$, which is consistent with the first two lines, since $P_{1n} = P_{11} = 1$.

Next let us make sure that the logic of the definition is sound, specifically that $P_{mn}$ is being defined in terms of $P_{ij}$ for $i \leq m$ and $j \leq n$, with at least one of the inequalities strict. There is no problem with the first two lines, since these are not recursive. The third line is okay, since $m < n$, and $P_{mn}$ is being defined in terms of $P_{mm}$. The fourth line is also okay, since here $P_{mm}$ is being defined in terms of $P_{m,m-1}$. Finally, the last line is okay, since the subscripts satisfy the desired inequalities.

Finally, we need to check the content of each line. (Note that so far we have not even discussed what $P_{mn}$ means!) The first line says that there is only one way to write the number 1 as the sum of positive integers, none of which exceeds $n$, and that is patently true, namely as $1 = 1$. The second line says that there is only one way to write the number $m$ as the sum of positive integers, none of which exceeds 1, and that, too, is obvious, namely $m = 1 + 1 + \cdots + 1$. The third line says that the number of ways to write $m$ as the sum of integers not exceeding $n$ is the same as the number of ways to write $m$ as the sum of integers not exceeding $m$ as long as $m < n$. This again is true, since we could never use a number from $\{m+1, m+2, \ldots, n\}$ in such a sum anyway. Now we begin to get to the meat. The fourth line says that the number of ways to write $m$ as the sum of positive integers not exceeding $m$ is 1 plus the number of ways to write $m$ as the sum of positive integers not exceeding $m - 1$. Indeed, there is exactly one way to write $m$ as the sum of positive integers not exceeding $m$ that actually uses $m$, namely $m = m$; all the rest use only numbers less than or equal to $m - 1$. This verifies line four. The real heart of the matter is line five. How can we write $m$ as the sum of positive integers not exceeding $n$? We may use an $n$, or we may not. There are exactly $P_{m,n-1}$ ways to form the sum without using $n$, since in that case each summand is less than or equal to $n - 1$. If we do use at least one $n$, then we have $m = n + (m - n)$. The number of ways this can be done, then, is the same as the number of ways to complete the partition by writing $(m - n)$ as the sum of positive integers not exceeding $n$. Thus there are $P_{m-n,n}$ ways to write $m$ as the sum of numbers not exceeding $n$, at least one of which equals $n$. By the sum rule, we have $P_{mn} = P_{m,n-1} + P_{m-n,n}$, as desired.

**c)** We expand each $P_{mn}$ according to the definition. For the first problem we have $P_5 = P_{55} = 1 + P_{54} = 1 + P_{53} + P_{14} = 1 + P_{52} + P_{23} + 1 = 1 + P_{51} + P_{32} + P_{22} + 1 = 1 + 1 + P_{31} + P_{12} + 1 + P_{21} + 1 = 1 + 1 + 1 + 1 + 1 + 1 + 1 = 7$. For the second problem we have $P_6 = P_{66} = 1 + P_{65} = 1 + P_{64} + P_{15} = 1 + P_{63} + P_{24} + 1 = 1 + P_{62} + P_{33} + P_{22} + 1 = 1 + P_{61} + P_{42} + 1 + P_{32} + 1 + P_{21} + 1 = 1 + 1 + P_{41} + P_{22} + 1 + P_{31} + P_{12} + 1 + 1 + 1 = 1 + 1 + 1 + 1 + P_{21} + 1 + 1 + 1 + 1 + 1 + 1 = 1 + 1 + 1 + 1 + 1 + 1 + 1 + 1 + 1 + 1 + 1 = 11$.

**29.** We prove this by induction on $m$. The base case is $m = 1$, so we need to compute $A(1, 2)$. Line four of the definition tells us that $A(1, 2) = A(0, A(1, 1))$. Since $A(1, 1) = 2$, by line three, we see that $A(1, 2) = A(0, 2)$. Now line one of the definition applies, and we see that $A(1, 2) = A(0, 2) = 2 \cdot 2 = 4$, as desired. For the inductive step, assume that $A(m - 1, 2) = 4$, and consider $A(m, 2)$. Applying first line four of the definition, then line three, and then the inductive hypothesis, we have

$$A(m, 2) = A(m - 1, A(m, 1)) = A(m - 1, 2) = 4.$$

**31.** It is often the case in proofs by induction that you need to prove something stronger than the given proposition, in order to have a stronger inductive hypothesis to work with. That is the case here. We will prove the statement "$A(m, k) > A(m, l)$ if $k > l$ for all $m$, $k$, and $l$," and we will use **double induction**, inducting first on $m$, and then within the inductive step for that induction, inducting on $k$ (using the second principle of mathematical induction). Note that this stronger statement implies the statement we are trying to prove—just take $k = l + 1$.

The base case is $m = 0$, in which the statement at hand reduces (by line one of the definition) to the true implication that if $k > l$, then $2k > 2l$. Next we assume the inductive hypothesis, namely that $A(m, x) > A(m, y)$ for all values of $x$ and $y$ with $x > y$. We want now to show that if $k > l$, then $A(m + 1, k) > A(m + 1, l)$. This we will do by induction on $k$. For the base case, $k = 0$, there is nothing to prove, since the condition $k > l$ is vacuous. Similarly, if $k = 1$, then $A(m + 1, k) = 2$ and $A(m + 1, l) = 0$ (since necessarily $l = 0$), so the desired inequality holds. So assume the inductive hypothesis (using the second principle of induction), that $A(m+1, r) > A(m+1, s)$ whenever $k > r > s$, where $k \geq 2$. We need to show that $A(m + 1, k) > A(m + 1, l)$ if $k > l$. Now $A(m + 1, k) = A(m, A(m + 1, k - 1))$ by line four of the definition. Since $k - 1 \geq l$, we apply the inductive hypothesis on $k$ to yield $A(m + 1, k - 1) > A(m + 1, l - 1)$, and therefore by the inductive hypothesis on $m$, we have $A(m, A(m+1, k-1)) > A(m, A(m+1, l-1))$. But this latter value equals $A(m + 1, l)$, as long as $l \geq 2$. Thus we have shown that $A(m + 1, k) > A(m + 1, l)$ as long as $l \geq 2$. On the other hand, if $l = 0$ or 1, then $A(m + 1, l) \leq 2$ (by lines two and three of the definition), whereas $A(m + 1, 2) = 4$ by Exercise 29. Therefore $A(m + 1, k) \geq A(m + 1, 2) > A(m + 1, l)$. This completes the proof.

**33.** We repeatedly invoke the result of Exercise 32, which says that $A(m + 1, j) \geq A(m, j)$. Indeed, we have $A(i, j) \geq A(i - 1, j) \geq \cdots \geq A(0, j) = 2j \geq j$.

**35.** Let $P(n)$ be the statement "$F(n)$ is well-defined." We need to show that $P(n)$ is true for all $n$. We do this by induction, using the second principle. First $P(0)$ is true, since $F(0)$ is well-defined by the specification of $F(0)$. Next assume that $P(k)$ is true for all $k < n$. We want to show that $P(n)$ is also true, in other words that $F(n)$ is well-defined. Since the definition gave $F(n)$ in terms of $F(0)$ through $F(n - 1)$, and since we are assuming that these are all well-defined (our inductive hypothesis), we conclude that $F(n)$ is well-defined, as desired.

⇒ **SECTION 3.4   Recursive Algorithms**

*Recursive algorithms are important theoretical entities, but they often cause a lot of grief on first encounter. Sometimes it is helpful to "play computer" very carefully to see how a recursive algorithm works. However it is good to avoid doing that after you get the idea. Instead, convince yourself that if the recursive algorithm handles the base case correctly, and handles the recursive step correctly (gives the correct answer assuming the correct answer was obtained on the recursive call), then the algorithm works. Let the computer worry about actually "recursing all the way down to the base case"!*

**1.** The key idea for this recursive procedure is that $nx = (n - 1)x + x$. Thus we compute $nx$ by calling the procedure recursively, with $n$ replaced by $n - 1$, and adding $x$. The base case is $1 \cdot x = x$.

> **procedure** *product*($n$ : positive integer, $x$ : integer)
> **if** $n = 1$ **then** *product*$(n, x) := x$
> **else** *product*$(n, x) := $ *product*$(n - 1, x) + x$

3.  We recurse on the size of the list. If there is only one element, then it is the smallest. Otherwise, we find the smallest element in the list consisting of all but the last element of our original list, and compare it with the last element of the original list. Whichever is smaller is the answer. (We assume that there is already a function min, defined for two arguments, which returns the smaller.)

> **procedure** *smallest*$(a_1, a_2, \ldots, a_n$ : integers)
> **if** $n = 1$ **then** *smallest*$(a_1, a_2, \ldots, a_n) := a_1$
> **else** *smallest*$(a_1, a_2, \ldots, a_n) := \min($ *smallest*$(a_1, a_2, \ldots, a_{n-1}), a_n)$

5.  We need to worry about which of our arguments is the larger. Since we are given $a < b$ as input, we need to make sure always to call the algorithm with the first argument less than the second. There need to be two stopping conditions: when $a = 0$ (in which case the answer is $b$), and when the two arguments have become equal (in which case the answer is their common value). Otherwise we use the recursive condition that $gcd(a, b) = gcd(a, b - a)$, taking care to reverse the arguments if necessary.

> **procedure** *gcd*$(a, b$ : integers with $a < b)$
> **if** $a = 0$ **then** *gcd*$(a, b) := b$
> **else if** $a = b - a$ **then** *gcd*$(a, b) := a$
> **else if** $a < b - a$ **then** *gcd*$(a, b) := $ *gcd*$(a, b - a)$
> **else** *gcd*$(a, b) := $ *gcd*$(b - a, a)$

7.  Algorithm 1 uses $2^n$ multiplications by $a$, one for each factor of $a$ in the product $a^{2^n}$. The algorithm in Exercise 6, based on squaring, uses only $n$ multiplications (each of which is a multiplication of a number by itself). For instance, to compute $a^{2^4} = a^{16}$, the algorithm will compute $a \cdot a = a^2$ (one multiplication), then $a^2 \cdot a^2 = a^4$ (a second multiplication), then $a^4 \cdot a^4 = a^8$ (a third), and finally $a^8 \cdot a^8 = a^{16}$ (a fourth multiplication).

9.  Algorithm 1 uses $n$ multiplications by $a$, one for each factor of $a$ in the product $a^n$. The algorithm in Exercise 8 will use $O(\log n)$ multiplications as it computes squares. Furthermore, in addition to squaring, sometimes a multiplication by $a$ is needed; this will add at most another $O(\log n)$ multiplications. Thus a total of $O(\log n)$ multiplications are used altogether.

11.  This is very similar to the recursive procedure for computing the Fibonacci numbers. Note that we can combine the two base cases (stopping rules) into one.

> **procedure** *sequence*$(n$ : nonnegative integer)
> **if** $n < 2$ **then** *sequence*$(n) := n + 1$
> **else** *sequence*$(n) := $ *sequence*$(n - 1) \cdot $ *sequence*$(n - 2)$

13.  The iterative version is much more efficient. The analysis is exactly the same as that for the Fibonacci sequence given in this section. Indeed, the $n^{\text{th}}$ term in this sequence is actually just $2^{f_n}$, as is easily shown by induction.

15.  We use the recursive definition of the reversal of a string given in Exercise 19 of Section 3.3, namely that $(vy)^R = y(v^R)$, where $y$ is the last symbol in the string and $v$ is the substring consisting of all but the last symbol.

> **procedure** $reverse(b_1 b_2 \ldots b_n : \text{bit string})$
> **if** $n = 0$ **then** $reverse(b_1 b_2 \ldots b_n) := \lambda$
> **else** $reverse(b_1 b_2 \ldots b_n) := b_n \, reverse(b_1 b_2 \ldots b_{n-1})$

**17.** Essentially all we do is to write down the definition as a procedure.

> **procedure** $ackermann(m, n : \text{nonnegative integers})$
> **if** $m = 0$ **then** $ackermann(m, n) := 2 \cdot n$
> **else if** $n = 0$ **then** $ackermann(m, n) := 0$
> **else if** $n = 1$ **then** $ackermann(m, n) := 2$
> **else** $ackermann(m, n) := ackermann(m - 1, ackermann(m, n - 1))$

$\Rightarrow$ **SECTION 3.5    Program Correctness**

*Entire books have been written on program verification; obviously here we barely scratch the surface. In some sense program verification is just a very careful stepping through a program to prove that it works correctly. There should be no problem verifying anything except loops; indeed it may seem that there is nothing to prove. Loops are harder to deal with. The trick is to find the right invariant. Once you have the invariant, it again is really a matter of stepping through one pass of the loop to make sure that the invariant is satisfied at the end of that pass, given that it was satisfied at the beginning. Analogous to our remark in the comments for Section 3.1, there is a deep theorem of logic (or theoretical computer science) which says essentially that there is no algorithm for proving correct programs correct, so the task is much more an art than a science.*

*Your proofs must be valid proofs, of course. You may use the rules of inference discussed in Section 3.1. What is special about proofs of program correctness is the addition of some special rules for this setting. These exercises (and the examples in the text) may seem overly simple, but unfortunately it is extremely hard to prove all but the simplest programs correct.*

**1.** We suppose that initially $x = 0$. The segment causes two things to happen. First $y$ is assigned the value of 1. Next the value of $x + y$ is computed to be $0 + 1 = 1$, and so $z$ is assigned the value 1. Therefore at the end $z$ has the value 1, so the final assertion is satisfied.

**3.** We suppose that initially $y = 3$. The effect of the first two statements is to assign $x$ the value 2 and $z$ the value $2 + 3 = 5$. Next, when the **if**...**then** statement is encountered, since the value of $y$ is 3, and $3 > 0$ is true, the statement $z := z + 1$ assigns the value $5 + 1 = 6$ to $z$ (and the **else** clause is not executed). Therefore at the end, $z$ has the value 6, so the final assertion $z = 6$ is true.

**5.** We generalize the rule of inference for the **if**...**then**...**else** statement, given before Example 3. Let $p$ be the initial assertion, and let $q$ be the final assertion. If condition 1 is true, then $S_1$ will get executed, so we need $(p \wedge \text{condition 1})\{S_1\}q$. Similarly, if condition 2 is true, but condition 1 is false, then $S_2$ will get executed, so we need $(p \wedge \neg(\text{condition 1}) \wedge \text{condition 2})\{S_2\}q$. This pattern continues, until the last statement we need is $(p \wedge \neg(\text{condition 1}) \wedge \neg(\text{condition 2}) \wedge \cdots \wedge \neg(\text{condition } n-1))\{S_n\}q$. Given all of these, we can conclude that $pTq$, where $T$ is the entire statement. In symbols, we have

$(p \wedge \text{condition 1})\{S_1\}q$

$(p \wedge \neg(\text{condition 1}) \wedge \text{condition 2})\{S_2\}q$

$\quad \vdots$

$(p \wedge \neg(\text{condition 1}) \wedge \neg(\text{condition 2}) \wedge \cdots \wedge \neg(\text{condition } n-1))\{S_n\}q$

$\overline{\therefore\ p\{\textbf{if condition 1 then } S_1 \textbf{ else if condition 2 then } S_2 \textbf{ else if}\ldots\textbf{else } S_n\}q\,.}$

**7.** The problem is similar to Example 4. We will use the loop invariant $p$: "$power = x^{i-1}$ and $i \leq n+1$." Now $p$ is true initially, since before the loop starts, $i = 1$ and $power = 1 = x^0 = x^{1-1}$. (There is a technicality here: we define $0^0$ to equal 1 in order for this to be correct if $x = 0$. There is no harm in this, since $n > 0$, so if $x = 0$, then the program certainly computes the correct answer $x^n = 0$.) We must now show that if $p$ is true and $i \leq n$ before some pass through the loop, then $p$ remains true after that pass. The loop increments $i$ by one. Hence since $i \leq n$ before this pass through the loop, $i \leq n+1$ after this pass. Also the loop assigns $power \cdot x$ to $power$. By the inductive hypothesis, $power$ started with the value $x^{i-1}$ (the old value of $i$). Therefore its new value is $x^{i-1} \cdot x = x^i = x^{(i+1)-1}$. But since $i + 1$ is the new value of $i$, the statement $power = x^{i-1}$ is true at the completion of this pass through the loop. Hence $p$ remains true, so $p$ is a loop invariant. Furthermore, the loop terminates after $n$ traversals, with $i = n + 1$, since $i$ is assigned the value 1 prior to entering the loop, $i$ is incremented by 1 on each pass, and the loop terminates when $i > n$. At termination we have $(i \leq n + 1) \wedge \neg(i \leq n)$, so $i = n + 1$. Hence $power = x^{(n+1)-1} = x^n$, as desired.

**9.** We will break the problem up into the various statements that are left unproved in Example 5.

We must show that $p\{S_1\}q$, where $p$ is the assertion that $m$ and $n$ are integers, and $q$ is the proposition $p \wedge (a = |n|)$. This follows from Example 3 and the fact that the values of $m$ and $n$ have not been tampered with.

We must show that $q\{S_2\}r$, where $r$ is the proposition $q \wedge (k = 0) \wedge (x = 0)$. This is clear, since in $S_2$, none of $m$, $n$, or $a$ have been altered, but $k$ and $x$ have been assigned the value 0.

We must show that $(x = mk) \wedge (k \leq a)$ is an invariant for the loop in $S_3$. Assume that this statement is true before a pass through the loop. In the loop, $k$ is incremented by 1. If $k < a$ (the condition of the loop), then at the end of the pass, $k < a+1$, so $k \leq a$. Furthermore, since $x = mk$ at the beginning of the pass, and $x$ is incremented by $m$ inside the loop, we have $x = mk+m = m(k+1)$ at the end of the pass, which is precisely the statement that $x = mk$ for the updated value of $k$. When the loop terminates (which it clearly does after $a$ iterations), clearly $k = a$ (since $(k \leq a) \wedge \neg(k < a)$), and so $x = ma$ at this point.

Finally we must show that $s\{S_4\}t$, where $s$ is the proposition $(x = ma) \wedge (a = |n|)$, and $t$ is the proposition $product = mn$. The program segment $S_4$ assigns the value $x$ or $-x$ to $product$, depending on the sign of $n$. We need to consider the two cases. If $n < 0$, then since $a = |n|$ we know that $a = -n$. Therefore $product = -x = -(ma) = -m(-n) = mn$. If $n \not< 0$, then since $a = |n|$ we know that $a = n$. Therefore $product = x = ma = mn$.

**11.** To say that the program assertion $p\{S\}q_1$ is true is to say that if $p$ is true before $S$ is executed, then $q_1$ is true after $S$ is executed. To prove this, let us assume that $p$ is true and then $S$ is executed. Since $p\{S\}q_0$, we know that after $S$ is executed $q_0$ is true. By modus ponens, since $q_0$ is true and $q_0 \rightarrow q_1$ is true, we know that $q_1$ is true, as desired.

⇒ **SUPPLEMENTARY EXERCISES FOR CHAPTER 3**

1.  An odd number is one of the form $2n + 1$, where $n$ is an integer. We are given two odd numbers, say $2a + 1$ and $2b + 1$. Their product is $(2a + 1)(2b + 1) = 4ab + 2a + 2b + 1 = 2(2ab + a + b) + 1$. This last expression shows that the product is odd, since it is of the form $2n + 1$, with $n = 2ab + a + b$.

3.  The sum of two irrational numbers need not be irrational. If fact, if $x$ is any irrational number, then so is $-x$, but $x + (-x) = 0$ is rational. Thus for example, $\sqrt{2} + (-\sqrt{2})$ is a sum of two irrational numbers that is rational.

5.  This is not a valid argument. It is of the form $p \to q$ and $q$; therefore $p$. This is the fallacy of affirming the conclusion. In this particular case, not only is the argument invalid, but the conclusion is false. If $n = -6$, then $n^2 > 25$, but $n \not> 5$. However, note that the counterexample is not the reason the argument is invalid; one can give invalid arguments to justify true propositions as well, and they are just as wrong.

7.  There are four cases, depending on the signs of $x$ and $y$. If $x$ and $y$ are both nonnegative, then so is $xy$, and we have $|xy| = xy = |x||y|$. If $x$ and $y$ are both negative, then $xy$ is positive, and we have $|xy| = xy = (-x)(-y) = |x||y|$. If $x$ is nonnegative and $y$ is negative, then $xy$ is nonpositive, and we have $|xy| = -(xy) = x(-y) = |x||y|$. Finally, if $x$ is negative and $y$ is nonnegative, then $xy$ is nonpositive, and we have $|xy| = -(xy) = (-x)y = |x||y|$.

9.  The statement need not be true if the $x_i$'s are not distinct, since by definition we cannot have a function $P$ such that $P(x) = y_1$ and $P(x) = y_2$ with $y_1 \neq y_2$. So we add that hypothesis. Following the hint, we define the function $P$ by

$$P(x) = \sum_{i=1}^{n} \left( \prod_{i \neq j} \frac{x - x_j}{x_i - x_j} \right) y_i \,.$$

Since the $x_i$'s are all distinct, and the product is taken over only those values of $j$ with $j \neq i$, the denominator is not zero, so our function is well defined. Clearly it is a polynomial, since the only place that the variable $x$ appears is in the numerator, and the only operations involved (aside from subtraction of and division by constants) are multiplication and addition. All that remains to prove is that $P(x_{i_0}) = y_{i_0}$ for each $i_0$. If we let $x = x_{i_0}$, then for $i = i_0$, the fraction which appears in the formula, $(x - x_j)/(x_i - x_j)$, is equal to $(x_{i_0} - x_j)/(x_{i_0} - x_j) = 1$ for all $j \neq i_0$. Therefore the product is 1 for $i = i_0$. On the other hand, if $i \neq i_0$, then the product is 0, since it includes the term $(x_{i_0} - x_{i_0})/(x_i - x_{i_0})$ when $j = i_0$. Therefore the sum reduces to just $1 \cdot y_{i_0} = y_{i_0}$, as desired.

11. We prove this by induction on $n$. If $n = 1$ (base case), then the equation reads $1 \cdot 2^0 = (1 - 1) \cdot 2^1 + 1$, which is the true statement $1 = 1$. Assume that the statement is true for $n$:

$$1 \cdot 2^0 + 2 \cdot 2^1 + 3 \cdot 2^2 + \cdots + n \cdot 2^{n-1} = (n - 1) \cdot 2^n + 1 \,.$$

We must show that it is true for $n + 1$. Thus we have

$$1 \cdot 2^0 + 2 \cdot 2^1 + 3 \cdot 2^2 + \cdots + n \cdot 2^{n-1} + (n + 1) \cdot 2^n$$
$$= (n - 1) \cdot 2^n + 1 + (n + 1) \cdot 2^n \quad \text{(by the inductive hypothesis)}$$
$$= (2n) \cdot 2^n + 1$$
$$= n \cdot 2^{n+1} + 1$$
$$= ((n + 1) - 1) \cdot 2^{n+1} + 1 \,,$$

exactly as desired.

**13.** We prove this by induction on $n$. If $n = 1$ (base case), then the equation reads $1/(1 \cdot 4) = 1/4$, which is true. Assume that the statement is true for $n$:

$$\frac{1}{1 \cdot 4} + \frac{1}{4 \cdot 7} + \cdots + \frac{1}{(3n - 2)(3n + 1)} = \frac{n}{3n + 1}.$$

We must show that it is true for $n + 1$. Thus we have

$$\frac{1}{1 \cdot 4} + \frac{1}{4 \cdot 7} + \cdots + \frac{1}{(3n - 2)(3n + 1)} + \frac{1}{(3(n + 1) - 2)(3(n + 1) + 1)}$$

$$= \frac{n}{3n + 1} + \frac{1}{(3(n + 1) - 2)(3(n + 1) + 1)} \quad \text{(by the inductive hypothesis)}$$

$$= \frac{n}{3n + 1} + \frac{1}{(3n + 1)(3n + 4)}$$

$$= \frac{1}{3n + 1}\left(n + \frac{1}{3n + 4}\right)$$

$$= \frac{1}{3n + 1}\left(\frac{3n^2 + 4n + 1}{3n + 4}\right)$$

$$= \frac{1}{3n + 1}\left(\frac{(3n + 1)(n + 1)}{3n + 4}\right)$$

$$= \frac{n + 1}{3n + 4}$$

$$= \frac{n + 1}{3(n + 1) + 1},$$

exactly as desired.

**15.** Let $P(n)$ be the statement $2^n > n^3$. We want to prove that $P(n)$ is true for all $n > 9$. The base case is $n = 10$, in which we have $2^{10} = 1024 > 1000$. Assume $P(n)$; we want to show $P(n + 1)$. Then we have

$$(n + 1)^3 = n^3 + 3n^2 + 3n + 1$$

$$\leq n^3 + 3n^2 + 3n^2 + 3n^2 \quad \text{(since } n \geq 1\text{)}$$

$$= n^3 + 9n^2$$

$$< n^3 + n^3 \quad \text{(since } n > 9\text{)}$$

$$= 2n^3 < 2 \cdot 2^n \quad \text{(by the inductive hypothesis)}$$

$$= 2^{n+1},$$

as desired.

**17.** This problem deals with factors in algebra. We have to be just a little clever. Let $P(n)$ be the statement that $a - b$ is a factor of $a^n - b^n$. We want to show that $P(n)$ is true for all positive integers $n$, and of course we will do so by induction. If $n = 1$, then we have the trivial statement that $a - b$ is a factor of $a - b$. Next assume the inductive hypothesis, that $P(n)$ is true. We want to show $P(n + 1)$, that $a - b$ is a factor of $a^{n+1} - b^{n+1}$. The trick is to rewrite $a^{n+1} - b^{n+1}$ by subtracting and adding $ab^n$ (and hence not changing its value). We obtain $a^{n+1} - b^{n+1} = a^{n+1} - ab^n + ab^n - b^{n+1} = a(a^n - b^n) + b^n(a - b)$. Now this expression contains two terms. By the inductive hypothesis, $a - b$ is a factor of the first term. Obviously $a - b$ is a factor of the second. Therefore $a - b$ is a factor of the entire expression, and we are done.

**19.** Let $P(n)$ be the given equation. It is certainly true for $n = 0$, since it reads $a = a$ in that case. Assume that $P(n)$ is true:

$$a + (a + d) + \cdots + (a + nd) = \frac{(n+1)(2a + nd)}{2}.$$

Then

$$a + (a + d) + \cdots + (a + nd) + (a + (n+1)d)$$

$$= \frac{(n+1)(2a + nd)}{2} + (a + (n+1)d) \quad \text{(by the inductive hypothesis)}$$

$$= \frac{(n+1)(2a + nd) + 2(a + (n+1)d)}{2}$$

$$= \frac{(n+1)(2a + nd) + 2a + nd + nd + 2d}{2}$$

$$= \frac{(n+2)(2a + nd) + (n+2)d}{2}$$

$$= \frac{(n+2)(2a + (n+1)d)}{2},$$

which is exactly $P(n+1)$.

**21.** The base case is wrong. The statement makes no sense for $n = 1$, since the last term on the left-hand side would then be $1/(0 \cdot 1)$, which is undefined. The first $n$ for which it makes sense is $n = 2$, when it reads

$$\frac{1}{1 \cdot 2} = \frac{3}{2} - \frac{1}{2}.$$

Of course this statement is false, since $1/2 \neq 1$. Therefore the base case fails, and so the proof is invalid.

**23.** We will prove by induction that $n$ circles divide the plane into $n^2 - n + 2$ regions. One circle certainly divides the plane into two regions (the inside and the outside), and $1^2 - 1 + 2 = 2$. Thus the statement is correct for $n = 1$. We assume that the statement is true for $n$ circles, and consider it for $n + 1$ circles. Let us imagine an arrangement of $n + 1$ circles in the plane, each pair intersecting in exactly two points, no point common to three circles. If we remove one circle, then we are left with $n$ circles, and by the inductive hypothesis they divide the plane into $n^2 - n + 2$ regions. Now let us draw the circle that we removed, starting at a point at which it intersects another circle. As we proceed around the circle, every time we encounter a point on one of the circles that was already there, we cut off a new region (in other words, we divide one old region into two). Therefore the number of regions that are added on account of this circle is equal to the number of points of intersection of this circle with the other $n$ circles. We are told that each other circle intersects this one in exactly two points. Therefore there are a total of $2n$ points of intersection, and hence $2n$ new regions. Therefore the number of regions determined by $n + 1$ circles is $n^2 - n + 2 + 2n = n^2 + n + 2 = (n+1)^2 - (n+1) + 2$ (the last equality is just algebra). Thus we have derived that the statement is also true for $n + 1$, and our proof is complete.

**25.** We will give a proof by contradiction. Let us consider the set $B = \{\, b\sqrt{2} \mid b \text{ and } b\sqrt{2} \text{ are positive integers} \,\}$. Clearly $B$ is a subset of the set of positive integers. Now if $\sqrt{2}$ is rational, say $\sqrt{2} = p/q$, then $B \neq \varnothing$, since $q\sqrt{2} = p \in B$. Therefore by the well-ordering property, $B$ contains a smallest element, say $a = b\sqrt{2}$. Then $a\sqrt{2} - a = a\sqrt{2} - b\sqrt{2} = (a - b)\sqrt{2}$. Since $a\sqrt{2} = 2b$ and $a$ are both integers, so is this quantity. Furthermore, it is a positive integer, since it equals $a(\sqrt{2} - 1)$ and

$\sqrt{2} - 1 > 0$. Therefore $a\sqrt{2} - a \in B$. But clearly $a\sqrt{2} - a < a$, since $\sqrt{2} < 2$. This contradicts our choice of $a$ to be the smallest element of $B$. Therefore our original assumption that $\sqrt{2}$ is rational is false.

27. We will prove this by contradiction. Suppose the well-ordering property were false. Let $S$ be a counterexample: a nonempty set of nonnegative integers that contains no smallest element. Let $P(n)$ be the statement "$i \notin S$ for all $i \leq n$." We will show that $P(n)$ is true for all $n$ (which will contradict the assertion that $S$ is nonempty). Now $P(0)$ must be true, because if $0 \in S$ then clearly $S$ would have a smallest element, namely 0. Suppose now that $P(n)$ is true, so that $i \notin S$ for $i = 1, 2, \ldots, n$. We must show that $P(n + 1)$ is true, which amounts to showing that $n + 1 \notin S$. If $n + 1 \in S$, then $n + 1$ would be the smallest element of $S$, and this would contradict our assumption. Therefore $n + 1 \notin S$. Thus we have shown that $P(n)$ is true for all $n$, which means that there can be no elements of $S$. This contradicts our assumption that $S \neq \emptyset$, and our proof by contradiction is complete.

29. We begin by computing $f(n)$ for the first few values of $n$, using the recursive definition. Thus we have $f(1) = 1$, $f(2) = f(1) + 4 - 1 = 1 + 4 - 1 = 4$, $f(3) = f(2) + 6 - 1 = 4 + 6 - 1 = 9$, $f(4) = f(3) + 8 - 1 = 9 + 8 - 1 = 16$. The pattern seems clear, so we conjecture that $f(n) = n^2$. Now we prove this by induction. The base case we have already verified. So assume that $f(n) = n^2$. All we have to do is show that $f(n + 1) = (n + 1)^2$. By the recursive definition we have $f(n + 1) = f(n) + 2(n + 1) - 1$. This equals $n^2 + 2(n + 1) - 1$ by the inductive hypothesis, and by algebra we have $n^2 + 2(n + 1) - 1 = (n + 1)^2$, as desired.

31. The recursive definition says that we can "grow" strings in $S$ by appending 0's on the left and 1's on the right, as many as we wish.

    a) The only string of length 0 in $S$ is $\lambda$. There are two strings of length 1 in $S$, obtained either by appending a 0 to the front of $\lambda$ or a 1 to the end of $\lambda$, namely the strings 0 and 1. The strings of length 2 in $S$ come from the strings of length 1 by appending either a 0 to the front or a 1 to the end; they are 00, 01, and 11. Similarly, we can append a 0 to the front or a 1 to the end of any of these strings to get the strings of length 3 in $S$, namely 000, 001, 011, and 111. Continuing in this manner, we see that the other strings in $S$ of length less than or equal to 5 are 0000, 0001, 0011, 0111, 1111, 00000, 00001, 00011, 00111, 01111, and 11111.

    b) The simplest way to describe these strings is $\{\, 0^m 1^n \mid m$ and $n$ are nonnegative integers $\}$.

33. There is of course the empty string, with 0 symbols. By the first recursive rule, we get the string (). If we apply the first recursive rule to this string, then we get (()), and if we apply the second recursive rule, then we get ()(). These are the only strings in $B$ with four or fewer symbols.

35. The definition simply says that $N$ of a string is a count of the parentheses, with each left parenthesis counting $+1$ and each right parenthesis counting $-1$.

    a) There is one left parenthesis and one right parenthesis, so $N(()) = 1 - 1 = 0$.

    b) There are 3 left parentheses and 5 right parentheses, so $N()))()(() = 3 - 5 = -2$.

    c) There are 4 left parentheses and 2 right parentheses, so $N((()(()) = 4 - 2 = 2$.

    d) There are 6 left parentheses and 6 right parentheses, so $N(()((()))(())) = 6 - 6 = 0$.

**37.** The basic idea, of course, is to turn the definition into a procedure. The recursive part of the definition tells us how to find elements of $B$ from shorter elements of $B$. The naive approach, however, is not very good, because we end up adding to $B$ strings that already are there. For example, the string $()()()$ occurs in two different ways from the rule "$xy \in B$ if $x, y \in B$": by letting $x = ()()$ and $y = ()$, and by letting $x = ()$ and $y = ()()$.

To avoid this problem, we will keep two lists of strings, whose union is the set $B(n)$ of balanced strings of parentheses of length not exceeding $n$. The set $S(n)$ will be those balanced strings $w$ of length at most $n$ such that $w = uv$, where $u, v \neq \lambda$ and $u$ and $v$ are balanced. The set $T(n)$ will be all other balanced strings of length at most $n$. Note that, for example, $\lambda \in T$, $() \in T$, $(()) \in T$, but $()() \in S$. Since all the strings in $B$ are of even length, we really only need to work with even values of $n$, dragging the odd values along for the ride.

> **procedure** $generate(n : \text{nonnegative integer})$
> **if** $n$ is odd **then**
> **begin**
> > $S := S(n - 1)$ {the $S$ constructed by $generate(n - 1)$}
> > $T := T(n - 1)$ {the $T$ constructed by $generate(n - 1)$}
>
> **end**
> **else if** $n = 0$ **then**
> **begin**
> > $S := \emptyset$
> > $T := \{\lambda\}$
>
> **end**
> **else**
> **begin**
> > $S' := S(n - 2)$ {the $S$ constructed by $generate(n - 2)$}
> > $T' := T(n - 2)$ {the $T$ constructed by $generate(n - 2)$}
> > $T := T' \cup \{ (x) \mid x \in T' \cup S' \wedge \text{length}(x) = n - 2 \}$
> > $S := S' \cup \{ xy \mid x \in T' \wedge y \in T' \cup S' \wedge \text{length}(xy) = n \}$
>
> **end**
> $\{ T \cup S$ is the set of balanced strings of length at most $n \}$

**39.** There are two cases. If $x \leq y$ initially, then the statement $x := y$ is not executed, so $x$ and $y$ remain unchanged and $x \leq y$ is a true final assertion. If $x > y$ initially, then the statement $x := y$ is executed, so $x = y$ at the end, and thus $x \leq y$ is again a true final assertion. These are the only two possibilities associated with the initial condition **T** (**true**), so our proof is complete.

# CHAPTER 4
# Counting

⇒ **SECTION 4.1    The Basics of Counting**

*The secret to solving counting problems is to look at the problem the right way and apply the correct rules (usual the product rule or the sum rule), with often some common sense and cleverness thrown in. This is usually easier said than done, but it gets easier the more problems you do. Often you need to count more than you want and then subtract the overcount. (This notion is made more precise in Section 5.4, where the inclusion-exclusion principle is discussed explicitly.) Counting problems are sometimes ambiguous, so it is possible that your answer, although different from the answer we obtain, is the correct answer to a different interpretation of the problem; try to figure out if that is the case.*

*If you have trouble with a problem, change the parameters to make them more manageable (if necessary) and try to list the set in question explicitly. This will often give you an idea of what is going on and suggest a general method of attack that will solve the problem as given. For example, in Exercise 9 you are asked about bit strings of length 10. If you are having difficulty, investigate the analogous question about bit strings of length 2 or 3, where you can write down the entire set, and see if a pattern develops. (In some sense, mathematics is just a study of interesting patterns.) Sometimes tree diagrams make the analysis in these small cases easier to keep track of.*

*Finally, do not be misled, if you find these exercises easy, into thinking that combinatorial problems are a piece of cake. It is very easy to ask combinatorial questions that look just like the ones asked here but which in fact are extremely difficult, if not impossible. For example, try your hand at the following problem: how many strings are there, using 10 A's, 12 B's, 11 C's, and 15 D's, such that no A is followed by a B, and no C is followed by a D?*

1. This problem illustrates the difference between the product rule and the sum rule. If we must make one choice *and* then another choice, the product rule applies, as in part (**a**). If we must make one choice *or* another choice, the sum rule applies, as in part (**b**). We assume in this problem that there are no double majors.

   **a)** The product rule applies here, since we want to do two things, one after the other. First, since there are 18 mathematics majors, and we are to choose one of them, there are 18 ways to choose the mathematics major. Then we must choose the computer science major from among the 325 computer science majors, and that can clearly be done in 325 ways. Therefore there are, by the product rule, $18 \cdot 325 = 5850$ ways to pick the two representatives.

   **b)** The sum rule applies here, since we want to do one of two mutually exclusive things. We can either choose a mathematics major to be the representative, or we can choose a computer science major. There are 18 ways to choose a mathematics major, and there are 325 ways to choose a computer science major. Since these two actions are mutually exclusive (no one is both a mathematics major and a computer science major), and since we want to do one of them or the other, there are $18 + 325 = 343$ ways to pick the representative.

3. **a)** The product rule applies, since the student will perform each of 10 tasks, one after the other. There are 4 ways to do each task. Therefore there are $4 \cdot 4 \cdots 4 = 4^{10} = 1{,}048{,}576$ ways to answer the questions on the test.

   **b)** This is identical to part **(a)**, except that now there are 5 ways to answer each question—give any of the 4 answers or give no answer at all. Therefore there are $5^{10} = 9{,}765{,}625$ ways to answer the questions on the test.

5. The product rule applies here, since a flight is determined by choosing an airline for the flight from New York to Denver (which can be done in 6 ways) and then choosing an airline for the flight from Denver to San Francisco (which can be done in 7 ways). Therefore there are $6 \cdot 7 = 42$ different possibilities for the entire flight.

7. Three-letter initials are determined by specifying the first initial (26 ways), then the second initial (26 ways), and then the third initial (26 ways). Therefore by the product rule there are $26 \cdot 26 \cdot 26 = 26^3 = 17{,}576$ possible three-letter initials.

9. A bit string is determined by choosing the bits in the string, one after another, so the product rule applies, with each factor being a 2 (the bit can be either a 1 or a 0). We want to count the number of bit strings of length 10, except that we are not free to choose either the first bit or the last bit (they are mandated to be 1's). Therefore there are 8 choices to make, and the product rule tells us that there are $2^8 = 256$ such strings.

11. This is a trick question, since it is easier than one might expect. Since the string is given to consist entirely of 1's, there is nothing to choose except the length. Since there are $n + 1$ possible lengths not exceeding $n$ (if we include the empty string, of length 0), the answer is simply $n + 1$.

13. By the sum rule, we can count the number of strings of length 4 or less by counting the number of strings of length $i$, for $0 \leq i \leq 4$, and then adding the results. Now there are 26 letters to choose from, and a string of length $i$ is specified by choosing its characters, one after another. Therefore by the product rule, there are $26^i$ strings of length $i$. The answer to the question is thus $\sum_{i=0}^{4} 26^i = 1 + 26 + 676 + 17576 + 456976 = 475{,}255$.

15. This problem deals with the set of positive integers between 100 and 999, inclusive. Note that there are exactly $999 - 100 + 1 = 900$ such numbers. A second way to see this is to note that to specify a three-digit number, we need to choose the first digit to be nonzero (which can be done in 9 ways) and then the second and third digits (which can each be done in 10 ways), for a total of $9 \cdot 10 \cdot 10 = 900$ ways, by the product rule. A third way to see this (perhaps most relevant for this problem) is to note that a number of the desired form is a number less than or equal to 999 (and there are 999 such numbers) but not less than or equal to 99 (and there are 99 such numbers); therefore there are $999 - 99 = 900$ numbers in the desired range.

   **a)** Every seventh number—7, 14, and so on—is divisible by 7. Therefore the number of positive integers less than or equal to $n$ and divisible by 7 is $\lfloor n/7 \rfloor$ (the floor function is used—we have to round down—because the first six positive integers are not multiples of 7; for example there are only $\lfloor 20/7 \rfloor = 2$ multiples of 7 less than or equal to 20). So we find that there are $\lfloor 999/7 \rfloor = 142$ multiples of 7 not exceeding 999, of which $\lfloor 99/7 \rfloor = 14$ do not exceed 99. Therefore there are exactly $142 - 14 = 128$ numbers in the desired range divisible by 7.

**b)** This is similar to part **(a)**, with 7 replaced by 2, but with the added twist that we want to count the numbers *not* divisible by 2. Mimicking the analysis in part **(a)**, we see that there are $\lfloor 999/2 \rfloor = 499$ even numbers not exceeding 999, and therefore $999 - 499 = 500$ odd ones; there are similarly $99 - \lfloor 99/2 \rfloor = 50$ odd numbers less than or equal to 99. Therefore there are $500 - 50 = 450$ odd numbers between 100 and 999 inclusive.

**c)** There are just 9 possible digits that a three-digit number can start with. If all of its digits are to be the same, then there is no choice after the leading digit has been specified. Therefore there are 9 such numbers.

**d)** This is similar to part **(b)**, except that 2 is replaced by 4. Following the analysis there, we find that there are $999 - \lfloor 999/4 \rfloor = 750$ positive integers less than or equal to 999 not divisible by 4, and $99 - \lfloor 99/4 \rfloor = 75$ such positive integers less than or equal to 99. Therefore there are $750 - 75 = 675$ three-digit integers not divisible by 4.

**e)** The method is similar to that used in the earlier parts. There are $\lfloor 999/3 \rfloor - \lfloor 99/3 \rfloor = 300$ three-digit numbers divisible by 3, and $\lfloor 999/4 \rfloor - \lfloor 99/4 \rfloor = 225$ three-digit numbers divisible by 4. Moreover there are $\lfloor 999/12 \rfloor - \lfloor 99/12 \rfloor = 75$ numbers divisible by both 3 and 4, i.e., divisible by 12. In order to count each number divisible by 3 or 4 once and only once, we need to add the number of numbers divisible by 3 to the number of numbers divisible by 4, and then subtract the number of numbers divisible by both 3 and 4 so as not to count them twice. Therefore the answer is $300 + 225 - 75 = 450$.

**f)** In part **(e)** we found that there were 450 three-digit integers that are divisible by either 3 or 4. The others, of course, are not. Therefore there are $900 - 450 = 450$ three-digit integers that are not divisible by either 3 or 4.

**g)** We saw in part **(e)** that there are 300 three-digit numbers divisible by 3 and that 75 of them are also divisible by 4. The remainder of those 300 numbers, therefore, are not divisible by 4. Thus the answer is $300 - 75 = 225$.

**h)** We saw in part **(e)** that there are 75 three-digit numbers divisible by both 3 and 4.

17. There are 50 choices to make, each of which can be done in 3 ways, namely by choosing the governor, choosing the senior senator, or choosing the junior senator. By the product rule the answer is therefore $3^{50} \approx 7 \times 10^{23}$.

19. By the sum rule, we need to add the number of license plates of the first type and the number of license plates of the second type. By the product rule there are $26 \cdot 26 \cdot 10 \cdot 10 \cdot 10 \cdot 10 = 6{,}760{,}000$ license plates consisting of 2 letters followed by 4 digits; and there are $10 \cdot 10 \cdot 26 \cdot 26 \cdot 26 \cdot 26 = 45{,}697{,}600$ license plates consisting of 2 digits followed by 4 letters. Therefore the answer is $6{,}760{,}000 + 45{,}697{,}600 = 52{,}457{,}600$.

21. For all parts of this problem, we need to find the number of one-to-one functions from a set with 5 elements to a set with $k$ elements. To specify such a function, we need to make 5 choices, in succession, namely the values of the function at each of the 5 elements in its domain. Therefore the product rule applies. The first choice can be made in $k$ ways, since any element of the codomain can be the image of the first element of the domain. After that choice has been made, there are only $k - 1$ elements of the codomain available to be the image of the second element of the domain, since images must be distinct for the function to be one-to-one. Similarly, for the third element of the domain, there are $k - 2$ possible choices for a function value. Continuing in this way, and applying the product rule, we see that there are $k(k - 1)(k - 2)(k - 3)(k - 4)$ one-to-one functions from a set with 5 elements to a set with $k$ elements.

**a)** By the analysis above, the answer is $4 \cdot 3 \cdot 2 \cdot 1 \cdot 0 = 0$, what we would expect since there are no one-to-one functions from a set to a strictly smaller set.

**b)** By the analysis above, the answer is $5 \cdot 4 \cdot 3 \cdot 2 \cdot 1 = 120$.

**c)** By the analysis above, the answer is $6 \cdot 5 \cdot 4 \cdot 3 \cdot 2 = 720$.

**d)** By the analysis above, the answer is $7 \cdot 6 \cdot 5 \cdot 4 \cdot 3 = 2520$.

23. **a)** There can clearly be no one-to-one function from $\{1, 2, \ldots, n\}$ to $\{0, 1\}$ if $n > 2$. If $n = 1$, then there are 2 such functions, the one that sends 1 to 0, and the one that sends 1 to 1. If $n = 2$, then there are again 2 such functions, since once it is determined where 1 is sent, the function must send 2 to the other value in the codomain.

    **b)** If the function assigns 0 to both 1 and $n$, then there are $n - 2$ function values free to be chosen. Each can be chosen in 2 ways. Therefore by the product rule (since we have to choose values for all the elements of the domain), there are $2^{n-2}$ such functions.

    **c)** If $n = 1$, then there are no such functions, since there are no positive integers less than $n$. So assume $n > 1$. In order to specify such a function, we have to decide which of the numbers from 1 to $n - 1$, inclusive, will get sent to 1. There are $n - 1$ ways to make this choice. There is no choice for the remaining numbers from 1 to $n - 1$, inclusive, since they all must get sent to 0. Finally, we are free to specify the value of the function at $n$, and this may be done in 2 ways. Hence by the product rule, the final answer is $2(n - 1)$.

25. The trick here is to realize that a palindrome of length $n$ is completely determined by its first $\lceil n/2 \rceil$ bits. This is true because once these bits are specified, the remaining bits, read from right to left, must be identical to the first $\lfloor n/2 \rfloor$ bits, read from left to right. Furthermore, these first $\lceil n/2 \rceil$ bits can be specified at will, and by the product rule there are $2^{\lceil n/2 \rceil}$ ways to do so.

27. By the result of Example 10, there are $C = 6,400,000,000$ possible numbers of the form $NXX - NXX - XXXX$. To determine the number of different telephone numbers worldwide, then, we need to determine how many country codes there are and multiply by $C$. There are clearly 10 country codes of length 1, 100 country codes of length 2, and 1000 country codes of length 3. Thus there are $10 + 100 + 1000 = 1110$ country codes in all, by the sum rule. Our final answer is $1110 \cdot C = 7,104,000,000,000$.

29. We assume that what is intended is that each of the 4 letters is to be used exactly once. There are at least two ways to do this problem. First let us break it into two cases, depending on whether the $a$ comes at the end of the string or not. If $a$ is not at the end, then there are 3 places to put it. After we have placed the $a$, there are only 2 places to put the $b$, since it cannot go into the position occupied by the $a$ and it cannot go into the position following the $a$. Then there are 2 positions in which the $c$ can go, and only 1 position for the $d$. Therefore there are by the product rule $3 \cdot 2 \cdot 2 \cdot 1 = 12$ allowable strings in which the $a$ does not come last. Second, if the $a$ comes last, then there are $3 \cdot 2 \cdot 1 = 6$ ways to arrange the letters $b$, $c$, and $d$ in the first three positions. The answer then, by the sum rule, is $12 + 6 = 18$.

    Here is another approach. Ignore for a moment the restriction that a $b$ cannot follow an $a$. Then we need to choose the letter which comes first (which can be done in 4 ways), then the letter which comes second (which can be done in 3 ways, since one letter has already been used), then the letter which comes third (which can be done in 2 ways, since two of the letters have already been used), and finally the letter which comes last (which can only be done in 1 way, since there is only one unused letter at that point). Therefore there are, by the product rule, $4 \cdot 3 \cdot 2 \cdot 1 = 24$ such strings. Now we need to subtract from this total the number of strings in which the $a$ is followed by the $b$. To count these, let us imagine the $a$ and $b$ glued together into one superletter, $ab$. Now there are 3 things to arrange. We can choose any of them (the letters $c$ or $d$ or the superletter $ab$) to come first, and that can be done in 3 ways. We can choose either of the other two to come second (which can be done in 2 ways), and we are forced to choose the remaining one to come third. By the product rule, there are $3 \cdot 2 \cdot 1 = 6$ ways to make these choices. Therefore our final answer is $24 - 6 = 18$.

31.  There are at least two approaches that are effective here. In our first tree, we let each branching point represent a decision as to whether to include the next element in the set (starting with the largest element). At the top of the tree, for example, we can either choose to include 24 or to exclude it (denoted ¬24). We branch one way for each possibility. In our figure, the entire subtree to the right represents those sets which do not include 24, and the subtree to the left represents those that do. At the point below and to the left of the 24, we have only one branch, ¬11, since after we have included 24 in our set, we cannot include 11, because the sum would not be less than 28 if we did. At the point below and to the right of the ¬24, however, we again branch twice, since we can choose either to include 11 or to exclude it. To answer the question, we look at the points in the last row of the tree. Each represents a set whose sum is less than 28. For example, the sixth point from the right represents the set $\{11, 3\}$. Since there are 17 such points, the answer to the problem is 17.

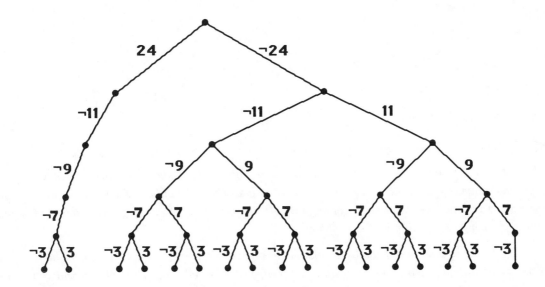

Our other solution is more compact. In the tree below we show branches from a point only for the inclusion of new numbers in the set. The set formed by including no more numbers is represented by the point itself. This time *every* point represents a set. For example, the point at the top represents the empty set, the point below and to the right of the number 11 represents the set $\{11\}$, and the leftmost point on the bottom row represents the set $\{3, 7, 9\}$. In general the set that a point represents is the set of numbers found on the path up the tree from that point to the root of the tree (the point at the top). We only included branches when the sum would be less than 28. Since there are 17 points altogether in this figure, the answer to the problem is 17.

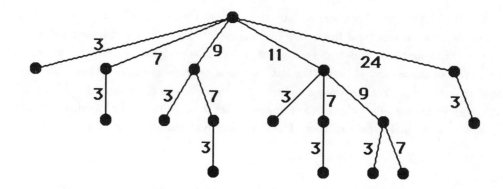

**33.** We want to prove $P(m)$, the sum rule for $m$ tasks, which says that if tasks $T_1$, $T_2$, ..., $T_m$ can be done in $n_1$, $n_2$, ..., $n_m$ ways, respectively, and no two of them can be done at the same time, then there are $n_1 + n_2 + \cdots + n_m$ ways to do one of the tasks. The base case is $m = 2$, and that has already been given. Now assume that $P(m)$ is true, and we want to prove $P(m+1)$. There are $m + 1$ tasks, no two of which can be done at the same time; we want to do one of them. Either we choose one from among the first $m$, or we choose the task $T_{m+1}$. By the sum rule for two tasks, the number of ways we can do this is $n + n_{m+1}$, where $n$ is the number of ways we can do one of the tasks among the first $m$. But by the inductive hypothesis, $n = n_1 + n_2 + \cdots + n_m$. Therefore the number of ways we can do one of the $m + 1$ tasks is $n_1 + n_2 + \cdots + n_m + n_{m+1}$, as desired.

⇒ **SECTION 4.2    The Pigeonhole Principle**

*The pigeonhole principle seems so trivial that it is difficult to realize how powerful it is in solving some mathematical problems. As usual with combinatorial problems, the trick is to look at things the right way, which usually means coming up with the clever insight after perhaps hours of agonizing and frustrating exploration with a problem.*

*Try to solve these problems by invoking the pigeonhole principle explicitly, even if you can see other ways of doing them; you will gain some insights by formulating the problem and your solution in this way. The trick, of course, is to figure out what should be the pigeons and what should be the pigeonholes. Many of the the hints of Section 4.1 apply here, as well as general problem-solving techniques, especially the willingness to play with a problem for a long time before giving up.*

*Many of the elegant applications are quite subtle and difficult, and there are even more subtle and difficult applications not touched on here. Not every problem, of course, fits into the model of one of the examples in the text. In particular Exercise 22 looks deceptively like a problem amenable to the technique discussed in Example 8. Keep in mind that the process of grappling with problems such as these is worthwhile and educational in itself, even if you never find the solution.*

1. There are 6 classes: these are the pigeons. There are 5 days on which classes may meet (Monday through Friday): these are the pigeonholes. Each class must meet on a day (each pigeon must occupy a pigeonhole). By the pigeonhole principle, at least one day must contain at least two classes.

3. There are 2 colors: these are the pigeonholes. We want to know the least number of pigeons needed to insure that at least one of the pigeonholes contains two pigeons. By the pigeonhole principle, the answer is 3. Therefore if 3 socks are taken from the drawer, at least 2 must have the same color. On the other hand 2 socks is not enough, because one might be brown and the other black. Note that the number of socks was irrelevant (assuming it was at least 3).

5. Let the $n$ consecutive integers be denoted $x + 1$, $x + 2$, ..., $x + n$, where $x$ is some integer. We want to show that exactly one of these is divisible by $n$. There are $n$ possible remainders when an integer is divided by $n$, namely 0, 1, 2, ..., $n - 1$. There are two possibilities for the remainders of our collection of $n$ numbers: either they cover all the possible remainders (in which case exactly one of our numbers has a remainder of 0 and is therefore divisible by $n$), or they do not. If they do not, then by the pigeonhole principle, since there are then fewer than $n$ pigeonholes (remainders) for $n$ pigeons (the numbers in our collection), at least one remainder must occur twice. In other words, it must be the case that $x + i$ and $x + j$ have the same remainder when divided by $n$ for some pair of numbers $i$ and $j$ with $0 < i < j \leq n$. Since $x + i$ and $x + j$ have the same remainder when divided by $n$, if we subtract $x + i$ from $x + j$, then we will get a number divisible by $n$. This means that $j - i$ is divisible by $n$. But this is impossible, since $j - i$ is a positive integer strictly less than $n$. Therefore the first possibility must hold, that exactly one of the numbers in our collection is divisible by $n$.

7. The generalized pigeonhole principle applies here. The pigeons are the students (no slur intended), and the pigeonholes are the states, 50 in number. By the generalized pigeonhole principle, if we want there to be at least 100 pigeons in at least one of the pigeonholes, then we need to have a total of $N$ pigeons so that $\lceil N/50 \rceil \geq 100$. This will be the case as long as $N \geq 99 \cdot 50 + 1 = 4951$. Therefore we need at least 4951 students to guarantee that at least 100 come from a single state.

9. Let $d_j$ be $jx - N(jx)$, where $N(jx)$ is the integer closest to $jx$, for $1 \leq j \leq n$. We want to show that $|d_j| < 1/n$ for some $j$. Note that each $d_j$ is an irrational number strictly between $-1/2$ and $1/2$ (since $jx$ is irrational and every irrational number is closer than $1/2$ to the nearest integer). The proof is slightly messier if $n$ is odd, so let us assume that $n$ is even. Consider the $n$ intervals

$$\left(0, \frac{1}{n}\right), \left(\frac{1}{n}, \frac{2}{n}\right), \ldots, \left(\frac{(n/2) - 1}{n}, \frac{1}{2}\right), \left(-\frac{1}{n}, 0\right), \left(-\frac{2}{n}, -\frac{1}{n}\right), \ldots, \left(-\frac{1}{2}, -\frac{(n/2) - 1}{n}\right).$$

The intervals are the pigeonholes and the $d_j$'s are the pigeons. If the interval $(0, 1/n)$ or $(-1/n, 0)$ is occupied, then we are done, since the $d_j$ in that interval tells us which $j$ makes $|d_j| < 1/n$. If not, then there are $n$ pigeons for at most $n - 2$ pigeonholes, so by the pigeonhole principle there is some interval, say $((k - 1)/n, k/n)$, with two pigeons in it, say $d_r$ and $d_s$, with $r < s$. Now we will consider $sx - rx$ and show that it is within $1/n$ of its nearest integer; that will complete our proof, since $sx - rx = (s - r)x$, and $s - r$ is a positive integer less than $n$.

We can write $rx = N(rx) + d_r$ and $sx = N(sx) + d_s$, where $(k - 1)/n \leq d_r < k/n$ and $(k - 1)/n \leq d_s < k/n$. Subtracting, we have that $sx - rx = [N(sx) - N(rx)] + [d_s - d_r]$. Now the quantity in the first pair of square brackets is an integer. Furthermore the quantity in the second pair of square brackets is the difference of two numbers in the interval $((k - 1)/n, k/n)$ and hence has absolute value less than $1/n$ (the extreme case would be when one of them is very close to $(k-1)/n$ and the other is very close to $k/n$). Therefore by definition of "closest integer," $sx - rx$ is at most a distance $1/n$ from its closest integer, i.e., $|(sx - rx) - N(sx - rx)| < 1/n$, as desired. (The case in which $n$ is odd is similar, but we need to extend our intervals slightly past $\pm 1/2$, using $n + 1$ intervals rather than $n$. This is okay, since when we subtract 2 from $n+1$ we still have more pigeons than pigeonholes.)

11. One way to do this is to have the sequence contain 4 groups of 4 numbers each, so that the numbers within each group are decreasing, and so that the numbers between groups are increasing. For example, we could take the sequence to be 4, 3, 2, 1; 8, 7, 6, 5; 12, 11, 10, 9; 16, 15, 14, 13. There can be no increasing subsequence of 5 terms, because any increasing subsequence can have only one element from each of the 4 groups. There can be no decreasing subsequence of 5 terms, because any decreasing subsequence cannot have elements from more than one group.

13. This is actually a fairly hard problem, in terms of what we need to keep track of. Call the given sequence $a_1, a_2, \ldots, a_n$. We will keep track of the lengths of long increasing or decreasing subsequences by assigning values $i_k$ and $d_k$ for each $k$ from 1 to $n$, indicating the length of the longest increasing subsequence ending with $a_k$ and the length of the longest decreasing subsequence ending with $a_k$, respectively. Thus $i_1 = d_1 = 1$, since $a_1$ is both an increasing and a decreasing subsequence of length 1. If $a_2 < a_1$, then $i_2 = 1$ and $d_2 = 2$, since the longest increasing subsequence ending at $a_2$ is just $a_2$, but the longest decreasing subsequence ending at $a_2$ is $a_1, a_2$. If $a_2 > a_1$, then it is the other way around: $i_2 = 2$ and $d_2 = 1$. In general, we can determine $i_k$ in the following manner (the determination of $d_k$ is similar, with the roles of $i$ and $d$, and the roles of $<$ and $>$, reversed). We look at the numbers $a_1, a_2, \ldots, a_{k-1}$. For each $a_j$ which is less than $a_k$, we know that the value of $d_k$ is at least $i_j + 1$, since the increasing subsequence of length $i_j$ ending at $a_j$ can be extended by following it by $a_k$, resulting in an increasing subsequence of length $i_j + 1$, ending at $a_k$. Furthermore, there is no other way of producing an increasing subsequence ending at $a_k$, other than the subsequence of length 1. Thus we set $i_k$ equal to either 1 or the maximum of the numbers $i_j + 1$ for those values of $j < k$ for which $a_j < a_k$. Finally, once we have determined all the values $i_k$ and $d_k$, we choose the largest of these $2n$ numbers as our answer.

The procedure just described, however, does not keep track of what the longest subsequence is, so we need to use two more sets of variables, $iprev_k$ and $dprev_k$. These will point back to the terms in the sequence that caused the values of $i_k$ and $d_k$ to be what they are. To retrieve the longest increasing or decreasing subsequence, once we know which type it is and where it ends, we follow these pointers, thereby exhibiting the subsequence backwards. We will not write the pseudocode for this final phase of the algorithm.

```
procedure long subsequence(a_1, a_2, ..., a_n : distinct integers)
for k := 1 to n
begin
      i_k := 1; d_k := 1
      iprev_k := k; dprev_k := k
      for j := 1 to k - 1
      begin
            if a_j < a_k and i_j + 1 > i_k then
            begin
                  i_k := i_j + 1
                  iprev_k := j
```

> **end**
> **if** $a_j > a_k$ and $d_j + 1 > d_k$ **then**
> **begin**
> $\qquad d_k := d_j + 1$
> $\qquad dprev_k := j$
> **end**
> **end**
> **end** {at this point correct values of $i_k$ and $d_k$ have all been assigned}
> $longest := 1$
> **for** $k := 2$ **to** $n$
> **begin**
> $\qquad$ **if** $i_k > longest$ **then** $longest := i_k$
> $\qquad$ **if** $d_k > longest$ **then** $longest := d_k$
> **end**
> {$longest$ is the length of the longest increasing or decreasing subsequence}

15. We can prove these statements using both the result and the method of Example 11. First note that the role of "mutual friend" and "mutual enemy" is symmetric, so it is really enough to prove one of these statements; the other will follow by interchanging the roles. So let us prove that in any group of 10 people, either there are 3 mutual friends or 4 mutual enemies. Consider one person; call this person $A$. Of the 9 other people, either there must be 6 enemies of $A$, or there must be 4 friends of $A$ (if there were 5 or fewer enemies and 3 or fewer friends, that would only account for 8 people). We need to consider the two cases separately. First suppose that $A$ has 6 enemies. Apply the result of Example 11 to these 6 people: among them either there are 3 mutual friends or there are 3 mutual enemies. If there are 3 mutual friends, then we are done. If there are 3 mutual enemies, then these 3 people, together with $A$, form a group of 4 mutual enemies, and again we are done. That finishes the first case. The second case was that $A$ had 4 friends. If any pair of these people are friends, then they, together with $A$, form the desired group of 3 mutual friends. Otherwise, these 4 people are the desired group of 4 mutual enemies. Thus in either case we have found either 3 mutual friends or 4 mutual enemies.

17. First we need to figure out how many distinct combinations of initials and birthdays there are. The product rule tells us that since there are 26 ways to choose each of the 3 initials and 366 ways to choose the birthday, there are $26 \cdot 26 \cdot 26 \cdot 366 = 6{,}432{,}816$ such combinations. By the generalized pigeonhole principle, with these combinations as the pigeonholes and the 25 million people as the pigeons, there must be at least $\lceil 25{,}000{,}000/6{,}432{,}816 \rceil = 4$ people with the same combination.

19. The 38 time periods are the pigeonholes, and the 677 classes are the pigeons. By the generalized pigeonhole principle there is some time period in which at least $\lceil 677/38 \rceil = 18$ classes are meeting. Since each class must meet in a different room, we need 18 rooms.

21. This problem is similar to Example 8, so we follow the method of solution suggested there. Let $a_j$ be the number of matches held during or before the $j^{\text{th}}$ hour. Then $a_1, a_2, \ldots, a_{75}$ is an increasing sequence of distinct positive integers, since there was at least one match held every hour. Furthermore $1 \le a_j \le 125$, since there were only 125 matches altogether. Moreover, $a_1 + 24, a_2 + 24, \ldots, a_{75} + 24$ is also an increasing sequence of distinct positive integers, with $25 \le a_i + 24 \le 149$.

Now the 150 positive integers $a_1, a_2, \ldots, a_{75}, a_1 + 24, a_2 + 24, \ldots, a_{75} + 24$ are all less than or equal to 149. Hence by the pigeonhole principle two of these integers are equal. Since the integers

$a_1$, $a_2$, ..., $a_{75}$ are all distinct, and the integers $a_1 + 24$, $a_2 + 24$, ..., $a_{75} + 24$ are all distinct, there must be distinct indices $i$ and $j$ such that $a_j = a_i + 24$. This means that exactly 24 matches were held from the beginning of hour $i + 1$ to the end of hour $j$, precisely the occurrence we wanted to find.

**23.** This is exactly a restatement of the generalized pigeonhole principle. The pigeonholes are the elements in the codomain (the elements of the set $T$), and the pigeons are the elements of the domain (the elements of the set $S$). To say that a pigeon $s$ is in pigeonhole $t$ is just to say that $f(s) = t$. The elements $s_1$, $s_2$, ..., $s_m$ are just the $m$ pigeons guaranteed by the generalized pigeonhole principle to occupy a common pigeonhole.

**25. a)** Assuming that each $i_k \leq n$, there are only $n$ pigeonholes (namely 1, 2, ..., $n$) for the $n^2 + 1$ numbers $i_1$, $i_2$, ..., $i_{n^2+1}$. Hence by the generalized pigeonhole principle at least $\lceil (n^2 + 1)/n \rceil = n + 1$ of the numbers are in the same pigeonhole, i.e., equal.

**b)** If $a_{k_j} < a_{k_{j+1}}$, then the subsequence consisting of $a_{k_j}$ followed by the increasing subsequence of length $i_{k_{j+1}}$ starting at $a_{k_j}$ contradicts the fact that $i_{k_j} = i_{k_{j+1}}$. Hence $a_{k_j} > a_{k_{j+1}}$.

**c)** If there is no increasing subsequence of length greater than $n$, then parts **(a)** and **(b)** apply. Therefore we have $a_{k_{n+1}} > a_{k_n} > \cdots > a_{k_2} > a_{k_1}$, a decreasing subsequence of length $n + 1$.

$\Rightarrow$ **SECTION 4.3   Permutations and Combinations**

*In this section we look at counting problems more systematically than in Section 4.1. We have some formulas that apply in many instances, and the trick is to recognize the instances. If an ordered arrangement without repetitions is asked for, then the formula for permutations applies; if an unordered selection without repetition is asked for, then the formula for combinations applies. Of course the product rule and the sum rule (and common sense and cleverness) are still needed to solve some of these problems—having formulas for permutations and combinations does not reduce the solving of counting problems to an algorithm by any means.*

*Again the general comments of Section 4.1 apply. Try to solve problems more than one way and come up with the same answer—you will learn from the process of looking at the same problem from two or more different angles, and you will be (almost) sure that your answer is correct. Exercise 16 through Exercise 20 are particularly worthwhile in this regard.*

**1.** Permutations are ordered arrangements. Thus we need to list all the ordered arrangements of all 3 of these letters. There are 6 such: $a, b, c$; $a, c, b$; $b, a, c$; $b, c, a$; $c, a, b$; and $c, b, a$. Note that we have listed them in alphabetical order. Algorithms for generating permutations and combinations are discussed in Section 4.6.

**3.** If we want the permutation to end with $a$, then we may as well forget about the $a$, and just count the number of permutations of $\{b, c, d, e, f, g\}$. Any permutation of these 6 letters, followed by $a$, will be a permutation of the desired type, and conversely. Therefore the answer is $P(6, 6) = 6! = 720$.

5. We simply plug into the formula $P(n, r) = n(n - 1)(n - 2) \cdots (n - r + 1)$, given in Theorem 1. Note that there are $r$ terms in this product, starting with $n$. This is the same as $P(n, r) = n!/(n - r)!$, but the latter formula is not as nice for computation, since it ignores the fact that each of the factors in the denominator cancels one factor in the numerator. Thus to compute $n!$ and $(n - r)!$ and then to divide is to do a lot of extra arithmetic. Of course if the denominator is 1, then there is no extra work, so we note that $P(n, n) = P(n, n - 1) = n!$.

   a) $P(6, 3) = 6 \cdot 5 \cdot 4 = 120$

   b) $P(6, 5) = 6! = 720$

   c) $P(8, 1) = 8$

   d) $P(8, 5) = 8 \cdot 7 \cdot 6 \cdot 5 \cdot 4 = 6720$

   e) $P(8, 8) = 8! = 40,320$

   f) $P(10, 9) = 10! = 3,628,800$

7. This is $P(9, 5) = 9 \cdot 8 \cdot 7 \cdot 6 \cdot 5 = 15,120$ by Theorem 1.

9. We need to pick 3 horses from the 12 horses in the race, and we need to arrange them in order (first, second, and third), in order to specify the win, place, and show. Thus there are $P(12, 3) = 12 \cdot 11 \cdot 10 = 1320$ possibilities.

11. We assume that the row has a distinguished head. Consider the order in which the men appear relative to each other. There are $n$ men, and any of the $P(n, n) = n!$ arrangements is allowed. Similarly, there are $n!$ arrangements in which the women can appear. Now the men and women must alternate, and there are the same number of men and women; therefore there are exactly two possibilities: either the row starts with a man and ends with a woman ($MWMW \ldots MW$) or else it starts with a woman and ends with a man ($WMWM \ldots WM$). We have three tasks to perform, then: arrange the men among themselves, arrange the women among themselves, and decide which sex starts the row. By the product rule there are $n! \cdot n! \cdot 2 = 2(n!)^2$ ways in which this can be done.

13. We assume that a combination is called for, not a permutation, since we are told to *select a set*, not *form an arrangement*. We need to choose 5 things from 26, so there are $C(26, 5) = 26 \cdot 25 \cdot 24 \cdot 23 \cdot 22/5! = 65,780$ ways to do so.

15. We know that there are $2^{100}$ subsets of a set with 100 elements. All of them have more than one element except the empty set and the 100 subsets consisting of one element each. Therefore the answer is $2^{100} - 101$.

17. There are at least two ways to do this. For our first approach, we first decide where in the 4-permutation the number 47 is to go. There are 4 possibilities (first, second, third, and fourth). That leaves 3 slots to fill, in order, from the 99 other positive integers not exceeding 100, and there are $P(99, 3)$ ways to do so. Therefore the answer (by the product rule) is $4 \cdot P(99, 3) = 4 \cdot 99 \cdot 98 \cdot 97 = 3,764,376$.

   Alternatively, let us count the number of 4-permutations without restriction, and then subtract the number of 4-permutations that violate the restriction. There are $P(100, 4)$ 4-permutations of the positive integers not exceeding 100. There are $P(99, 4)$ 4-permutations of the numbers not exceeding 100 that do not include 47, since the set $\{1, 2, \ldots, 46, 48, \ldots, 99, 100\}$ has 99 elements. Therefore the answer is $P(100, 4) - P(99, 4)$, which has the same value obtained above.

19. We take the first approach used in Exercise 17. To specify a 4-permutation of the positive integers not exceeding 100 which contains 19, 47, and 73, we can first decide which slot the 19 is to occupy; there are 4 choices. After making that decision, we then decide which slot the 47 is to occupy; there are 3 slots left, so that task can be done in 3 ways. Similarly, there are two ways to decide which of the remaining slots the 73 is to go in. Finally, of the 97 numbers not yet used, we need to choose 1 to fill the only vacant slot; there are of course 97 ways to do so. Therefore the answer is $4 \cdot 3 \cdot 2 \cdot 97 = 2328$.

21. We need to agree on what "consecutive" means in this context, to avoid ambiguity. Let us assume it means consecutive in the usual ordering of the integers, not consecutive in the permutation. For example, the permutation $5, 6, 32, 7$ is to be counted, since it contains the consecutive numbers 5, 6, and 7 in their correct order (even though separated by the 32). In order to specify such a 4-permutation, we first need to choose the 3 consecutive integers. They can be anything from $\{1, 2, 3\}$ to $\{98, 99, 100\}$; thus there are 98 possibilities. Next we need to decide which slot is to contain a number not in this set; there are 4 possibilities. Finally, we need to decide which of the 97 other positive integers not exceeding 100 is to fill this slot, and there are of course 97 choices. Thus our first attempt at an answer gives us, by the product rule, $98 \cdot 4 \cdot 97$.

    Unfortunately, this answer is not correct, since we have counted some 4-permutations more than once. Consider the 4-permutation $4, 5, 6, 7$, for example. We cannot tell whether it arose from choosing 4, 5, and 6 as the consecutive numbers, or from choosing 5, 6, and 7. (These are the only two ways it could have arisen.) In fact, any 4-permutation consisting of 4 consecutive numbers, in order, has been double counted. Therefore to correct our count, we need to subtract the number of such 4-permutations. Clearly there are 97 of them (they can begin with any number from 1 to 97). Further thought shows that any other 4-permutation in our collection arises in a unique way (in other words, there is a unique subsequence of three consecutive integers). Thus our final answer is $98 \cdot 4 \cdot 97 - 97 = 37{,}927$.

    If we had interpreted the problem differently, insisting that the consecutive numbers be consecutive in the 4-permutation as well, then the answer would have been $98 \cdot 2 \cdot 97 - 97 = 18{,}915$, since there would be only 2 places to put the fourth number—in slot one or in slot four.

23. To specify such a license plate we need to write down a 3-permutation of the set of 26 letters and follow it by a 3-permutation of the set of 10 digits. By the product rule, the answer is therefore $P(26, 3) \cdot P(10, 3) = 26 \cdot 25 \cdot 24 \cdot 10 \cdot 9 \cdot 8 = 11{,}232{,}000$.

25. This identity can be proved algebraically or combinatorially. Algebraically, we compute the right-hand side as follows (using twice the fact that $(x+1)x! = (x+1)!$):

$$\frac{(n+1)C(n, k-1)}{k} = \frac{(n+1)n!}{(k-1)!(n-(k-1))!k}$$
$$= \frac{(n+1)!}{k!(n-(k-1))!}$$
$$= \frac{(n+1)!}{k!((n+1)-k)!},$$

which is exactly the left-hand side.

    For a combinatorial argument, we need to construct a situation in which both sides count the same thing. Suppose we have a set of $n+1$ people, and we wish to choose $k$ of them. Clearly there are $C(n+1, k)$ ways to do this. On the other hand, we can choose our set of $k$ people by first choosing one person to be in the set (there are $n + 1$ choices), and then choosing $k - 1$ additional people to be in the set, from the $n$ people remaining. This can be done in $C(n, k - 1)$ ways. Therefore apparently there are $(n + 1)C(n, k - 1)$ ways to choose the set of $k$ people. However, we have overcounted: there are $k$ ways that every such set can be chosen, since once we have the set, we realize that any of the $k$ people could have been chosen first. Thus we have overcounted by a factor of $k$, and the real answer is $(n+1)C(n, k-1)/k$ (we correct for the overcounting by dividing by $k$). Comparing our two approaches, one yielding the answer $C(n+1, k)$, and the other yielding the answer $(n+1)C(n, k-1)/k$, we conclude that $C(n + 1, k) = (n + 1)C(n, k - 1)/k$.

Finally, we are asked to use this identity to give a recursive definition of the $C(n, k)$'s. Note that this identity expresses $C(n, k)$ in terms of $C(i, j)$ for values of $i$ and $j$ less than $n$ and $k$, respectively (namely $i = n - 1$ and $j = k - 1$). Thus the identity will be the recursive part of the definition. We need the base cases to handle the case of $n = 0$ or $k = 0$. Our full definition becomes:

$$C(n, k) = \begin{cases} 1 & \text{if } k = 0 \\ 0 & \text{if } k > 0 \text{ and } n = 0 \\ nC(n - 1, k - 1)/k & \text{if } n > 0 \text{ and } k > 0. \end{cases}$$

Actually, if we assume (as we usually do) that $k \leq n$, then we do not need the second line of the definition. Note that $C(n, k) = 0$ for $n < k$ under the definition given here, which is consistent with the combinatorial definition, since there are no ways to choose $k$ different elements from a set with fewer than $k$ elements.

27. The coefficients are the binomial coefficients $C(5, i)$, as $i$ runs from 0 to 5, namely 1, 5, 10, 10, 5, 1. Therefore $(x + y)^5 = \sum_{i=0}^{5} C(5, i) x^{5-i} y^i = x^5 + 5x^4 y + 10x^3 y^2 + 10x^2 y^3 + 5xy^4 + y^5$.

29. There is one term for each $i$ from 0 to 100, so there are 101 terms.

31. Using the formula we have

$$\begin{aligned} C(n, k - 1) + C(n, k) &= \frac{n!}{(k - 1)!(n - (k - 1))!} + \frac{n!}{k!(n - k)!} \\ &= \frac{n!k + n!(n - k + 1)}{k!(n - k + 1)!} \quad \text{(having found common denominator)} \\ &= \frac{(n + 1)n!}{k!((n + 1) - k)!} = \frac{(n + 1)!}{k!((n + 1) - k)!} = C(n + 1, k). \end{aligned}$$

33. **a)** We need to find something to count so that the left-hand side of the equation counts it in one way and the right-hand side counts it in a different way. After much thought, we might try the following. We will count the number of bit strings of length $n + r + 1$ containing exactly $r$ 0's and $n + 1$ 1's. There are $C(n + r + 1, r)$ such strings, since a string is completely specified by deciding which $r$ of the bits are to be the 0's. To see that the left-hand side of the identity counts the same thing, let $l + 1$ be the position of the last 1 in the string. Since there are $n + 1$ 1's, we know that $l$ cannot be less than $n$. Thus there are disjoint cases for each $l$ from $n$ to $n + r$. For each such $l$, we completely determine the string by deciding which of the $l$ positions in the string before the last 1 are to be 0's. Since there are $n$ 1's in this range, there are $l - n$ 0's. Thus there are $C(l, l - n)$ ways to choose the positions of the 0's. Now by the sum rule, the total number of bit strings will be $\sum_{l=n}^{n+r} C(l, l - n)$. By making the change of variable $k = l - n$, this transforms into the left-hand side, and we are finished.

**b)** We need to prove this by induction on $r$; Pascal's identity will enter at the crucial step. We let $P(r)$ be the statement to be proved. The base case is clear, since the equation reduces to $C(n,0) = C(n+1,0)$, which is the true proposition $1 = 1$. Assuming the inductive hypothesis, we derive $P(r+1)$ in the usual way.

$$\sum_{k=0}^{r+1} C(n+k,k) = \left(\sum_{k=0}^{r} C(n+k,k)\right) + C(n+r+1,r+1)$$
$$= C(n+r+1,r) + C(n+r+1,r+1) \quad \text{(by the inductive hypothesis)}$$
$$= C(n+(r+1)+1,r+1) \quad \text{(by Pascal's identity)}.$$

35. Theorem 7 says that $C(n,0) - C(n,1) + C(n,2) - \cdots \pm C(n,n) = 0$. If we put all the negative terms on the other side, we obtain $C(n,0) + C(n,2) + C(n,4) + \cdots = C(n,1) + C(n,3) + \cdots$ (one side ends at $C(n,n)$ and the other side ends at $C(n,n-1)$—which is which depends on whether $n$ is even or odd). Now the left-hand side counts the number of subsets with even cardinality of a set with $n$ elements, and the right-hand side counts the number of subsets with odd cardinality of the same set. That these two quantities are equal is precisely what we wanted to prove.

$\Rightarrow$ **SECTION 4.4    Discrete Probability**

*Calculating probabilities is one of the most immediate applications of combinatorics. Many people play games in which discrete probability plays a role, whether it is card games like poker or bridge, board games, or state lotteries. Probability is also important in making decisions in such areas as business and medicine—for example, in deciding how high a deductible to have on your automobile insurance. This section only scratches the surface, of course, but it is surprising how many useful calculations can be made using just the techniques discussed in this section.*

*The process is basically the same in each problem. First count the number of possible, equally likely, outcomes; this is the denominator of the probability you are seeking. Then count the number of ways that the event you are looking for can happen; this is the numerator. We have given approximate decimal answers to many of the problems, since the human mind can comprehend the magnitude of a number much better this way than by looking at a fraction with large numerator and denominator.*

1. There are 52 equally likely cards to be selected, and 4 of them are aces. Therefore the probability is $4/52 = 1/13$.

3. Among the first 100 positive integers there are exactly 50 odd ones. Therefore the probability is $50/100 = 1/2$.

5. One way to do this is to look at the 36 equally likely outcomes of the roll of two dice, which we can represent by the set of ordered pairs $(i,j)$ with $1 \leq i, j \leq 6$. A better way is to argue as follows. Whatever the number of spots showing on the first die, the sum will be even if and only if the number of spots showing on the second die has the same parity (even or odd) as the first. Since there are 3 even faces (2, 4, and 6) and 3 odd faces (1, 3, and 5), the probability is $3/6 = 1/2$.

7. There are $2^6 = 64$ possible outcomes, represented by all the sequences of length 6 of $H$'s and $T$'s. Only one of those sequences, $HHHHHH$, represents the event under consideration, so the probability is $1/64$.

9. We need to compute the number of ways to hold two pairs. To specify the hand we first choose the ranks the pairs will be (such as kings and fives); there are $C(13,2) = 78$ ways to do this, since we need to choose 2 ranks from the 13 possible ranks. Then we need to decide which 2 cards of each of the ranks of the pairs we want to include. There are 4 cards of each rank (4 suits), so there are $C(4,2) = 6$ ways to make each of these two choices. Finally, we need to decide which card to choose for the fifth card in the hand. We cannot choose any card in either of the 2 ranks that are already represented (we do not want to construct a full house by accident), so there are $52 - 8 = 44$ cards to choose from and hence $C(44,1) = 44$ ways to make the choice. Putting this all together by the product rule, there are $78 \cdot 6 \cdot 6 \cdot 44 = 123{,}552$ different hands classified as "two pairs."

   Since each hand is equally likely, and since there are $C(52,5) = 2{,}598{,}960$ different hands (see Example 5), the probability of holding two pairs is $123552/2598960 = 198/4165 \approx 0.0475$.

11. First we need to compute the number of ways to hold a straight. We can specify the hand by first choosing the starting (lowest) rank for the straight. Since the straight can start with any card from the set $\{A,2,3,4,5,6,7,8,9,10\}$, there are $C(10,1) = 10$ ways to do this. Then we need to decide which card of each of the ranks in the straight we want to include. There are 4 cards of each rank (4 suits), so there are $C(4,1) = 4$ ways to make each of these 5 choices. Putting this all together by the product rule, there are $10 \cdot 4^5 = 10{,}240$ different hands containing a straight. (For poker buffs, it should be pointed out that a hand is classified as a "straight" in poker if it contains a straight but does not contain a straight flush, which is a straight in which all of the cards are in the same suit. Since there are $10 \cdot 4 = 40$ straight flushes, we would need to subtract 40 from our answer above in order to find the number of hands classified as a "straight." Also, some poker books do not count $A,2,3,4,5$ as a straight.)

   Since each hand is equally likely, and since there are $C(52,5) = 2{,}598{,}960$ different hands (see Example 5), the probability of holding a hand containing a straight is $10240/2598960 = 128/32487 \approx 0.00394$.

13. Looked at properly, this is the same as Exercise 7. There are 2 equally likely outcomes for the parity on the roll of a die—even and odd. Of the $2^6 = 64$ outcomes in the roll of a die 6 times, only one consists of 6 odd numbers. Therefore the probability is $1/64$.

15. We need to count the number of positive integers not exceeding 100 that are divisible by 5 or 7. Using an analysis similar to Exercise 15e in Section 4.1, we see that there are $\lfloor 100/5 \rfloor = 20$ numbers in that range divisible by 5 and $\lfloor 100/7 \rfloor = 14$ divisible by 7. However, we have counted the numbers 35 and 70 twice, since they are divisible by both 5 and 7 (i.e., divisible by 35). Therefore there are $20 + 14 - 2 = 32$ such numbers. (We needed to subtract 2 to compensate for the double counting.) Now since there are 100 equally likely numbers in the set, the probability of choosing one of these 32 numbers is $32/100 = 8/25 = 0.32$.

17. There is only one winning choice of numbers, namely the same 8 numbers the computer chooses. Therefore the probability of winning is $1/C(100,8) \approx 1/(1.86 \times 10^{11})$.

19. **a)** There are 18 red numbers and 38 numbers in all, so the probability is $18/38 = 9/19 \approx 0.474$.
    **b)** There are $38^2$ equally likely outcomes for 2 spins, since each spin can result in 38 different outcomes. Of these, $18^2$ are a pair of black numbers. Therefore the probability is $18^2/38^2 = 81/361 \approx 0.224$.

**c)** There are 2 outcomes being considered here, so the probability is $2/38 = 1/19$.

**d)** We are interpreting this question as asking for the probability that on each of five consecutive spins of the wheel, a number other than 0 or 00 comes up. (The other possible interpretation is as asking for the probability that it is not the case that five times in a row the wheel lands on 0 or 00. The answer under that interpretation is $1 - (2^5/38^5) = 2476098/2476099$, which equals 1 for all practical purposes.) There are $38^5$ equally likely outcomes in 5 spins of the wheel. Since 36 outcomes on each spin are not 0 or 00, there are $36^5$ outcomes being considered. Therefore the probability is $36^5/38^5 = 1889568/2476099 \approx 0.763$.

**e)** There are $38^2$ equally likely outcomes. The number of outcomes that meet the conditions specified here is $6 \cdot (38-6) = 192$ (by the product rule). Therefore the probability is $192/38^2 = 48/361 \approx 0.133$.

⇒ **SECTION 4.5    Generalized Permutations and Combinations**

*As in the previous section, we have formulas that give us the answer to some combinatorial problems, if we can figure out which formula applies to which problem, and in what way it applies. Here, even more than in previous sections, the ability to see a problem from the right perspective is the key to solving it. Expect to spend several minutes staring at each problem before any insight comes. Reread the examples in the section and try to imagine yourself going through the thought processes explained there. Gradually your mind will begin to think in the same terms. In particular, ask yourself what is being selected from what, whether ordered or unordered selections are to be made, and whether repetition is allowed. In most case, after you have answered these questions, you can find the appropriate formula from Table 1.*

**1.** Since order is important here, and since repetition is allowed, this is a simple application of the product rule. There are 3 ways in which the first element can be selected, 3 ways in which the second element can be selected, and so on, with finally 3 ways in which the fifth element can be selected, so there are $3^5 = 243$ ways in which the 5 elements can be selected. The general formula is that there are $n^k$ ways to select $k$ elements from a set of $n$ elements, in order, with unlimited repetition allowed.

**3.** Since we are considering strings, clearly order matters. The choice for each position in the string is from the set of 26 letters. Therefore, using the same reasoning as in Exercise 1, we see that there are $26^6 = 308,915,776$ strings.

**5.** We assume that the jobs and the employees are distinguishable. For each job, we have to decide which employee gets that job. Thus there are 5 ways in which the first job can be assigned, 5 ways in which the second job can be assigned, and 5 ways in which the third job can be assigned. Therefore by the multiplication principle (just as in Exercise 1), there are $5^3 = 125$ ways in which the assignments can be made.

**7.** Since the selection is to be an unordered one, the theory of Theorem 2 applies. We want to choose $r = 3$ items from a set with $n = 5$ elements. Theorem 2 tells us that there are $C(5 + 3 - 1, 3) = C(7,3) = 7 \cdot 6 \cdot 5/(3 \cdot 2) = 35$ ways to do so. (Equivalently, this problem is asking us to count the number of nonnegative integer solutions to $x_1 + x_2 + x_3 + x_4 + x_5 = 3$, where $x_i$ represents the number of times that the $i^{th}$ element of the 5-element set gets selected.)

9. Let $b_1$, $b_2$, ..., $b_8$ be the number of bagels of the 8 types listed (in the order listed) that are selected. Order does not matter: we are presumably putting the bagels into a bag to take home, and the order in which we put them there is irrelevant.

a) If we want to choose 6 bagels, then we are asking for the number of nonnegative solutions to the equation $b_1 + b_2 + \cdots + b_8 = 6$. Theorem 2 applies, with $n = 8$ and $r = 6$, giving us the answer $C(8 + 6 - 1, 6) = C(13, 6) = 1716$.

b) This is the same as part (a), except that $r = 12$ rather than 6. Thus there are $C(8 + 12 - 1, 12) = C(19, 12) = C(19, 7) = 50{,}388$ ways to make the selection. (Note that $C(19, 7)$ was easier to compute than $C(19, 12)$, and since they are equal, we chose the latter form.)

c) This is the same as part (a), except that $r = 24$ rather than 6. Thus there are $C(8 + 24 - 1, 24) = C(31, 24) = C(31, 7) = 2{,}629{,}575$ ways to make the selection.

d) This one is more complicated. Here we want to solve the equation $b_1 + b_2 + \cdots + b_8 = 12$, subject to the constraint that each $b_i \geq 1$. We reduce this problem to the form in which Theorem 2 is applicable with the following trick. Let $b_i' = b_i - 1$; then $b_i'$ represents the number of bagels of type $i$, in excess of the required 1, that are selected. If we substitute $b_i = b_i' + 1$ into the original equation, we obtain $(b_1' + 1) + (b_2' + 1) + \cdots + (b_8' + 1) = 12$, which reduces to $b_1' + b_2' + \cdots + b_8' = 4$. In other words, we are asking how many ways are there to choose the 4 extra bagels (in excess of the required 1 of each type) from among the 8 types, repetitions allowed. By Theorem 2 the number of solutions is $C(8 + 4 - 1, 4) = C(11, 4) = 330$.

e) This final part is even trickier. First let us ignore the restriction that there can be no more than 2 salty bagels (i.e., that $b_4 \leq 2$). We will take into account, however, the restriction that there must be at least 3 egg bagels (i.e., that $b_3 \geq 3$). Thus we want to count the number of solutions to the equation $b_1 + b_2 + \cdots + b_8 = 12$, subject to the condition that $b_i \geq 0$ for all $i$ and $b_3 \geq 3$. As in part (d), we use the trick of choosing the 3 egg bagels at the outset, leaving only 9 bagels free to be chosen; equivalently, we set $b_3' = b_3 - 3$, to represent the extra egg bagels, above the required 3, that are chosen. Now Theorem 2 applies to the number of solutions of $b_1 + b_2 + b_3' + b_4 + \cdots + b_8 = 9$, so there are $C(8 + 9 - 1, 9) = C(16, 9) = C(16, 7) = 11{,}440$ ways to make this selection.

Next we need to worry about the restriction that $b_4 \leq 2$. We will impose this restriction by subtracting from our answer so far the number of ways to violate this restriction (while still obeying the restriction that $b_3 \geq 3$). The difference will be the desired answer. To violate the restriction means to have $b_4 \geq 3$. Thus we want to count the number of solutions to $b_1 + b_2 + \cdots + b_8 = 12$, with $b_3 \geq 3$ and $b_4 \geq 3$. Using the same technique as we have just used, this is equal to the number of nonnegative solutions to the equation $b_1 + b_2 + b_3' + b_4' + b_5 + \cdots + b_8 = 6$ (the 6 on the right being $12 - 3 - 3$). By Theorem 2 there are $C(8 + 6 - 1, 6) = C(13, 6) = 1716$ ways to make this selection. Therefore our final answer is $11440 - 1716 = 9724$.

11. Assuming that the warehouses are distinguishable, let $w_i$ be the number of books stored in warehouse $i$. Then we are asked for the number of solutions to the equation $w_1 + w_2 + w_3 = 3000$. By Theorem 2, there are $C(3 + 3000 - 1, 3000) = C(3002, 3000) = C(3002, 2) = 4{,}504{,}501$ of them.

13. a) Let $x_1 = x_1' + 1$; thus $x_1'$ is the value that $x_1$ has in excess of its required 1. Then the problem asks for the number of nonnegative solutions to $x_1' + x_2 + x_3 + x_4 + x_5 = 20$. By Theorem 2 there are $C(5 + 20 - 1, 20) = C(24, 20) = C(24, 4) = 10{,}626$ of them.

b) Substitute $x_i = x_i' + 2$ into the equation for each $i$; thus $x_i'$ is the value that $x_i$ has in excess of its required 2. Then the problem asks for the number of nonnegative solutions to $x_1' + x_2' + x_3' + x_4' + x_5' = 11$. By Theorem 2 there are $C(5 + 11 - 1, 11) = C(15, 11) = C(15, 4) = 1365$ of them.

c) There are $C(5 + 21 - 1, 21) = C(25, 21) = C(25, 4) = 12650$ solutions with no restriction on $x_1$. The restriction on $x_1$ will be violated if $x_1 \geq 11$. Following the procedure in part (a), we find that there are $C(5 + 10 - 1, 10) = C(14, 10) = C(14, 4) = 1001$ solutions in which the restriction is violated. Therefore there are $12650 - 1001 = 11{,}649$ solutions of the equation with its restriction.

d) First let us impose the restrictions that $x_3 \geq 15$ and $x_2 \geq 1$. Then the problem is equivalent to counting the number of solutions to $x_1 + x_2' + x_3' + x_4 + x_5 = 5$, subject to the constraints that $x_1 \leq 3$ and $x_2' \leq 2$ (the latter coming from the original restriction that $x_2 < 4$). Note that these two restrictions cannot be violated simultaneously. Thus if we count the number of solutions to $x_1 + x_2' + x_3' + x_4 + x_5 = 5$, subtract the number of its solutions in which $x_1 \geq 4$, and subtract the numbers of its solutions in which $x_2' \geq 3$, then we will have the answer. By Theorem 2, there are $C(5 + 5 - 1, 5) = C(9, 5) = C(9, 4) = 126$ solutions of the unrestricted equation. Applying the first restriction reduces the equation to $x_1' + x_2' + x_3' + x_4 + x_5 = 1$, which has $C(5 + 1 - 1, 1) = C(5, 1) = 5$ solutions. Applying the second restriction reduces the equation to $x_1 + x_2 + x_3' + x_4 + x_5 = 2$, which has $C(5 + 2 - 1, 2) = C(6, 2) = 15$ solutions. Therefore the answer is $126 - 5 - 15 = 106$.

15. Let $d_1$, $d_2$, ..., $d_6$ be the digits of a number less than $1{,}000{,}000$; they can each be anything from 0 to 9 (in other words, we may as well assume that there are leading 0's if necessary to make the number exactly 6 digits long). If we want the sum of the digits to equal 19, then we are asking for the number of solutions to the equation $d_1 + d_2 + \cdots + d_6 = 19$ with $0 \leq d_i \leq 9$ for each $i$. Ignoring the upper bound restriction, there are, by Theorem 2, $C(6 + 19 - 1, 19) = C(24, 19) = C(24, 5) = 42504$ of them. We must subtract the number of solutions in which the restriction is violated. If the digits are to add up to 19 and one or more of them is to exceed 9, then exactly one of them will have to exceed 9, since $10 + 10 > 19$. There are 6 ways to choose the digit that will exceed 9. Once we have made that choice (without loss of generality assume it is $d_1$ that is to be made greater than or equal to 10), then we count the number of solutions to the equation by counting the number of solutions to $d_1' + d_2 + \cdots + d_6 = 19 - 10 = 9$; by Theorem 2 there are $C(6 + 9 - 1, 9) = C(14, 9) = C(14, 5) = 2002$ of them. Thus there are $6 \cdot 2002 = 12012$ solutions which violate the restriction. Subtracting this from the 42504 solutions altogether, we find that $42504 - 12012 = 30{,}492$ is the answer to the problem.

17. We assume that each problem is worth a whole number of points. Then we want to find the number of integer solutions to $x_1 + x_2 + \cdots + x_{10} = 100$, subject to the constraint that each $x_i \geq 5$. Letting $x_i'$ be the number of points assigned to problem $i$ in excess of its required 5, and substituting $x_i = x_i' + 5$ into the equation, we obtain the equivalent equation $x_1' + x_2' + \cdots + x_{10}' = 50$. By Theorem 2, the number of solutions is given by $C(10 + 50 - 1, 50) = C(59, 50) = C(59, 9) = 12{,}565{,}671{,}261$.

19. There are at least two good ways to do this problem. First we present a solution in the spirit of this section. Let us place the 1's and some gaps in a row. A 1 will come first, followed by a gap, followed by another 1, another gap, a third 1, a third gap, a fourth 1, and a fourth gap. Into the gaps we must place the 12 0's that are in this string. Let $g_1$, $g_2$, $g_3$, and $g_4$ be the numbers of 0's placed in gaps 1 through 4, respectively. The only restriction is that each $g_i \geq 2$. Thus we want to count the number of solutions to the equation $g_1 + g_2 + g_3 + g_4 = 12$, with $g_i \geq 2$ for each $i$. Letting $g_i = g_i' + 2$, we want to count, equivalently, the number of nonnegative solutions to $g_1' + g_2' + g_3' + g_4' = 4$. By Theorem 2, there are $C(4 + 4 - 1, 4) = C(7, 4) = C(7, 3) = 35$ solutions. Thus our answer is 35.

Here is another way to solve the problem. Since each 1 must be followed by two 0's, suppose we glue 00 to the right end of each 1. This uses up 8 of the 0's, leaving 4 unused 0's. Now we have 8 objects, namely 4 0's and 4 100's. We want to find the number of strings we can form with these

8 objects, starting with a 100. After placing the 100 first, there are 7 places left for objects, 3 of which have to be 100's. Clearly there are $C(7,3) = 35$ ways to choose the positions for the 100's, so our answer is 35.

21. This is a direct application of Theorem 3, with $n = 11$, $n_1 = 5$, $n_2 = 2$, $n_3 = n_4 = 1$, and $n_5 = 2$ (where $n_1$ represents the number of $A$'s, etc.). Thus the answer is $11!/(5!2!1!1!2!) = 83{,}160$.

23. We need to use the sum rule at the outermost level here, adding the number of strings using each subset of letters. There are quite a few cases. First, there are 3 strings of length 1, namely $O$, $R$, and $N$. There are several strings of length 2. If the string uses no $O$'s, then there are 2; if it uses 1 $O$, then there are 2 ways to choose the other letter, and 2 ways to permute the letters in the string, so there are 4; and of course there is just 1 string of length 2 using 2 $O$'s. Strings of length 3 can use 1, 2, or 3 $O$'s. A little thought shows that the number of such strings is $3! = 6$, 6, and 1, respectively. There are 3 possibilities of the choice of letters for strings of length 4. If we omit an $O$, then there are $4!/2! = 12$ strings; if we omit either of the other letters (2 ways to choose the letter), then there are 4 strings. Finally, there are $5!/3! = 20$ strings of length 5. This gives a total of $3 + 2 + 4 + 1 + 6 + 6 + 1 + 12 + 2 \cdot 4 + 20 = 63$ strings using some or all of the letters.

25. We assume that all the fruit is to be eaten; in other words, this process ends after 7 days. This is a permutation problem since the order in which the fruit is consumed matters (indeed, there is nothing else that matters here). Theorem 3 applies, with $n = 7$, $n_1 = 3$, $n_2 = 2$, and $n_3 = 2$. The answer is therefore $7!/(3!2!2!) = 210$.

27. When $(x_1 + x_2 + \cdots + x_m)^n$ is expanded, each term will clearly be of the form $Cx_1^{n_1} x_2^{n_2} \cdots x_m^{n_m}$, for some constants $C$ which depend on the exponents, where the exponents sum to $n$. Thus the form of the given formula is correct, and the only question is whether the constants are correct. We need to count the number of ways in which a product of one term from each of the $n$ factors can be $x_1^{n_1} x_2^{n_2} \cdots x_m^{n_m}$. In order for this to happen, we must choose $n_1$ $x_1$'s, $n_2$ $x_2$'s, $\ldots$, $n_m$ $x_m$'s. By Theorem 3 this can be done in

$$C(n; n_1, n_2, \ldots, n_m) = \frac{n!}{n_1! n_2! \cdots n_m!}$$

ways.

29. By the multinomial theorem, given in Exercise 27, the coefficient is

$$C(10; 3, 2, 5) = \frac{10!}{3!2!5!} = \frac{10 \cdot 9 \cdot 8 \cdot 7 \cdot 6}{12} = 2520.$$

⇒ **SECTION 4.6   Generating Permutations and Combinations**

*This section is quite different from the rest of this chapter. It is really about algorithms and programming. These algorithms are not easy, and it would be worthwhile to "play computer" with them to get a feeling for how they work. In constructing such algorithms yourself, try assuming that you will list the permutations or combinations in a nice order (such as lexicographic order); then figure out how to find the "next" one in this order.*

**1.** We use Algorithm 1 to find the next permutation. Our notation follows that algorithm, with $j$ being the largest subscript such that $a_j < a_{j+1}$ and $k$ being the subscript of the smallest number to the right of $a_j$ which is larger than $a_j$.

**a)** Since $4 > 3 > 2$, we know that the 1 is our $a_j$. The smallest integer to the right of 1 and greater than 1 is 2, so $k = 4$. We interchange $a_j$ and $a_k$, giving the permutation 2431, and then we reverse the entire substring to the right of the position now occupied by the 2, giving the answer 2134.

**b)** The first integer from the right that is less than its right neighbor is the 2 in position 4. Therefore $j = 4$ here, and of course $k$ has to be 5. The next permutation is the one that we get by interchanging the fourth and fifth numbers, 54132. (Note that the last phase of the algorithm, reversing the end of the string, was vacuous this time—there was only one element to the right of position 4, so no reversing was necessary.)

**c)** Since $5 > 3$, we know that the 4 is our $a_j$. The smallest integer to the right of 4 and greater than 4 is $a_k = 5$. We interchange $a_j$ and $a_k$, giving the permutation 12543, and then we reverse the entire substring to the right of the position now occupied by the 5, giving the answer 12534.

**d)** Since $3 > 1$, we know that the 2 is our $a_j$. The smallest integer to the right of 2 and greater than 2 is $a_k = 3$. We interchange $a_j$ and $a_k$, giving the permutation 45321, and then we reverse the entire substring to the right of the position now occupied by the 3, giving the answer 45312.

**e)** The first integer from the right that is less than its right neighbor is the 3 in position 6. Therefore $j = 6$ here, and of course $k$ has to be 7. The next permutation is the one that we get by interchanging the sixth and seventh numbers, 6714253. As in part **(b)**, no reversing was necessary.

**f)** Since $8 > 7 > 6 > 4$, we know that the 2 is our $a_j$, so $j = 4$. The smallest integer to the right of 2 and greater than 2 is $a_8 = 4$. We interchange $a_4$ and $a_8$, giving the permutation 31548762, and then we reverse the entire substring to the right of the position now occupied by the 4, giving the answer 31542678.

**3.** We begin with the permutation 1234. Then we apply Algorithm 1 23 times in succession, giving us the other 23 permutations in lexicographic order: 1243, 1324, 1342, 1423, 1432, 2134, 2143, 2314, 2341, 2413, 2431, 3124, 3142, 3214, 3241, 3412, 3421, 4123, 4132, 4213, 4231, 4312, and 4321. The last permutation is the one entirely in decreasing order. Each application of Algorithm 1 follows the pattern in Exercise 1.

**5.** We begin with the first 3-combination, namely $\{1, 2, 3\}$. Let us trace through Algorithm 3 to find the next. Note that $n = 5$ and $r = 3$.; also $a_1 = 1$, $a_2 = 2$, and $a_3 = 3$. We set $i$ equal to 3 and then decrease $i$ until $a_i \neq 5 - 3 + i$. This inequality is already satisfied for $i = 3$, since $a_3 \neq 5$. At this point we increment $a_i$ by 1 (so that now $a_3 = 4$), and fill the remaining spaces with consecutive integers following $a_i$ (in this case there are no more remaining spaces). Thus our second 3-combination is $\{1, 2, 4\}$. The next call to Algorithm 3 works the same way, producing the third 3-combination, namely $\{1, 2, 5\}$. To get the fourth 3-combination, we again call Algorithm 3. This time the $i$ that we find is 2, since $5 = a_3 = 5 - 3 + 3$. Therefore the second element in the list is incremented, namely goes from a 2 to a 3, and the third element is the next largest element after 3, namely 4. Thus this 3-combination is $\{1, 3, 4\}$. Another call to the algorithm gives us $\{1, 3, 5\}$, and another call gives us $\{1, 4, 5\}$. Now when we call the algorithm, we find $i = 1$, since in this case the last two elements are the two largest elements in the set. Thus $a_1$ is increased to 2, and the remainder of the list is filled with the next two consecutive integers, giving us $\{2, 3, 4\}$. Continuing in this manner, we get the rest of the 3-combinations: $\{2, 3, 5\}$, $\{2, 4, 5\}$, $\{3, 4, 5\}$.

7. Clearly the next largest $r$-combination must differ from the old one in position $i$, since positions $i+1$, $i+2, \ldots, r$ are occupied by the largest possible numbers (namely $i+n-r+1$ to $n$). Also $a_i + 1$ is the smallest possible number that can be put in position $i$ if we want an $r$-combination greater than the given one, and then similarly $a_i + 2$, $a_i + 3$, $\ldots$, $a_i + r - i + 1$ are the smallest allowable numbers for positions $i+1$ to $r$. Therefore there is no $r$-combination between the given one and the one that Algorithm 3 produces, which is exactly what we had to prove.

9. One way to do this problem (and to have done Exercise 8) is to generate the $r$-combinations using Algorithm 3, and then to find all the permutations of each, using Algorithm 1 (except that now the elements to be permuted are not the integers from 1 to $r$, but are instead the $r$ elements of the $r$-combination currently being used). Thus we start with the first 3-combination, $\{1, 2, 3\}$, and we list all 6 of its permutations: 123, 132, 213, 231, 312, 321. Next we find the next 3-combination, namely $\{1, 2, 4\}$, and list all of its permutations: 124, 142, 214, 241, 412, 421. We continue in this manner to generate the remaining 48 3-permutations of $\{1, 2, 3, 4, 5\}$: 125, 152, 215, 251, 512, 521; 134, 143, 314, 341, 413, 431; 135, 153, 315, 351, 513, 531; 145, 154, 415, 451, 514, 541; 234, 243, 324, 342, 423, 432; 235, 253, 325, 352, 523, 532; 245, 254, 425, 452, 524, 542; 345, 354, 435, 453, 534, 543. There are of course $P(5, 3) = 5 \cdot 4 \cdot 3 = 60$ items in our list.

11. One way to show that a function is a bijection is to find its inverse, since only bijections can have inverses. Note that the sizes of the two sets in question are the same, since there are $n!$ nonnegative integers less than $n!$, and there are $n!$ permutations of $\{1, 2, \ldots, n\}$. In this case, since Cantor expansions are unique, we need to take the digits $a_1$, $a_2$, $\ldots$, $a_{n-1}$ of the Cantor expansion of a nonnegative integer $m$ less than $n!$ (so that $m = a_1 1! + a_2 2! + \cdots + a_{n-1}(n-1)!$), and produce a permutation with these $a_k$'s satisfying the definition given above Exercise 10—indeed the only such permutation.

We will fill the positions in the permutation one at a time. First we put $n$ into position $n - a_{n-1}$; clearly $a_{n-1}$ will be the number of integers less than $n$ that follow $n$ in the permutation, since exactly $a_{n-1}$ positions remain empty to the right of where we put the $n$. Next we renumber the free positions (the ones other than the one into which we put $n$), from left to right, as $1, 2, \ldots, n-1$. Under this numbering, we put $n-1$ into position $(n-1) - a_{n-2}$. Again it is clear that $a_{n-2}$ will be the number of integers less than $n-1$ that follow $n-1$ in the permutation. We continue in this manner, renumbering the free positions, from left to right, as $1, 2, \ldots, n-k+1$, and then placing $n-k+1$ in position $(n-k+1) - a_{n-k}$, for $k = 1, 2, \ldots, n-1$. Finally we place 1 in the only remaining position.

13. The algorithm is really given in our solution to Exercise 11. To produce all the permutations, we find the permutation corresponding to $i$, where $0 \leq i < n!$, under the correspondence given in Exercise 11. To do this, we need to find the digits in the Cantor expansion of $i$, starting with the digit $a_{n-1}$. In what follows, that digit will be called $c$. We use $k$ to keep track of which digit we are working on; as $k$ goes from 1 to $n - 1$, we will be computing the digit $a_{n-k}$ in the Cantor expansion and inserting $n - k + 1$ into the proper location in the permutation. (At the end, we need to insert 1 into the only remaining position.) We will call the positions in the permutation $p_1$, $p_2$, $\ldots$, $p_n$. We write only the procedure which computes the permutation corresponding to $i$; obviously to get all the permutations we simply call this procedure for each $i$ from 0 to $n! - 1$.

> **procedure** *Cantor permutation*$(n, i :$ integers with $n \geq 1$ and $0 \leq i < n!)$
> $x := n$ {to help in computing Cantor digits}
> **for** $j := 1$ **to** $n$ {initialize permutation to be all 0's}

```
           p_j := 0
  for k := 1 to n − 1  {figure out where to place n − k + 1 }
  begin
               c := ⌊x/(n − k)!⌋  {the Cantor digit}
               x := x − c(n − k)!  {what's left of x }
               h := n  {now find the (c + 1)^th free position from the right}
               while p_h ≠ 0
                       h := h − 1
               for j := 1 to c
               begin
                       h := h − 1
                       while p_h ≠ 0
                               h := h − 1
               end
               p_h := n − k + 1  {here is the key step}
  end
  h := 1  {now find the last free position}
  while p_h ≠ 0
          h := h + 1
  p_h := 1
  { p_1, p_2, . . . , p_n is the permutation corresponding to i }
```

⇒ **SUPPLEMENTARY EXERCISES FOR CHAPTER 4**

1. In each part of this problem we have $n = 10$ and $r = 6$.

   **a)** If the items are to be chosen in order with no repetition allowed, then we need a simple permutation. Therefore the answer is $P(10,6) = 10 \cdot 9 \cdot 8 \cdot 7 \cdot 6 \cdot 5 = 151,200$.

   **b)** If repetition is allowed, then this is just a simple application of the product rule, with 6 tasks, each of which can be done in 10 ways. Therefore the answer is $10^6 = 1,000,000$.

   **c)** If the items are to be chosen without regard to order but with no repetition allowed, then we need a simple combination. Therefore the answer is $C(10,6) = C(10,4) = 10 \cdot 9 \cdot 8 \cdot 7 \cdot /(4 \cdot 3 \cdot 2) = 210$.

   **d)** Unordered choices with repetition allowed are counted by $C(n + r − 1, r)$, which in this case is $C(15,6) = 5005$.

3. The student has 3 choices for each question: true, false, and no answer. There are 100 questions, so by the product rule there are $3^{100} \approx 5 \times 10^{47}$ ways to answer the test.

5. **a)** We want a combination with repetition allowed, with $n = 28$ and $r = 3$. By Theorem 2 of Section 4.5 there are $C(28 + 3 − 1, 3) = C(30,3) = 4060$ possibilities.

   **b)** This is just a simple application of the product rule. There are 28 ways to choose the ice cream, 8 ways to choose the sauce, and 12 ways to choose the topping, so there are $28 \cdot 8 \cdot 12 = 2688$ possible small sundaes.

   **c)** By the product rule, we have to multiply together the number of ways to choose the ice cream, the number of ways to choose the sauce, and the number of ways to choose the topping. There are $C(28 + 3 − 1, 3)$ ways to choose the ice cream, just as in part **(a)**. There are $C(8,2)$ ways to choose the sauce, since repetition is not allowed. There are similarly $C(12,3)$ ways to choose the toppings. Multiplying these numbers together, we find that the answer is $4060 \cdot 28 \cdot 220 = 25,009,600$ different large sundaes.

7. We can solve this problem by counting the number of numbers that have the given digit in 1, 2, or 3 places.

a) The digit 0 appears in 1 place in some two-digit numbers and in some three-digit numbers. There are clearly 9 two-digit numbers in which 0 appears, namely $10, 20, \ldots, 90$. We can count the number of three-digit numbers in which 0 appears exactly once as follows: first choose the place in which it is to appear (2 ways, since it cannot be the leading digit), then choose the left-most of the remaining digits (9 ways, since it cannot be a 0), then choose the final digit (also 9 ways). Therefore there are $9 + 2 \cdot 9 \cdot 9 = 171$ numbers in which the 0 appears exactly once, accounting for 171 appearances of the digit 0. Finally there are another 9 numbers in which the digit 0 appears twice, namely 100, $200, \ldots, 900$. This accounts for 18 more 0's. And of course the number 1000 contributes 3 0's. Therefore our final answer is $171 + 18 + 3 = 192$.

b) The analysis for the digit 1 is not the same as for the digit 0, since we can have leading 1's but not leading 0's. One 1 appears in the one-digit numbers. Two-digit numbers can have a 1 in the ones place (and there are 9 of these, namely $11, 21, \ldots, 91$), or in the tens place (and there are 10 of these, namely 10 through 19). Of course the number 11 is counted in both places, but that is proper, since we want to count each appearance of a 1. Therefore there are $10 + 9 = 19$ 1's appearing in two-digit numbers. Similarly, the three-digit numbers have 90 1's appearing in the ones place (every tenth number, and there are 900 numbers), 90 1's in the tens place (10 per decade, and there are 9 decades), and 100 1's in the hundreds place (100 through 199); therefore there are 280 ones appearing in three-digit numbers. Finally there is a 1 in 1000, so the final answer is $1 + 19 + 280 + 1 = 301$.

c) The analysis for the digit 2 is exactly the same as for the digit 1, with the exception that we do not get any 2's in 1000. Therefore the answer is $301 - 1 = 300$.

d) The analysis for the digit 9 is exactly the same as for the digit 2, so the answer is again 300.

Let us check all of the answers to this problem simultaneously. There are 300 each of the digits 2 through 9, for a total of 2400 digits. There are 192 0's and 301 1's. Therefore $2400 + 192 + 301 = 2893$ digits are used altogether. Let us count this another way. There are 9 one-digit numbers, 90 two-digit numbers, 900 three-digit numbers, and 1 four-digit number, so the total number of digits is $9 \cdot 1 + 90 \cdot 2 + 900 \cdot 3 + 1 \cdot 4 = 2893$. This agreement tends to confirm our analysis.

9. This is a negative instance of the generalized pigeonhole principle. The worst case would be if the student gets each fortune 3 times, for a total of $3 \times 213 = 639$ meals. If the student ate 640 or more meals, then the student will get the same fortune at least $\lceil 640/213 \rceil = 4$ times.

11. We have no guarantee ahead of time that this will work, but we will try applying the pigeonhole principle. Let us count the number of different possible sums. If the numbers in the set do not exceed 50, then the largest possible sum of a 5-element subset will be $50 + 49 + 48 + 47 + 46 = 240$. The smallest possible sum will be $1 + 2 + 3 + 4 + 5 = 15$. Therefore the sum has to be a number between 15 and 240, inclusive, and there are $240 - 15 + 1 = 226$ such numbers. Now let us count the number of different subsets. That is of course $C(10, 5) = 252$. Since there are more subsets (pigeons) than sums (pigeonholes), we know that there must be two subsets with the same sum.

13. We assume that the drawings of the cards is done without replacement (i.e., no repetition allowed).

a) The worst case would be that we drew 1 ace and the 48 cards which are not aces, a total of 49 cards. Therefore we need to draw 50 cards to guarantee at least 2 aces (and it is clear that 50 is sufficient, since at worst 2 of the 4 aces would then be left in the deck).

**b)** The same analysis as in part **(a)** applies, so again the answer is 50.

**c)** In this problem we can use the pigeonhole principle. If we drew 13 cards, then they might all be of different kinds (we assume that "kind" means rank). If we drew 14 cards, however, then since there are only 13 kinds we would be assured of having at least two of the same kind. (The drawn cards are the pigeons and the kinds are the pigeonholes.)

**d)** If we drew 4 cards, they might all be of the same kind. However, if we draw 5 cards, then since there are only 4 of one kind, we are assured of seeing at least two different kinds.

15. This problem can be solved by the pigeonhole principle if we look at it correctly. Let $s_i$ be the sum of the first $i$ of these numbers, where $1 \leq i \leq m$. Now if $s_i \equiv 0 \pmod{m}$ for some $i$, then we have our desired consecutive terms whose sum is divisible by $m$. Otherwise the numbers $s_1 \bmod m$, $s_2 \bmod m, \ldots, s_m \bmod m$ are all integers in the set $\{1, 2, \ldots, m-1\}$. By the pigeonhole principle we know that two of them are the same, say $s_i \bmod m = s_j \bmod m$ with $i < j$. Then $s_j - s_i$ is divisible by $m$. But $s_j - s_i$ is just the sum of the $(i+1)^{\text{th}}$ through $j^{\text{th}}$ terms in the sequence, and we are done.

17. The decimal expansion of a rational number $a/b$ (we can assume that $a$ and $b$ are positive integers) can be obtained by long division of the number $b$ into the number $a$, where $a$ is written with a decimal point and an arbitrarily long string of 0's following it. The basic step in long division is finding the next digit of the quotient, which is just $\lfloor r/b \rfloor$, where $r$ is the current remainder with the next digit of the dividend brought down. Now in our case, eventually the dividend has nothing but 0's to bring down. Furthermore there are only $b$ possible remainders, namely the numbers from 0 to $b-1$. Thus at some point in our calculation after we have passed the decimal point, we will, by the pigeonhole principle, be looking at exactly the same situation as we had previously. From that point onward, then, the calculation must follow the same pattern as it did previously. In particular, the digits of the quotient will repeat.

For example, to compute the decimal expansion of the rational number 349/11, we divide 11 into 349.00.... The first digit of the quotient is 3, and the remainder is 1. The next digit of the quotient is 1 and the remainder is 8. At this point there are only 0's left to bring down. The next digit of the quotient is a 7 with a remainder of 3, and then a quotient digit of 2 with a remainder of 8. We are now in exactly the same situation as at the previous appearance of a remainder of 8, so the quotient digits 72 repeat forever. Thus $349/11 = 31.\overline{72}$.

19. **a)** This is a simple combination, so the answer is $C(20, 12) = 125{,}970$.

**b)** The only choice is the choice of a variety, so the answer is 20.

**c)** We assume that order does not matter (all the donuts will go into a bag). Therefore, since repetitions are allowed, Theorem 2 of Section 4.5 applies, and the answer is $C(20 + 12 - 1, 12) = C(31, 12) = 141{,}120{,}525$.

**d)** We can simply subtract from our answer to part **(c)** our answer to part **(b)**, which asks for the number of ways this restriction can be violated. Therefore the answer is $141{,}120{,}505$.

**e)** We put the 6 blueberry filled donuts into our bag, and the problem becomes one of choosing 6 donuts with no restrictions. In analogy with part **(c)**, we obtain the answer $C(20 + 6 - 1, 6) = C(25, 6) = 177{,}100$.

**f)** There are $C(20 + 5 - 1, 5) = C(24, 5) = 42504$ ways to choose at least 7 blueberry donuts among our dozen (the calculation is essentially the same as that in part **(e)**). Our answer is therefore 42504 less than our unrestricted answer to part **(c)**: $141120525 - 42504 = 141{,}078{,}021$.

**21.** There are $C(52, 13)$ possible hands. A hand with no pairs must contain exactly one of each rank. The only choice involved, therefore, is the suit for each of the 13 cards. There are 4 ways to specify the suit, and there are 13 tasks to be performed. Therefore there are $4^{13}$ hands with no pairs. The probability of drawing such a hand is thus $4^{13}/C(52, 13) = 67108864/635013559600 = 4194304/39688347475 \approx 0.000106$.

**23. a)** The given equation is equivalent to $n(n-1)/2 = 45$. The quadratic formula (or factoring) tells us that the roots are $n = 10$ and $n = -9$. Since $n$ is assumed to be nonnegative, the only relevant solution is $n = 10$.
**b)** The given equation is equivalent to $n(n-1)(n-2)/6 = n(n-1)$. Since $P(n, 2)$ is not defined for $n < 2$, we know that neither $n$ nor $n-1$ is 0, so we can divide both sides by these factors, obtaining $n - 2 = 6$, whence $n = 8$.
**c)** Recall the identity $C(n, k) = C(n, n - k)$. The given equation fits that model if $n = 7$ and $k = 5$. Hence $n = 7$ is a solution. That there are no more solutions follows from the fact that $C(n, k)$ is an increasing function in $k$ for $0 \leq k \leq n/2$, and hence there are no other numbers $i$ and $j$ for which $C(n, i) = C(n, j)$.

**25.** The left-hand side gives the number of ways to choose $r$ items from a set of $n$ items. The right-hand side gives the number of ways to choose $n - r$ items from a set of $n$ items. However, these two choices are the same, since choosing $r$ items is equivalent to selecting the $n - r$ items not to choose.

**27.** Let us start with the right-hand side and use Pascal's identity. We have
$$C(n + 2, r + 1) - 2C(n + 1, r + 1) + C(n, r + 1)$$
$$= C(n + 1, r + 1) + C(n + 1, r) - 2C(n + 1, r + 1) + C(n, r + 1)$$
$$= C(n + 1, r) - C(n + 1, r + 1) + C(n, r + 1)$$
$$= C(n, r) + C(n, r - 1) - \big(C(n, r + 1) + C(n, r)\big) + C(n, r + 1)$$
$$= C(n, r - 1),$$
which is the left-hand side.

**29.** We assume that there are no restrictions, and that the students and advisors are to be considered distinct. Then there are 5 ways to assign each student, so by the product rule there are $5^{24} \approx 6 \times 10^{16}$ ways to assign all of them.

**31.** For all parts of this problem, Theorem 2 in Section 4.5 is used.
**a)** We let $x_1 = x_1' + 2$, $x_2 = x_2' + 3$, and $x_3 = x_3' + 4$. Then the restrictions are equivalent to requiring that each of the $x_i'$'s be nonnegative. Therefore we want the number of nonnegative integer solutions to the equation $x_1' + x_2' + x_3' = 8$. There are $C(3 + 8 - 1, 8) = C(10, 8) = C(10, 2) = 45$ of them.
**b)** The number of solutions with $x_3 > 5$ is the same as the number of solutions to $x_1 + x_2 + x_3' = 11$, where $x_3 = x_3' + 6$. There are $C(3 + 11 - 1, 11) = C(13, 11) = C(13, 2) = 78$ of these. Now we want to subtract the number of solutions for which also $x_1 \geq 6$. This is equivalent to the number of solutions to $x_1' + x_2 + x_3' = 5$, where $x_1 = x_1' + 6$. There are $C(3 + 5 - 1, 5) = C(7, 5) = C(7, 2) = 21$ of these. Therefore the answer to the problem is $78 - 21 = 57$.
**c)** Arguing as in part **(b)**, we know that there are 78 solutions to the equation $x_1 + x_2 + x_3' = 11$, which is equivalent to the number of solutions to $x_1 + x_2 + x_3 = 17$ with $x_3 > 5$. We now need to subtract the number of these solutions that violate one or both of the restrictions $x_1 < 4$ and

$x_2 < 3$. The number of solutions with $x_1 \geq 4$ is the number of solutions to $x_1' + x_2 + x_3' = 7$, namely $C(3 + 7 - 1, 7) = C(9, 7) = C(9, 2) = 36$. The number of solutions with $x_2 \geq 3$ is the number of solutions to $x_1 + x_2' + x_3' = 8$, namely $C(3 + 8 - 1, 7) = C(10, 8) = C(10, 2) = 45$. However, there are also solutions in which both restrictions are violated, namely the solutions to $x_1' + x_2' + x_3' = 4$. There are $C(3 + 4 - 1, 4) = C(6, 4) = C(6, 2) = 15$ of these. Therefore the number of solutions in which one or both conditions are violated is $36 + 45 - 15 = 66$; we needed to subtract the 15 so as not to count these solutions twice. Putting this all together, we see that there are $78 - 66 = 12$ solutions of the given problem.

33. **a)** We want to find the number of $r$-element subsets for $r = 0, 1, 2, 3, 4$ and add. Therefore the answer is $C(10, 0) + C(10, 1) + C(10, 2) + C(10, 3) + C(10, 4) = 1 + 10 + 45 + 120 + 210 = 386$.
**b)** This time we want $C(10, 8) + C(10, 9) + C(10, 10) = C(10, 2) + C(10, 1) + C(10, 0) = 45 + 10 + 1 = 56$.
**c)** This time we want $C(10, 1) + C(10, 3) + C(10, 5) + C(10, 7) + C(10, 9) = C(10, 1) + C(10, 3) + C(10, 5) + C(10, 3) + C(10, 1) = 10 + 120 + 252 + 120 + 10 = 512$. We can also solve this problem by using the fact from Exercise 35 in Section 4.3 that a set has the same number of subsets with an even number of elements as it has subsets with an odd number of elements. Since the set has $2^{10} = 1024$ subsets altogether, half of these—512 of them—must have an odd number of elements.

35. Since the objects are identical, all that matters is the number of objects put into each container. If we let $x_i$ be the number of objects put into the $i^{\text{th}}$ container, then we are asking for the number of solutions to the equation $x_1 + x_2 + \cdots + x_m = n$ with the restriction that each $x_i \geq 1$. By the usual trick, this is equivalent to asking for the number of nonnegative integer solutions to $x_1' + x_2' + \cdots + x_m' = n - m$, where we have set $x_i = x_i' + 1$ to insure that each container gets at least one object. By Theorem 2 in Section 4.5, there are $C(m + (n - m) - 1, n - m) = C(n - 1, n - m)$ solutions. This can also be written as $C(n - 1, m - 1)$, since $(n - 1) - (n - m) = m - 1$. (Of course if $n < m$, then there are no solutions, since it would be impossible to put at least one object in each container. Our answer is consistent with this observation if we think of $C(x, y)$ as being 0 if $y > x$.)

37. For convenience let us assume that the finite set is $\{1, 2, \ldots, n\}$. If we call a permutation $a_1 a_2 \ldots a_r$, then we simply need to allow each of the variables $a_i$ to take on all $n$ of the values from 1 to $n$. This is essentially just counting in base $n$, so our algorithm will be similar to Algorithm 2 in Section 4.6. The procedure shown here generates the next permutation. To get all the permutations, we just start with $11 \ldots 1$ and call this procedure $r^n - 1$ times.

```
procedure next permutation(n : positive integer,
    a_1, a_2, ..., a_r : positive integers not exceeding n)
{this procedure replaces the input with the next permutation, repetitions allowed,
    in lexicographic order; assume that there is a next permutation,
    i.e., a_1 a_2 ... a_r ≠ nn ... n }
i := r
while a_i = n
begin
        a_i := 1
        i := i - 1
end
a_i := a_i + 1
{ a_1 a_2 ... a_r is the next permutation in lexicographic order }
```

# CHAPTER 5
# Advanced Counting Techniques

⇒ **SECTION 5.1    Recurrence Relations**

*This section is related to Section 3.3, in that recurrence relations are in some sense really recursive or inductive definitions. Many of the exercises in this set provide practice in setting up such relations from a given applied situation. In each problem of this type, ask yourself how the $n^{\text{th}}$ term of the sequence can be related to one or more previous terms; the answer is the desired recurrence relation.*

*Some of these exercises deal with solving recurrence relations by the iterative approach. The trick here is to be precise and patient. First write down $a_n$ in terms of $a_{n-1}$. Then use the recurrence relation with $n-1$ plugged in for $n$ to rewrite what you have in terms of $a_{n-2}$; simplify algebraically. Continue in this manner until a pattern emerges. Then write down what the expression is in terms of $a_0$ (or $a_1$, depending on the initial condition), following the pattern that developed in the first few terms. Usually at this point either the answer is what you have just written down, or else the answer can be obtained from what you have by summing a series. The iterative approach is not usually effective for recurrence relations of degree greater than 1 (i.e., in which $a_n$ depends on previous terms other than just $a_{n-1}$).*

*Exercise 25 is interesting and challenging, and shows that the inductive step may be quite non-trivial. Exercise 29 deals with onto functions; another—totally different—approach to counting onto functions is given in Section 5.5.*

1. We need to compute the terms of the sequence one at a time, since each term is dependent upon one or more of the previous terms.

    **a)** We are given $a_0 = 2$. Then by the recurrence relation $a_n = 6a_{n-1}$ we see (by letting $n = 1$) that $a_1 = 6a_0 = 6 \cdot 2 = 12$. Similarly $a_2 = 6a_1 = 6 \cdot 12 = 72$, then $a_3 = 6a_2 = 6 \cdot 72 = 432$, and $a_4 = 6a_3 = 6 \cdot 432 = 2592$.

    **b)** $a_1 = 2$ (given), $a_2 = a_1^2 = 2^2 = 4$, $a_3 = a_2^2 = 4^2 = 16$, $a_4 = a_3^2 = 16^2 = 256$, $a_5 = a_4^2 = 256^2 = 66536$

    **c)** This time each term depends on the two previous terms. We are given $a_0 = 1$ and $a_1 = 2$. To compute $a_2$ we let $n = 2$ in the recurrence relation, obtaining $a_2 = a_1 + 3a_0 = 2 + 3 \cdot 1 = 5$. Then we have $a_3 = a_2 + 3a_1 = 5 + 3 \cdot 2 = 11$ and $a_4 = a_3 + 3a_2 = 11 + 3 \cdot 5 = 26$.

    **d)** $a_0 = 1$ (given), $a_1 = 1$ (given), $a_2 = 2a_1 + 2^2a_0 = 2 \cdot 1 + 4 \cdot 1 = 6$, $a_3 = 3a_2 + 3^2a_1 = 3 \cdot 6 + 9 \cdot 1 = 27$, $a_4 = 4a_3 + 4^2a_2 = 4 \cdot 27 + 16 \cdot 6 = 204$

    **e)** We are given $a_0 = 1$, $a_1 = 2$, and $a_2 = 0$. Then $a_3 = a_2 + a_0 = 0 + 1 = 1$ and $a_4 = a_3 + a_1 = 1 + 2 = 3$.

3. In each case we have to substitute the given equation for $a_n$ into the recurrence relation $a_n = 8a_{n-1} - 16a_{n-2}$ and see if we get a true statement. Remember to make the appropriate substitutions for $n$ (either $n-1$ or $n-2$) on the right-hand side. What we are really doing here is performing the

inductive step in a proof by mathematical induction: if the formula is correct for $a_{n-1}$ (and also for $a_{n-2}$, etc., in some cases), then the formula is also correct for $a_n$.

**a)** Plugging $a_n = 0$ into the equation $a_n = 8a_{n-1} - 16a_{n-2}$, we obtain the true statement that $0 = 0$. Therefore $a_n = 0$ is a solution of the recurrence relation.

**b)** Plugging $a_n = 1$ into the equation $a_n = 8a_{n-1} - 16a_{n-2}$, we obtain the false statement $1 = 8 \cdot 1 - 16 \cdot 1 = -8$. Therefore $a_n = 1$ is not a solution.

**c)** Plugging $a_n = 2^n$ into the equation $a_n = 8a_{n-1} - 16a_{n-2}$, we obtain the statement $2^n = 8 \cdot 2^{n-1} - 16 \cdot 2^{n-2}$. By algebra, the right-hand side equals $2^{n-2}(8 \cdot 2 - 16) = 0$. Since this is not equal to the left-hand side, we conclude that $a_n = 2^n$ is not a solution.

**d)** Plugging $a_n = 4^n$ into the equation $a_n = 8a_{n-1} - 16a_{n-2}$, we obtain the statement $4^n = 8 \cdot 4^{n-1} - 16 \cdot 4^{n-2}$. By algebra, the right-hand side equals $4^{n-2}(8 \cdot 4 - 16) = 4^{n-2} \cdot 16 = 4^{n-2} \cdot 4^2 = 4^n$. Since this is the left-hand side, we conclude that $a_n = 4^n$ is a solution.

**e)** Plugging $a_n = n4^n$ into the equation $a_n = 8a_{n-1} - 16a_{n-2}$, we obtain the statement $n4^n = 8(n-1)4^{n-1} - 16(n-2)4^{n-2}$. By algebra, the right-hand side equals $4^{n-2}(8(n-1) \cdot 4 - 16(n-2)) = 4^{n-2}(32n - 32 - 16n + 32) = 4^{n-2}(16n) = 4^{n-2} \cdot 4^2 n = n4^n$. Since this is the left-hand side, we conclude that $a_n = n4^n$ is a solution.

**f)** Plugging $a_n = 2 \cdot 4^n + 3n4^n$ into the equation $a_n = 8a_{n-1} - 16a_{n-2}$, we obtain the statement $2 \cdot 4^n + 3n4^n = 8(2 \cdot 4^{n-1} + 3(n-1)4^{n-1}) - 16(2 \cdot 4^{n-2} + 3(n-2)4^{n-2})$. By algebra, the right-hand side equals $4^{n-2}(8 \cdot 2 \cdot 4 + 8 \cdot 3(n-1) \cdot 4 - 16 \cdot 2 - 16 \cdot 3(n-2)) = 4^{n-2}(64 + 96n - 96 - 32 - 48n + 96) = 4^{n-2}(48n + 32) = 4^{n-2} \cdot 4^2(3n + 2) = (2 + 3n)4^n$. Since this is the same as the left-hand side, we conclude that $a_n = 2 \cdot 4^n + 3n4^n$ is a solution.

**g)** Plugging $a_n = (-4)^n$ into the equation $a_n = 8a_{n-1} - 16a_{n-2}$, we obtain the statement $(-4)^n = 8 \cdot (-4)^{n-1} - 16 \cdot (-4)^{n-2}$. By algebra the right-hand side equals $(-4)^{n-2}(8 \cdot (-4) - 16) = (-4)^{n-2}(-48) = -3(-4)^n$. Since this is not equal to the left-hand side, we conclude that $a_n = (-4)^n$ is not a solution.

**h)** Plugging $a_n = n^2 4^n$ into the equation $a_n = 8a_{n-1} - 16a_{n-2}$, we obtain the statement $n^2 4^n = 8(n-1)^2 4^{n-1} - 16(n-2)^2 4^{n-2}$. By algebra, the right-hand side equals $4^{n-2}(8(n-1)^2 \cdot 4 - 16(n-2)^2) = 4^{n-2}(32(n^2 - 2n + 1) - 16(n^2 - 4n + 4)) = 4^{n-2}(32n^2 - 64n + 32 - 16n^2 + 64n - 64) = 4^{n-2}(16n^2 - 32) = 4^{n-2} \cdot 4^2(n^2 - 2)$. Since this is not equal to the left-hand side, we conclude that $a_n = n^2 4^n$ is not a solution.

5. In the iterative approach, we write $a_n$ in terms of $a_{n-1}$, then write $a_{n-1}$ in terms of $a_{n-2}$ (using the recurrence relation with $n-1$ plugged in for $n$), and so on. When we reach the end of this procedure, we use the given initial value of $a_0$. This will give us an explicit formula for the answer or it will give us a finite series, which we then sum to obtain an explicit formula for the answer.

**a)** We write

$$\begin{aligned}
a_n &= 3a_{n-1} \\
&= 3(3a_{n-2}) = 3^2 a_{n-2} \\
&= 3^2(3a_{n-3}) = 3^3 a_{n-3} \\
&\vdots \\
&= 3^n a_{n-n} = 3^n a_0 = 3^n \cdot 2.
\end{aligned}$$

Note that we figured out the last line by following the pattern that had developed in the first few lines. Therefore the answer is $2 \cdot 3^n$.

**b)** We write

$$a_n = 2 + a_{n-1}$$
$$= 2 + (2 + a_{n-2}) = (2 + 2) + a_{n-2} = (2 \cdot 2) + a_{n-2}$$
$$= (2 \cdot 2) + (2 + a_{n-3}) = (3 \cdot 2) + a_{n-3}$$
$$\vdots$$
$$= (n \cdot 2) + a_{n-n} = (n \cdot 2) + a_0 = (n \cdot 2) + 3 = 2n + 3.$$

Again we figured out the last line by following the pattern that had developed in the first few lines. Therefore the answer is $2n + 3$.

**c)** We write (note that it is more convenient to put the $a_{n-1}$ at the end)

$$a_n = n + a_{n-1}$$
$$= n + \big((n - 1) + a_{n-2}\big) = \big(n + (n - 1)\big) + a_{n-2}$$
$$= \big(n + (n - 1)\big) + \big((n - 2) + a_{n-3}\big) = \big(n + (n - 1) + (n - 2)\big) + a_{n-3}$$
$$\vdots$$
$$= \big(n + (n - 1) + (n - 2) + \cdots + (n - (n - 1))\big) + a_{n-n}$$
$$= \big(n + (n - 1) + (n - 2) + \cdots + 1\big) + a_0$$
$$= \frac{n(n + 1)}{2} + 1 = \frac{n^2 + n + 2}{2}.$$

Therefore the answer is $(n^2 + n + 2)/2$. The formula used to obtain the last line—for the sum of the first $n$ positive integers—was developed in Example 9 of Section 3.2.

**d)** We write

$$a_n = 3 + 2n + a_{n-1}$$
$$= 3 + 2n + \big(3 + 2(n - 1) + a_{n-2}\big) = \big(2 \cdot 3 + 2n + 2(n - 1)\big) + a_{n-2}$$
$$= \big(2 \cdot 3 + 2n + 2(n - 1)\big) + \big(3 + 2(n - 2) + a_{n-3}\big)$$
$$= \big(3 \cdot 3 + 2n + 2(n - 1) + 2(n - 2)\big) + a_{n-3}$$
$$\vdots$$
$$= \big(n \cdot 3 + 2n + 2(n - 1) + 2(n - 2) + \cdots + 2(n - (n - 1))\big) + a_{n-n}$$
$$= \big(n \cdot 3 + 2n + 2(n - 1) + 2(n - 2) + \cdots + 2 \cdot 1\big) + a_0$$
$$= 3n + 2 \cdot \frac{n(n + 1)}{2} + 4 = n^2 + 4n + 4.$$

Therefore the answer is $n^2 + 4n + 4$. Again we used the formula for the sum of the first $n$ positive integers developed in Example 9 of Section 3.2.

**e)** We write

$$a_n = -1 + 2a_{n-1}$$
$$= -1 + 2(-1 + 2a_{n-2}) = -3 + 4a_{n-2}$$
$$= -3 + 4(-1 + 2a_{n-3}) = -7 + 8a_{n-3}$$
$$= -7 + 8(-1 + 2a_{n-4}) = -15 + 16a_{n-4}$$
$$= -15 + 16(-1 + 2a_{n-5}) = -31 + 32a_{n-5}$$
$$\vdots$$
$$= -(2^n - 1) + 2^n a_{n-n} = -2^n + 1 + 2^n \cdot 1 = 1.$$

This time it was somewhat harder to figure out the pattern developing in the coefficients, but it became clear after we carried out the computation far enough. The answer, namely that $a_n = 1$ for all $n$, it clear in retrospect, after we found it, since $2 \cdot 1 - 1 = 1$.

**f)** We write

$$
\begin{aligned}
a_n &= 1 + 3a_{n-1} \\
&= 1 + 3(1 + 3a_{n-2}) = (1+3) + 3^2 a_{n-2} \\
&= (1+3) + 3^2(1 + 3a_{n-3}) = (1 + 3 + 3^2) + 3^3 a_{n-3} \\
&\ \ \vdots \\
&= (1 + 3 + 3^2 + \cdots + 3^{n-1}) + 3^n a_{n-n} \\
&= 1 + 3 + 3^2 + \cdots + 3^{n-1} + 3^n \\
&= \frac{3^{n+1} - 1}{3 - 1} \quad \text{(a geometric series)} \\
&= \frac{3^{n+1} - 1}{2}.
\end{aligned}
$$

Thus the answer is $a_n = (3^{n+1} - 1)/2$.

**g)** We write

$$
\begin{aligned}
a_n &= na_{n-1} = n(n-1)a_{n-2} \\
&= n(n-1)(n-2)a_{n-3} = n(n-1)(n-2)(n-3)a_{n-4} \\
&\ \ \vdots \\
&= n(n-1)(n-2)(n-3)\cdots(n-(n-1))\, a_{n-n} \\
&= n(n-1)(n-2)(n-3)\cdots 1 \cdot a_0 \\
&= n! \cdot 5 = 5n!.
\end{aligned}
$$

**h)** We write

$$
\begin{aligned}
a_n &= 2na_{n-1} \\
&= 2n\big(2(n-1)a_{n-2}\big) = 2^2\big(n(n-1)\big)a_{n-2} \\
&= 2^2\big(n(n-1)\big)\big(2(n-2)a_{n-3}\big) = 2^3\big(n(n-1)(n-2)\big)a_{n-3} \\
&\ \ \vdots \\
&= 2^n n(n-1)(n-2)(n-3)\cdots(n-(n-1))a_{n-n} \\
&= 2^n n(n-1)(n-2)(n-3)\cdots 1 \cdot a_0 \\
&= 2^n n!.
\end{aligned}
$$

**7. a)** Since the number of bacteria triples every hour, the recurrence relation should say that the number of bacteria after $n$ hours is 3 times the number of bacteria after $n-1$ hours. Letting $b_n$ denote the number of bacteria after $n$ hours, this statement translates into the recurrence relation $b_n = 3b_{n-1}$.
**b)** The given statement is the initial condition $b_0 = 100$ (the number of bacteria at the beginning is the number of bacteria after no hours have elapsed). We solve the recurrence relation by iteration: $b_n = 3b_{n-1} = 3^2 b_{n-2} = \cdots = 3^n b_{n-n} = 3^n b_0$. Letting $n = 10$ and knowing that $b_0 = 100$, we see that $b_{10} = 3^{10} \cdot 100 = 5{,}904{,}900$.

**9. a)** Let $c_n$ be the number of cars produced in the first $n$ months. The initial condition could be taken to be $c_0 = 0$ (no cars are made in the first 0 months). Since $n$ cars are made in the $n^{\text{th}}$ month, and since $c_{n-1}$ cars are made in the first $n-1$ months, we see that $c_n = c_{n-1} + n$.

b) The number of cars produced in the first year is $c_{12}$. To compute this we will solve the recurrence relation and initial condition, then plug in $n = 12$ (alternately, we could just compute the terms $c_1$, $c_2$, ..., $c_{12}$ directly from the definition). We proceed by iteration exactly as we did in Exercise 5c:

$$c_n = n + c_{n-1}$$
$$= n + \big((n-1) + c_{n-2}\big) = \big(n + (n-1)\big) + c_{n-2}$$
$$= \big(n + (n-1)\big) + \big((n-2) + c_{n-3}\big) = \big(n + (n-1) + (n-2)\big) + c_{n-3}$$
$$\vdots$$
$$= \big(n + (n-1) + (n-2) + \cdots + (n - (n-1))\big) + c_{n-n}$$
$$= \big(n + (n-1) + (n-2) + \cdots + 1\big) + c_0$$
$$= \frac{n(n+1)}{2} + 0 = \frac{n^2 + n}{2}.$$

Therefore the number of cars produced in the first month is $(12^2 + 12)/2 = 78$.

c) We found the formula in our solution to part (b).

11. We want to show that $H_n = 2^n - 1$ is a solution to the recurrence relation $H_n = 2H_{n-1} + 1$ with initial condition $H_1 = 1$. For $n = 1$ (the base case), this is simply the calculation that $2^1 - 1 = 1$. Assume that $H_n = 2^n - 1$. Then by the recurrence relation we have $H_{n+1} = 2H_n + 1$, whereupon if we substitute on the basis of the inductive hypothesis we obtain $2(2^n - 1) + 1 = 2^{n+1} - 2 + 1 = 2^{n+1} - 1$, exactly the formula for the case of $n + 1$. Thus we have shown that if the formula is correct for $n$, then it is also correct for $n + 1$, and our proof by induction is complete.

13. Let $b_n$ be the number of bit sequences of length $n$ that do not contain a pair of consecutive 0's. We want to derive a recurrence relation for $b_n$. Let us look at the beginning of a bit sequence of length $n$, containing no pair of consecutive 0's, and consider various cases. If the sequence starts with a 1, then the remainder of the sequence can be any bit sequence of length $n - 1$ that does not contain a pair of consecutive 0's. This latter number is just $b_{n-1}$. On the other hand, if the sequence starts with a 0, then the second bit must be a 1 (otherwise there would be two consecutive 0's). After these first two bits ( 01 ), however, the sequence may continue with any bit sequence of length $n - 2$ which does not contain a pair of consecutive 0's. There are $b_{n-2}$ of these. Since these are the only two possibilities, we have shown that $b_n = b_{n-1} + b_{n-2}$. The initial conditions must tell us what $b_0$ and $b_1$ are (alternately, we could ignore the empty sequence and specify $b_1$ and $b_2$). There is only one bit sequence of length 0 (namely the empty sequence), and it does not contain a pair of consecutive 0's, so $b_0 = 1$. Similarly, there are two bit sequences of length 1 (namely the sequences 0 and 1), and neither contains a pair of consecutive 0's, so $b_1 = 2$. (Alternatively, if we decide to specify $b_2$, then we need to set $b_2 = 3$, since the three bit sequences 01, 10, and 11 are the only ones of length 2 containing no pair of consecutive 0's.) Note that this recurrence relation is the recurrence relation for the Fibonacci numbers, so we see yet another application of this ubiquitous sequence (the sequence in this exercise picks up two terms later than the Fibonacci sequence, however).

15. We proceed in a manner similar to that of Exercise 13. Let $b_n$ be the number of bit sequences of length $n$ that contain a pair of consecutive 1's. A bit sequence of length $n$ containing a pair of consecutive 1's will fall into one of the following cases: either it will begin with a 0 and then be followed by a bit sequence of length $n - 1$ containing a pair of consecutive 1's; or it will begin with 10 and then

be followed by a bit sequence of length $n-2$ containing a pair of consecutive 1's; or it will begin with 11 and then be followed by any bit sequence of length $n-2$ (since we have already achieved the pair of consecutive 1's). Therefore we have $b_n = b_{n-1} + b_{n-2} + 2^{n-2}$. The initial conditions are that $b_0 = b_1 = 0$, since there are obviously no bit sequences of length less than 2 with a pair of consecutive 1's. (Alternately, we could specify $b_1 = 0$ and $b_2 = 1$ as the initial conditions.)

17. This problem is just like Exercise 15, but one bit harder. Let $b_n$ be the number of bit sequences of length $n$ that contain three consecutive 0's. The possible beginnings of such a sequence are 1, 01, 001, and 000. In the first three cases, the sequence must then continue with a bit sequence of length $n-1$, $n-2$, or $n-3$, respectively, containing three consecutive 0's, and there are $b_{n-1}$, $b_{n-2}$, and $b_{n-3}$ such sequences, respectively. In the last case, the remaining bits ($n-3$ of them) can be anything, so there are $2^{n-3}$ continuations. Putting this all together, we have $b_n = b_{n-1} + b_{n-2} + b_{n-3} + 2^{n-3}$. The initial conditions are $b_0 = b_1 = b_2 = 0$, since no bit sequence of length less than 3 can contain three consecutive 0's.

19. Let $s_n$ be the number of ways to climb $n$ stairs under the given conditions. We find the recurrence relation for $s_n$ by considering the first step. The problem tells us that the first step may encompass one stair or two. If it encompasses one stair, then the climb will continue exactly as if there were originally $n-1$ stairs to climb. On the other hand, if the climber took two stairs with the first step, then the climb will continue exactly as if there were originally $n-2$ stairs to climb. Since these are the only two possibilities (and they are disjoint), we have $s_n = s_{n-1} + s_{n-2}$. The initial conditions are $s_0 = 1$ (there is one way to climb no stairs—do nothing) and $s_1 = 1$ (there is one way to climb one stair—take a step). Note that the solution to this problem is, once again, essentially just the Fibonacci sequence.

21. This problem uses the results of Exercises 19 and 20.

    a) We are asked for $s_8$, using the notation of our solution to Exercise 19. Since $s_0$, $s_1$, $s_2$, ..., $s_8$ is 1, 1, 2, 3, 5, 8, 13, 21, 34 (each term here after the first two was obtained by adding the two previous terms), the answer is that there are 34 ways to climb the flight of 8 stairs.

    b) We are asked for $s_8$, where $s_n$ is the number of ways to climb a flight of $n$ stairs, taking one, two or three at a time. By the same line of reasoning as in Exercise 19, the recurrence relation is $s_n = s_{n-1} + s_{n-2} + s_{n-3}$. The initial conditions are $s_0 = s_1 = 1$ (as in Exercise 19) and $s_2 = 2$ (take the two stairs one at a time or in one big step). Therefore the sequence $s_0$, $s_1$, $s_2$, ..., $s_8$ is 1, 1, 2, 4, 7, 13, 24, 44, 81 (each term here after the first three was obtained by adding the three previous terms); the answer is that there are 81 ways to climb the flight of 8 stairs.

23. We need to solve Exercise 22 in order to do this one. The problem is exactly the same as ("isomorphic to," as a mathematician would say) the problem of climbing stairs in Exercise 19. The length of the message corresponds to the number of stairs; the signals correspond to the steps of size one and two. Therefore the solution to Exercise 22 is that $m_n = m_{n-1} + m_{n-2}$, where $m_n$ is the number of different messages that can be sent in (exactly) $n$ milliseconds, with initial conditions $m_0 = m_1 = 1$. We want $m_{10}$, so we compute this sequence (the Fibonacci sequence) out to $m_{10}$, obtaining 1, 1, 2, 3, 5, 8, 13, 21, 34, 55, 89. Therefore there are 89 different messages that can be sent in exactly 10 milliseconds. (If we allow only part of the time period to be used, and if we rule out the empty message, then the answer will be $1 + 2 + 3 + 5 + 8 + 13 + 21 + 34 + 55 + 89 = 231$.)

**25. a)** This problem is similar to Exercise 23 in the supplementary set of exercises in Chapter 3. Consider the plane already divided by $n-1$ lines into $R_{n-1}$ regions. The $n^{\text{th}}$ line is now added, intersecting each of the other $n-1$ lines in exactly one point, $n-1$ intersections in all. Think of drawing that line, beginning at one of its ends (out at "infinity"). (You should be drawing a picture as you read these words!) As we move toward the first point of intersection, we are dividing the unbounded region of the plane through which it is passing into two regions; the division is complete when we reach the first point of intersection. Then as we draw from the first point of intersection to the second, we cut off another region (in other words we divide another of the regions that were already there into two regions). This process continues as we encounter each point of intersection. By the time we have reached the last point of intersection, the number of regions has increased by $n-1$ (one for each point of intersection). Finally, as we move off to infinity, we divide the unbounded region through which we pass into two regions, increasing the count by yet 1 more. Thus there are exactly $n$ more regions than there were before the $n^{\text{th}}$ line was added. The analysis we have just completed shows that the recurrence relation we seek is $R_n = R_{n-1} + n$. The initial condition is $R_0 = 1$ (since there is just one region—the whole plane—when there are no lines). Alternately, we could specify $R_1 = 2$ as the initial condition.

**b)** The recurrence relation we have is precisely that in Exercise 5c, so the solution is $R_n = (n^2 + n + 2)/2$.

**27.** The easy way to do this problem is to invoke symmetry. A bit string of length 7 has an even number of 0's if and only if it has an odd number of 1's, since the sum of the number of 0's and the number of 1's, namely 7, is odd. Because of the symmetric role of 0 and 1, there must be just as many 7-bit strings with an even number of 0's as there are with an odd number of 0's, each therefore being $2^7/2$ (since there are $2^7$ bit strings altogether). Thus the answer is $2^{7-1} = 64$.

The solution can also be found using recurrence relations. Let $e_n$ be the number of bit strings of length $n$ with an even number of 0's. A bit string of length $n$ with an even number of 0's is either a bit string that starts with a 1 and is then followed by a bit string of length $n-1$ with an even number of 0's (of which there are $e_{n-1}$), or else it starts with a 0 and is then followed by a bit string of length $n-1$ with an odd number of 0's (of which there are $2^{n-1} - e_{n-1}$). Therefore we have the recurrence relation $e_n = e_{n-1} + (2^{n-1} - e_{n-1}) = 2^{n-1}$. In other words, it is a recurrence relation which is its own solution. In our case, $n = 7$, so there are $2^{7-1} = 64$ such strings.

**29.** If the codomain has only one element, then there is only one function (namely the function that takes each element of the domain to the unique element of the codomain). Therefore when $n = 1$ we have $S(m, n) = S(m, 1) = 1$, the initial condition we are asked to verify. Now assume that $m \geq n > 1$, and we want to count $S(m, n)$, the number of functions from a domain with $m$ elements *onto* a codomain with $n$ elements. The form of the recurrence relation we are supposed to verify suggests that what we want to do is to look at the non-onto functions. There are $n^m$ functions from the $m$-set to the $n$-set altogether (by the product rule, since we need to choose an element from the $n$-set, which can be done in $n$ ways, a total of $m$ times). Therefore we must show that there are $\sum_{k=1}^{n-1} C(n,k)S(m,k)$ functions from the domain to the codomain which are *not* onto. First we use the sum rule and break this count down into the disjoint cases determined by the number of elements—let us call it $k$—in the range of the function. Since we want the function not to be onto, $k$ can have any value from 1 to $n-1$, but $k$ cannot equal $n$. Once we have specified $k$, in order to specify a function we need to first specify the actual range, and this can be done in $C(n, k)$ ways, namely choosing the subset of $k$

elements from the codomain which are to constitute the range; and second choosing an *onto* function from the domain to this set of $k$ elements. This latter task can be done in $S(m,k)$ ways, since (and here is the key recursive point) we are defining $S(m,k)$ to be precisely this number. Therefore by the product rule there are $C(n,k)S(m,k)$ different functions with our original domain having a range of $k$ elements, and so by the sum rule there are $\sum_{k=1}^{n-1} C(n,k)S(m,k)$ non-onto functions from our original domain to our original codomain. Note that this two-dimensional recurrence relation can be used to compute $S(m,n)$ for any desired positive integers $m$ and $n$. Using it is much easier than trying to list all onto functions.

31. We have to do Exercise 30 before we can do this exercise.
    **a)** We found that the first differences were $\nabla a_n = 0$. Therefore the second differences are given by $\nabla^2 a_n = 0 - 0 = 0$.
    **b)** We found that the first differences were $\nabla a_n = 2n - 2(n-1) = 2$. Therefore the second differences are given by $\nabla^2 a_n = 2 - 2 = 0$.
    **c)** We found that the first differences were $\nabla a_n = n^2 - (n-1)^2 = 2n - 1$. Therefore the second differences are given by $\nabla^2 a_n = (2n-1) - (2(n-1)-1) = 2$.
    **d)** We found that the first differences were $\nabla a_n = 2^n - 2^{n-1} = 2^{n-1}$. Therefore the second differences are given by $\nabla^2 a_n = 2^{n-1} - 2^{n-2} = 2^{n-2}$.

33. This is just an exercise in algebra. The right-hand side of the given expression is by definition $a_n - 2\nabla a_n + \nabla a_n - \nabla a_{n-1} = a_n - \nabla a_n - \nabla a_{n-1} = a_n - (a_n - a_{n-1}) - (a_{n-1} - a_{n-2})$. Everything in this expression cancels except the last term, yielding $a_{n-2}$, as desired.

35. In order to express the recurrence relation $a_n = a_{n-1} + a_{n-2}$ in terms of $a_n$, $\nabla a_n$, and $\nabla^2 a_n$, we use the results of Exercise 32 (that $a_{n-1} = a_n - \nabla a_n$) and Exercise 33 (that $a_{n-2} = a_n - 2\nabla a_n + \nabla^2 a_n$). Thus the given recurrence relation is equivalent to $a_n = (a_n - \nabla a_n) + (a_n - 2\nabla a_n + \nabla^2 a_n)$, which simplifies algebraically to $a_n = 3\nabla a_n - \nabla^2 a_n$.

⇒ **SECTION 5.2    Solving Recurrence Relations**

*In many ways this section is extremely straightforward. Theorems 1, 2, and 3 (and their generalization as stated in the solution to Supplementary Exercise 11) give an algorithm for solving linear homogeneous recurrence relations with constant coefficients. The only difficulty that sometimes occurs is that the algebra involved becomes messy or impossible. (Although the Fundamental Theorem of Algebra says that every $n^{\text{th}}$ degree polynomial equation has exactly $n$ roots (counting multiplicities), there is in general no way to find out what the roots are exactly. For example, there is nothing analogous to the quadratic formula for equations of degree 5. Also, the roots may be irrational, as we saw in Example 4, or complex, as is discussed in Exercise 20 and Exercise 21. Patience is required with the algebra in such cases.) Exercise 16 through Exercise 19 deal with the interesting question of how to handle nonhomogeneous recurrence relations. Many other techniques are available in other special cases, analogously to the situation with differential equations.*

1. **a)** This is linear (the terms $a_i$ all appear to the first power), has constant coefficients ($3$, $4$, and $5$), and is homogeneous (no terms are functions of just $n$). It has degree $3$, since $a_n$ is expressed in terms of $a_{n-1}$, $a_{n-2}$, and $a_{n-3}$.

   **b)** This does not have constant coefficients, since the coefficient of $a_{n-1}$ is the nonconstant $2n$.

   **c)** This is linear, homogeneous, with constant coefficients. It has degree $4$, since $a_n$ is expressed in terms of $a_{n-1}$, $a_{n-2}$, $a_{n-3}$ and $a_{n-4}$ (the fact that the coefficient of $a_{n-2}$, for example, is $0$ is irrelevant—the degree is the largest $k$ such that $a_{n-k}$ is present).

   **d)** This is not homogeneous because of the $2$.

   **e)** This is not linear, since the term $a_{n-1}^2$ appears.

   **f)** This is linear, homogeneous, with constant coefficients. It has degree $2$.

3. The recurrence relation found in Exercise 22 of Section 5.1 was $m_n = m_{n-1} + m_{n-2}$, with initial conditions $m_0 = m_1 = 1$. To solve this, we look at the characteristic equation $r^2 - r - 1 = 0$ (exactly as in Example 4) and obtain, by the quadratic formula, the roots $r_1 = (1 + \sqrt{5})/2$ and $r_2 = (1 - \sqrt{5})/2$. Therefore from Theorem 1 we know that the solution is given by

$$m_n = \alpha_1 \left( \frac{1 + \sqrt{5}}{2} \right)^n + \alpha_2 \left( \frac{1 - \sqrt{5}}{2} \right)^n ,$$

for some constants $\alpha_1$ and $\alpha_2$. The initial conditions $m_0 = 1$ and $m_1 = 1$ allow us to determine these constants. We plug them into the equation displayed above and obtain

$$1 = m_0 = \alpha_1 + \alpha_2$$
$$1 = m_1 = \alpha_1 \left( \frac{1 + \sqrt{5}}{2} \right) + \alpha_2 \left( \frac{1 - \sqrt{5}}{2} \right) .$$

By algebra we solve these equations (one way is to solve the first for $\alpha_2$ in terms of $\alpha_1$, and plug that into the second equation to get one equation in $\alpha_1$, which can then be solved—the fact that these coefficients are messy irrational numbers involving $\sqrt{5}$ does not change the rules of algebra, of course). The solutions are $\alpha_1 = (5 + \sqrt{5})/10$ and $\alpha_2 = (5 - \sqrt{5})/10$. Therefore the specific solution is given by

$$m_n = \frac{5 + \sqrt{5}}{10} \left( \frac{1 + \sqrt{5}}{2} \right)^n + \frac{5 - \sqrt{5}}{10} \left( \frac{1 - \sqrt{5}}{2} \right)^n .$$

(Alternately, by not rationalizing the denominators when we solve for $\alpha_1$ and $\alpha_2$, we get $\alpha_1 = (1 + \sqrt{5})/(2\sqrt{5})$ and $\alpha_2 = -(1 - \sqrt{5})/(2\sqrt{5})$. With these expressions, we can write our solution as

$$m_n = \frac{1}{\sqrt{5}} \left( \frac{1 + \sqrt{5}}{2} \right)^{n+1} - \frac{1}{\sqrt{5}} \left( \frac{1 - \sqrt{5}}{2} \right)^{n+1} .$$

5. First we need to find a recurrence relation and initial conditions for the problem. Let $t_n$ be the number of ways to tile a $2 \times n$ board with $1 \times 2$ and $2 \times 2$ pieces. To obtain the recurrence relation, imagine what tiles are placed at the left-hand end of the board. We can place a $2 \times 2$ tile there, leaving a $2 \times (n-2)$ board to be tiled, which of course can be done in $t_{n-2}$ ways. We can place a $1 \times 2$ tile at the edge, oriented vertically, leaving a $2 \times (n-1)$ board to be tiled, which of course can be done in $t_{n-1}$ ways. Finally, we can place two $1 \times 2$ tiles horizontally, one above the other, leaving a $2 \times (n-2)$ board to be tiled, which of course can be done in $t_{n-2}$ ways. These three possibilities are disjoint. Therefore our recurrence relation is $t_n = t_{n-1} + 2t_{n-2}$. The initial conditions are $t_0 = t_1 = 1$, since

there is only one way to tile a $2 \times 0$ board (the way that uses no tiles) and only one way to tile a $2 \times 1$ board. This recurrence relation is the same one that appeared in Example 3; it has characteristic roots 2 and $-1$, so the general solution is

$$t_n = \alpha_1 2^n + \alpha_2(-1)^n .$$

To determine the coefficients we plug in the initial conditions, giving us the equations

$$1 = t_0 = \alpha_1 + \alpha_2$$
$$1 = t_1 = 2\alpha_1 - \alpha_2 .$$

Solving these yields $\alpha_1 = 2/3$ and $\alpha_2 = 1/3$, so our final solution is $t_n = 2^{n+1}/3 + (-1)^n/3$.

7. **a)** The amount $P_n$ in the account at the end of the $n^{\text{th}}$ year is equal to the amount at the end of the previous year ($P_{n-1}$), plus the 20% dividend on that amount ($0.2P_{n-1}$) plus the 45% dividend on the amount at the end of the year before that ($0.45P_{n-2}$). Thus we have $P_n = 1.2P_{n-1} + 0.45P_{n-2}$. We need two initial conditions, since the equation has degree 2. Clearly $P_0 = 100000$. The other initial condition is that $P_1 = 120000$, since there is only one dividend at the end of the first year.

**b)** Solving this recurrence relation requires looking at the characteristic equation $r^2 - 1.2r - 0.45 = 0$. By the quadratic formula, the roots are $r_1 = 1.5$ and $r_2 = -0.3$. Therefore the general solution of the recurrence relation is $P_n = \alpha_1(1.5)^n + \alpha_2(-0.3)^n$. Plugging in the initial conditions gives us the equations $100000 = \alpha_1 + \alpha_2$ and $120000 = 1.5\alpha_1 - 0.3\alpha_2$. These are easily solved to give $\alpha_1 = 250000/3$ and $\alpha_2 = 50000/3$. Therefore the solution of our problem is

$$P_n = \frac{250000}{3}(1.5)^n + \frac{50000}{3}(-0.3)^n .$$

9. **a)** We prove this by induction on $n$. We need to verify two base cases. For $n = 1$ we have $L_1 = 1 = 0 + 1 = f_0 + f_2$; and for $n = 2$ we have $L_2 = 3 = 1 + 2 = f_1 + f_3$. Assume the inductive hypothesis that $L_k = f_{k-1} + f_{k+1}$ for $k < n$. We must show that $L_n = f_{n-1} + f_{n+1}$. To do this, we let $k = n - 1$ and $k = n - 2$:

$$L_{n-1} = f_{n-2} + f_n$$
$$L_{n-2} = f_{n-3} + f_{n-1} .$$

If we add these two equations, we obtain

$$L_{n-1} + L_{n-2} = (f_{n-2} + f_{n-3}) + (f_n + f_{n-1}),$$

which is the same as

$$L_n = f_{n-1} + f_{n+1}$$

as desired, using the recurrence relations for the Lucas and Fibonacci numbers.

**b)** To find an explicit formula for the Lucas numbers, we need to solve the recurrence relation and initial conditions. Since the recurrence relation is the same as that of the Fibonacci numbers, we get the same general solution as in Example 4, namely

$$L_n = \alpha_1 \left(\frac{1 + \sqrt{5}}{2}\right)^n + \alpha_2 \left(\frac{1 - \sqrt{5}}{2}\right)^n ,$$

for some constants $\alpha_1$ and $\alpha_2$. The initial conditions are different, though. When we plug them in we get the system

$$2 = L_0 = \alpha_1 + \alpha_2$$
$$1 = L_1 = \alpha_1 \left(\frac{1 + \sqrt{5}}{2}\right) + \alpha_2 \left(\frac{1 - \sqrt{5}}{2}\right) .$$

By algebra we solve these equations, yielding $\alpha_1 = \alpha_1 = 1$. Therefore the specific solution is given by

$$L_n = \left(\frac{1+\sqrt{5}}{2}\right)^n + \left(\frac{1-\sqrt{5}}{2}\right)^n$$

11. This is a third degree equation. The characteristic equation is $r^3 - 7r - 6 = 0$. Assuming the composer of the problem has arranged that the roots are nice numbers, we use the rational root test, which says that rational roots must be of the form $\pm p/q$, where $p$ is a factor of the constant term (6 in this case) and $q$ is a factor of the coefficient of the leading term (the coefficient of $r^3$ is 1 in this case). Hence the possible rational roots are $\pm 1, \pm 2, \pm 3, \pm 6$. We find that $r = -1$ is a root, so one factor of $r^3 - 7r + 6$ is $r + 1$. Dividing $r + 1$ into $r^3 - 7r - 6$ by long (or synthetic) division, we find that $r^3 - 7r - 6 = (r+1)(r^2 - r - 6)$. By inspection we factor the rest, obtaining $r^3 - 7r - 6 = (r+1)(r-3)(r+2)$. Hence the roots are $-1$, $3$, and $-2$, so the general solution is $a_n = \alpha_1(-1)^n + \alpha_2 3^n + \alpha_3(-2)^n$. To find these coefficients, we plug in the initial conditions:

$$9 = a_0 = \alpha_1 + \alpha_2 + \alpha_3$$
$$10 = a_1 = -\alpha_1 + 3\alpha_2 - 2\alpha_3$$
$$32 = a_2 = \alpha_1 + 9\alpha_2 + 4\alpha_3 .$$

Solving this system of equations (by elimination, for instance), we get $\alpha_1 = 8$, $\alpha_2 = 4$, and $\alpha_3 = -3$. Therefore the specific solution is $a_n = 8(-1)^n + 4 \cdot 3^n - 3(-2)^n$.

13. This is a third degree equation. The characteristic equation is $r^3 - 2r^2 - 5r + 6 = 0$. By the rational root test, the possible rational roots are $\pm 1, \pm 2, \pm 3, \pm 6$. We find that $r = 1$ is a root. Dividing $r - 1$ into $r^3 - 2r^2 - 5r + 6$, we find that $r^3 - 2r^2 - 5r + 6 = (r-1)(r^2 - r - 6)$. By inspection we factor the rest, obtaining $r^3 - 2r^2 - 5r + 6 = (r-1)(r-3)(r+2)$. Hence the roots are $1$, $3$, and $-2$, so the general solution is $a_n = \alpha_1 1^n + \alpha_2 3^n + \alpha_3(-2)^n$, or more simply $a_n = \alpha_1 + \alpha_2 3^n + \alpha_3(-2)^n$. To find these coefficients, we plug in the initial conditions:

$$7 = a_0 = \alpha_1 + \alpha_2 + \alpha_3$$
$$-4 = a_1 = \alpha_1 + 3\alpha_2 - 2\alpha_3$$
$$8 = a_2 = \alpha_1 + 9\alpha_2 + 4\alpha_3 .$$

Solving this system of equations, we get $\alpha_1 = 5$, $\alpha_2 = -1$, and $\alpha_3 = 3$. Therefore the specific solution is $a_n = 5 - 3^n + 3(-2)^n$.

15. We almost follow the hint and let $a_{n+1}$ be the right-hand side of the stated identity. Clearly $a_1 = C(0,0) = 1$ and $a_2 = C(1,0) = 1$. Thus $a_1 = f_1$ and $a_2 = f_2$. Now if we can show that the sequence $\{a_n\}$ satisfies the same recurrence relation that the Fibonacci numbers do, namely $a_{n+1} = a_n + a_{n-1}$, then we will know that $a_n = f_n$ for all $n \geq 1$ (precisely what we want to show), since the solution of a second degree recurrence relation with two initial conditions is unique.

To show that $a_{n+1} = a_n + a_{n-1}$, we start with the right-hand side, which is, by our definition, $C(n-1,0) + C(n-2,1) + \cdots + C(n-1-k, k) + C(n-2,0) + C(n-3,1) + \cdots + C(n-2-l, l)$, where $k = \lfloor (n-1)/2 \rfloor$ and $l = \lfloor (n-2)/2 \rfloor$. Note that $k = l$ if $n$ is even, and $k = l + 1$ if $n$ is odd. Let us first take the case in which $k = l = (n-2)/2$. By Pascal's identity, we regroup the sum above and rewrite it as

$$C(n-1,0) + [C(n-2,0) + C(n-2,1)] + [C(n-3,1) + C(n-3,2)] + \cdots$$
$$+ [C(n-2-((n-2)/2-1),(n-2)/2-1) + C(n-1-(n-2)/2,(n-2)/2)]$$
$$+ C(n-2-(n-2)/2,(n-2)/2)$$
$$= C(n-1,0) + C(n-1,1) + C(n-2,2) + \cdots$$
$$+ C(n-(n-2)/2,(n-2)/2) + C(n-2-(n-2)/2,(n-2)/2)$$
$$= 1 + C(n-1,1) + C(n-2,2) + \cdots + C(n-(n-2)/2,(n-2)/2) + 1$$
$$= C(n,0) + C(n-1,1) + C(n-2,2) + \cdots + C(n-(n-2)/2,(n-2)/2)$$
$$+ C(n-n/2,n/2)$$
$$= C(n,0) + C(n-1,1) + C(n-2,2) + \cdots + C(n-j,j),$$

where $j = n/2 = \lfloor n/2 \rfloor$. This is precisely $a_{n+1}$, as desired. In case $n$ is odd, so that $k = (n-1)/2$ and $l = (n-3)/2$, we have a similar calculation (in this case the sum involving $k$ has one more term than the sum involving $l$):

$$C(n-1,0) + [C(n-2,0) + C(n-2,1)] + [C(n-3,1) + C(n-3,2)] + \cdots$$
$$+ [C(n-2-(n-3)/2,(n-3)/2) + C(n-1-(n-1)/2,(n-1)/2)]$$
$$= C(n-1,0) + C(n-1,1) + C(n-2,2) + \cdots + C(n-(n-1)/2,(n-1)/2)$$
$$= 1 + C(n-1,1) + C(n-2,2) + \cdots + C(n-(n-1)/2,(n-1)/2)$$
$$= C(n,0) + C(n-1,1) + C(n-2,2) + \cdots + C(n-j,j),$$

where $j = (n-1)/2 = \lfloor n/2 \rfloor$. Again, this is precisely $a_{n+1}$, as desired.

17. Exercise 16 tells us that the general solution to the nonhomogeneous linear recurrence relation

$$a_n = c_1 a_{n-1} + c_2 a_{n-2} + \cdots + c_k a_{n-k} + F(n)$$

can be found by finding one particular solution of this recurrence relation and adding it to the general solution to the corresponding homogeneous recurrence relation

$$a_n = c_1 a_{n-1} + c_2 a_{n-2} + \cdots + c_k a_{n-k}.$$

If we let $f_n$ be the particular solution to the nonhomogeneous recurrence relation and $g_n$ the general solution to the homogeneous recurrence relation (it will have some unspecified parameters $\alpha_1$, $\alpha_2$, ..., $\alpha_k$), then the general solution to the nonhomogeneous recurrence relation is $f_n + g_n$ (so it, too, will have some unspecified parameters $\alpha_1$, $\alpha_2$, ..., $\alpha_k$).

**a)** To show that $-2^{n+1}$ is a solution to $a_n = 3a_{n-1} + 2^n$, we simply substitute it in and see if we get a true statement. Upon substituting into the right-hand side we get $3a_{n-1} + 2^n = 3(-2^n) + 2^n = 2^n(-3+1) = -2^{n+1}$, which is precisely the left-hand side.

**b)** By Exercise 16 and the comments above, we need to find the general solution to the corresponding homogeneous recurrence relation $a_n = 3a_{n-1}$. This is easily seen to be $a_n = \alpha 3^n$ (either by the iterative method or by the method of this section with a linear characteristic equation). Putting these together as discussed above, we find the general solution to the given recurrence relation: $a_n = \alpha 3^n - 2^{n+1}$.

**c)** To find the solution with $a_0 = 1$, we need to plug this initial condition into our answer to part **(b)**. Doing so gives the equation $1 = \alpha - 2$, whence $\alpha = 3$. Therefore the solution to the given recurrence relation and initial condition is $a_n = 3 \cdot 3^n - 2^{n+1} = 3^{n+1} - 2^{n+1}$.

19. See the introductory remarks to Exercise 17, which apply here as well.

    **a)** We solve this problem by wishful thinking. Suppose that $a_n = An + B$, and substitute into the given recurrence relation. This gives us $An + B = 2\big(A(n-1) + B\big) + n + 5$, which simplifies to $(A+1)n + (-2A + B + 5) = 0$. Now if this is going to be true for all $n$, then both of the quantities in parentheses will have to be 0. In other words, we need to solve the simultaneous equations $A + 1 = 0$ and $-2A + B + 5 = 0$. The solution is $A = -1$ and $B = -7$. Therefore a solution to the recurrence relation is $a_n = -n - 7$.

    **b)** By Exercise 16 and the comments at the beginning of Exercise 17, we need to find the general solution to the corresponding homogeneous recurrence relation $a_n = 2a_{n-1}$. This is easily seen to be $a_n = \alpha 2^n$ (either by the iterative method or by the method of this section with a linear characteristic equation). Putting these together as discussed above, we find the general solution to the given recurrence relation: $a_n = \alpha 2^n - n - 7$.

    **c)** To find the solution with $a_0 = 4$, we need to plug this initial condition into our answer to part **(b)**. Doing so gives the equation $4 = \alpha - 7$, whence $\alpha = 11$. Therefore the solution to the given recurrence relation and initial condition is $a_n = 11 \cdot 2^n - n - 7$.

21. Nothing in the discussion of solving recurrence relations by the methods of this section relies on the roots of the characteristic equation being real numbers. Sometimes the roots are complex numbers (involving $i = \sqrt{-1}$). The situation is analogous to the fact that we sometimes get irrational numbers when solving the characteristic equation (for example, for the Fibonacci numbers), even though the coefficients are all integers and the terms in the sequence are all integers. It is just that we need irrational numbers in order to write down an algebraic solution. Here we need complex numbers in order to write down an algebraic solution, even though all the terms in the sequence are real.

    **a)** The characteristic equation is $r^4 - 1 = 0$. This factors as $(r-1)(r+1)(r^2+1) = 0$, so the roots are $r = 1$ and $r = -1$ (from the first two factors) and $r = i$ and $r = -i$ (from the third factor).

    **b)** By our work in part **(a)**, the general solution to the recurrence relation is $a_n = \alpha_1 + \alpha_2(-1)^n + \alpha_3 i^n + \alpha_4(-i)^n$. In order to figure out the $\alpha$'s we plug in the initial conditions, yielding the following system of linear equations:

$$1 = a_0 = \alpha_1 + \alpha_2 + \alpha_3 + \alpha_4$$
$$0 = a_1 = \alpha_1 - \alpha_2 + i\alpha_3 - i\alpha_4$$
$$-1 = a_2 = \alpha_1 + \alpha_2 - \alpha_3 - \alpha_4$$
$$1 = a_3 = \alpha_1 - \alpha_2 - i\alpha_3 + i\alpha_4.$$

    Remembering that $i$ is just a constant, we solve this system by elimination or other means. For instance, we could begin by subtracting the third equation from the first, to give $2 = 2\alpha_3 + 2\alpha_4$ and subtracting the fourth from the second to give $-1 = 2i\alpha_3 - 2i\alpha_4$. This gives us two equation in two unknowns. Solving them yields $\alpha_3 = (2i - 1)/(4i)$ which can be put into nicer form by multiplying by $i/i$, so $\alpha_3 = (2 + i)/4$; and then $\alpha_4 = 1 - \alpha_3 = (2 - i)/4$. We plug these values back into the first and fourth equations, obtaining $\alpha_1 + \alpha_2 = 0$ and $\alpha_1 - \alpha_2 = 1/2$. These tell us that $\alpha_1 = 1/4$ and $\alpha_2 = -1/4$. Therefore the answer to the problem is

$$a_n = \frac{1}{4} - \frac{1}{4}(-1)^n + \frac{2+i}{4}i^n + \frac{2-i}{4}(-i)^n.$$

⇒ **SECTION 5.3    Divide-and-Conquer Relations**

*Many of these exercises are fairly straightforward applications of Theorem 2 (or its special case, Theorem 1). The messiness of the algebra and analysis in this section is indicative of what often happens when trying to get reasonably precise estimates for the efficiency of complicated or clever algorithms.*

1. Let $f(n)$ be the number of comparisons needed in binary search for a list of $n$ elements. From Example 1 we know that $f$ satisfies the divide-and-conquer recurrence relation $f(n) = f(n/2) + 2$. Also, 2 comparisons are needed for a list with one element, i.e., $f(1) = 2$ (see Example 3 in Section 2.2 for further discussion). Thus $f(64) = f(32) + 2 = f(16) + 4 = f(8) + 6 = f(4) + 8 = f(2) + 10 = f(1) + 12 = 2 + 12 = 14$.

3. In the notation of Example 3 (all numerals in base 2), we want to multiply $a = 1110$ by $b = 1010$. Note that $n = 2$. Therefore $A_1 = 11$, $A_0 = 10$, $B_1 = 10$ and $B_0 = 10$. We need to form $A_1 - A_0 = 11 - 10 = 01$ and $B_0 - B_1 = 00$. Then we need the following three products: $A_1 B_1 = (11)(10)$, $(A_1 - A_0)(B_0 - B_1) = (01)(00)$, and $A_0 B_0 = (10)(10)$. In order to from these products, the algorithm would in fact recurse, but let us not worry about that, assuming instead that we have these answers, namely $A_1 B_1 = 0110$, $(A_1 - A_0)(B_0 - B_1) = 0000$, and $A_0 B_0 = 0100$. Now we need to shift these products various numbers of places to the left. We shift $A_1 B_1$ $2n = 4$ places and also $n = 2$ places, obtaining 01100000 and 011000; we shift $(A_1 - A_0)(B_0 - B_1)$ $n = 2$ places, obtaining 000000, and we shift $A_0 B_0$ $n = 2$ places and also no places, obtaining 010000 and 0100. Finally we add all five of these binary numbers, obtaining 10001100.

5. This problem is asking us to estimate the number of bit operations needed to do the shifts, additions, and subtractions in multiplying two $2n$-bit integers by the algorithm in Example 3. First recall from Example 6 in Section 2.4 that the number of bit operations needed for an addition of two $k$-bit numbers is at most $3k$; the same bound holds for subtraction. Let us assume that to shift a number $k$ bits also requires $k$ bit operations. Thus we need to count the number of additions and shifts of various sizes that occur in the fast multiplication algorithm. First, we need to perform two subtractions of $n$-bit numbers to get $A_1 - A_0$ and $B_0 - B_1$; these will take up to $6n$ bit operations altogether. We need to shift $A_1 B_1$ $2n$ places (requiring $2n$ bit operations), and also $n$ places (requiring $n$ bit operations); we need to shift $(A_1 - A_0)(B_0 - B_1)$ $n$ places (requiring $n$ bit operations); and we need to shift $A_0 B_0$ $n$ places, also requiring $n$ bit operations. This makes a total of $5n$ bit operations for the shifting. Finally we need to worry about the additions (which actually might include a subtraction if the middle term is negative). If we are clever, we can add the four terms that involve at most $3n$ bits first (that is, everything except the $2^{2n} A_1 B_1$). Three additions are required, each taking $9n$ bit operations, for a total of $27n$ bit operations. Finally we need to perform one addition involving a $4n$-bit number, taking $12n$ operations. This makes a total of $39n$ bit operations for the additions.

   Putting all these operations together, we need perhaps a total of $6n + 5n + 39n = 50n$ bit operations to perform all the additions, subtractions, and shifts. Obviously this bound is not exact; it depends on the actual implementation of these binary operations.

   Using $C = 50$ as estimated above, the recurrence relation for fast multiplication is $f(2n) = 3f(n) + 50n$, with $f(1) = 1$ (one multiplication of bits is all that is needed if we have 1-bit numbers). Thus we can compute $f(64)$ as follows: $f(2) = 3 \cdot 1 + 50 = 53$; $f(4) = 3 \cdot 53 + 100 = 259$; $f(8) = 3 \cdot 259 + 200 = 977$; $f(16) = 3 \cdot 977 + 400 = 3331$; $f(32) = 3 \cdot 3331 + 800 = 10793$; and finally $f(64) = 3 \cdot 10793 + 1600 = 33979$. Thus about 34,000 bit operations are needed.

**7.** We compute these from the bottom up. (In fact, it is easy to see by induction that $f(3^k) = k + 1$, so no computation is really needed at all.)

   **a)** $f(3) = f(1) + 1 = 1 + 1 = 2$

   **b)** $f(9) = f(3) + 1 = 2 + 1 = 3$; $f(27) = f(9) + 1 = 3 + 1 = 4$

   **c)** $f(81) = f(27) + 1 = 4 + 1 = 5$; $f(243) = f(81) + 1 = 5 + 1 = 6$; $f(729) = f(243) + 1 = 6 + 1 = 7$

**9.** We compute these from the bottom up.

   **a)** $f(5) = f(1) + 3 \cdot 5^2 = 4 + 75 = 79$

   **b)** $f(25) = f(5) + 3 \cdot 25^2 = 79 + 1875 = 1954$; $f(125) = f(25) + 3 \cdot 125^2 = 1954 + 46875 = 48{,}829$

   **c)** $f(625) = f(125) + 3 \cdot 625^2 = 48829 + 1171875 = 1220704$; $f(3125) = f(625) + 3 \cdot 3125^2 = 1220704 + 29296875 = 30{,}517{,}579$

**11.** We apply Theorem 2, with $a = 1$, $b = 2$, $c = 1$, and $d = 0$. Since $a = b^d$, we have $f(n) = O(n^d \log n) = O(\log n)$.

**13.** We apply Theorem 2, with $a = 2$, $b = 3$, $c = 4$, and $d = 0$. Since $a > b^d$, we have $f(n) = O(n^{\log_b a}) = O(n^{\log_3 2}) \approx O(n^{0.63})$.

**15.** After 1 round, there are 16 teams left; after 2 rounds, 8 teams; after 3 rounds, 4 teams; after 4 rounds, 2 teams; and after 5 rounds, only 1 team remains, so the tournament is over. In general, $k$ rounds are needed if there are $2^k$ teams (easily proved by induction).

**17.** Suppose $n = b^k$, so that $k = \log_b n$. We will prove by induction on $k$ that $f(b^k) = f(1)(b^k)^d + c(b^k)^d k$, which is what we are asked to prove, translated into this notation. If $k = 0$, then the equation reduces to $f(1) = f(1)$, certainly true. We assume the inductive hypothesis, that $f(b^k) = f(1)(b^k)^d + c(b^k)^d k$, and we try to prove that $f(b^{k+1}) = f(1)(b^{k+1})^d + c(b^{k+1})^d(k+1)$. By the recurrence relation for $f(n)$ in terms of $f(n/b)$, we have $f(b^{k+1}) = b^d f(b^k) + c(b^{k+1})^d$. Then we invoke the inductive hypothesis and work through the algebra:

$$b^d f(b^k) + c(b^{k+1})^d = b^d \big(f(1)(b^k)^d + c(b^k)^d k\big) + c(b^{k+1})^d$$
$$= f(1)b^{kd+d} + cb^{kd+d}k + c(b^{k+1})^d$$
$$= f(1)(b^{k+1})^d + c(b^{k+1})^d k + c(b^{k+1})^d$$
$$= f(1)(b^{k+1})^d + c(b^{k+1})^d(k+1).$$

**19.** The algebra is quite messy, but this is a straightforward proof by induction on $k = \log_b n$. If $k = 0$, so that $n = 1$, then we have the true statement

$$f(1) = C_1 + C_2 = \frac{b^d c}{b^d - a} + f(1) + \frac{b^d c}{a - b^d}$$

(since the fractions cancel each other out). Assume the inductive hypothesis, that for $n = b^k$ we have

$$f(n) = \frac{b^d c}{b^d - a} n^d + \left(f(1) + \frac{b^d c}{a - b^d}\right) n^{\log_b a}.$$

Then for $n = b^{k+1}$ we apply first the recurrence relation, then the inductive hypothesis, and finally some algebra:

$$f(n) = af\left(\frac{n}{b}\right) + cn^d$$

$$= a\left(\frac{b^d c}{b^d - a}\left(\frac{n}{b}\right)^d + \left(f(1) + \frac{b^d c}{a - b^d}\right)\left(\frac{n}{b}\right)^{\log_b a}\right) + cn^d$$

$$= \frac{b^d c}{b^d - a} \cdot n^d \cdot \frac{a}{b^d} + \left(f(1) + \frac{b^d c}{a - b^d}\right) n^{\log_b a} + cn^d$$

$$= n^d\left(\frac{ac}{b^d - a} + \frac{c(b^d - a)}{b^d - a}\right) + \left(f(1) + \frac{b^d c}{a - b^d}\right) n^{\log_b a}$$

$$= \frac{b^d c}{b^d - a} \cdot n^d + \left(f(1) + \frac{b^d c}{a - b^d}\right) n^{\log_b a}.$$

Thus we have verified that the equation holds for $k + 1$, and our induction proof is complete.

21. The equation given in Exercise 19 says that $f(n)$ is the sum of a constant times $n^d$ and a constant times $n^{\log_b a}$. Therefore we need to determine which term dominates, i.e., whether $d$ or $\log_b a$ is larger. But we are given $a > b^d$; hence $\log_b a > \log_b b^d = d$. It therefore follows (we are also using the fact that $f$ is increasing) that $f(n) = O(n^{\log_b a})$.

23. We use the result of Exercise 21, since $a = 5 > 4^1 = b^d$. Therefore $f(n) = O(n^{\log_b a}) = O(n^{\log_4 5}) \approx O(n^{1.16})$.

25. We use the result of Exercise 21, since $a = 8 > 2^2 = b^d$. Therefore $f(n) = O(n^{\log_b a}) = O(n^{\log_2 8}) = O(n^3)$.

⇒ SECTION 5.4   Inclusion-Exclusion

*Inclusion-exclusion is not a nice compact formula in practice, but it is often the best that is available. In Exercise 19, for example, the answer contains over 30 terms. The applications in this section are somewhat contrived, but much more interesting applications are presented in Section 5.5. The inclusion-exclusion principle in some sense gives a methodical way to apply common sense. Presumably anyone could solve a problem such as Exercise 9 by trial and error or other ad hoc techniques, given enough time; the inclusion-exclusion principle makes the solution straightforward. Be careful when using the inclusion-exclusion principle to get the signs right—some terms need to be subtracted and others need to be added. In general the sign changes when the size of the expression changes.*

1. In all cases we use the fact that $|A_1 \cup A_2| = |A_1| + |A_2| - |A_1 \cap A_2| = 12 + 18 - |A_1 \cap A_2| = 30 - |A_1 \cap A_2|$.
   a) Here $|A_1 \cap A_2| = 0$, so the answer is $30 - 0 = 30$.
   b) This time we are told that $|A_1 \cap A_2| = 1$, so the answer is $30 - 1 = 29$.
   c) This time we are told that $|A_1 \cap A_2| = 6$, so the answer is $30 - 6 = 24$.
   d) If $A_1 \subseteq A_2$, then $A_1 \cap A_2 = A_1$, so $|A_1 \cap A_2| = |A_1| = 12$. Therefore the answer is $30 - 12 = 18$.

3. We may as well treat percentages as if they were cardinalities—as if the population were exactly 100. Let $V$ be the set of households with television sets, and let $P$ be the set of households with phones. Then we are given $|V| = 96$, $|P| = 98$, and $|V \cap P| = 95$. Therefore $|V \cup P| = 96 + 98 - 95 = 99$, so only 1% of the households have neither telephones nor televisions.

5. For all parts we need to use the formula $|A_1 \cup A_2 \cup A_3| = |A_1| + |A_2| + |A_3| - |A_1 \cap A_2| - |A_1 \cap A_3| - |A_2 \cap A_3| + |A_1 \cap A_2 \cap A_3|$.

   **a)** If the sets are pairwise disjoint, then the cardinality of the union is the sum of the cardinalities, namely 300, since all but the first three terms on the right-hand side of the formula are equal to 0.

   **b)** Using the formula, we have $100 + 100 + 100 - 50 - 50 - 50 + 0 = 150$.

   **c)** Using the formula, we have $100 + 100 + 100 - 50 - 50 - 50 + 25 = 175$.

   **d)** In this case the answer is obviously 100. By the formula, the cardinality of each set on the right-hand side is 100, so we can arrive at this answer through the computation $100 + 100 + 100 - 100 - 100 - 100 + 100 = 100$.

7. We need to use the formula $|P \cup F \cup C| = |P| + |F| + |C| - |P \cap F| - |P \cap C| - |F \cap C| + |P \cap F \cap C|$, where, for example, $P$ is the set of students who have taken a course in Pascal. Thus we have $|P \cup F \cup C| = 1876 + 999 + 345 - 876 - 290 - 231 + 189 = 2012$. Therefore, since there are 2504 students altogether, we know that $2504 - 2012 = 492$ have taken none of these courses.

9. We need to use the inclusion-exclusion formula for four sets, $C$ (the students taking calculus), $D$ (the students taking discrete mathematics), $S$ (those taking data structures), and $L$ (those taking programming languages). The formula says $|C \cup D \cup S \cup L| = |C| + |D| + |S| + |L| - |C \cap D| - |C \cap S| - |C \cap L| - |D \cap S| - |D \cap L| - |S \cap L| + |C \cap D \cap S| + |C \cap D \cap L| + |C \cap S \cap L| + |D \cap S \cap L| - |C \cap D \cap S \cap L|$. Plugging the given information into this formula gives us a total of $507 + 292 + 312 + 344 - 0 - 14 - 213 - 211 - 43 - 0 + 0 + 0 + 0 + 0 - 0 = 974$.

11. There are clearly 50 odd positive integers not exceeding 100 (half of these 100 numbers are odd), and there are 10 squares (from $1^2$ to $10^2$). Furthermore, half of these squares are odd. Thus we compute the cardinality of the set in question to be $50 + 10 - 5 = 55$.

13. Let us count the strings that have 6 or more consecutive 0's. There are 4 strings that have 0's in the first six places, since there are $2 \cdot 2 = 4$ ways to specify the last two bits. Similarly, there are 4 strings that have 0's in bits 2 through 7, and there are 4 strings that have 0's in bits 3 through 8. We have overcounted, though. There are 2 strings that have 0's in bits 1 through 7 (the intersection of the first two sets mentioned above); 2 strings that have 0's in bits 2 through 8 (the intersection of the last two sets mentioned above); and 1 string that has 0's in all bits (the intersection of the first and last sets mentioned above). Moreover, there is 1 string with 0's in bits 1 through 8, the intersection of all three sets mentioned above. Putting this all together, we know that the number of strings with 6 consecutive 0's is $4 + 4 + 4 - 2 - 2 - 1 + 1 = 8$. Since there are $2^8 = 256$ strings in all, there must be $256 - 8 = 248$ that do not contain 6 consecutive 0's.

15. We need to use inclusion-exclusion with three sets. There are 7! permutations that begin 987, since there are 7 digits free to be permuted among the last 7 spaces (we are assuming that it is meant that the permutations are to start with 987 *in that order*, not with 897, for instance). Similarly, there are 8! permutations that have 45 in the fifth and sixth positions, and there are 7! that end with 123. (We assume that the intent is that these digits are to appear in the order given.) There are 5! permutations that begin with 987 and have 45 in the fifth and sixth positions; 4! that begin with 987 and end with 123; and 5! that have 45 in the fifth and sixth positions and end with 123. Finally, there are 2! permutations that begin with 987, have 45 in the fifth and sixth positions, and end with 123 (since only the 0 and the 6 are left to place). Therefore the total number of permutations meeting any of these conditions is $7! + 8! + 7! - 5! - 4! - 5! + 2! = 50{,}138$.

**17.** By inclusion-exclusion, the answer is $50 + 60 + 70 + 80 - 6 \cdot 5 + 4 \cdot 1 - 0 = 234$. Note that there were $C(4,2) = 6$ pairs to worry about (each with 5 elements in common) and $C(4,1) = 4$ triples to worry about (each with 1 element in common).

**19.** $|A_1 \cup A_2 \cup A_3 \cup A_4 \cup A_5| = |A_1| + |A_2| + |A_3| + |A_4| + |A_5| - |A_1 \cap A_2| - |A_1 \cap A_3| - |A_1 \cap A_4| - |A_1 \cap A_5| - |A_2 \cap A_3| - |A_2 \cap A_4| - |A_2 \cap A_5| - |A_3 \cap A_4| - |A_3 \cap A_5| - |A_4 \cap A_5| + |A_1 \cap A_2 \cap A_3| + |A_1 \cap A_2 \cap A_4| + |A_1 \cap A_2 \cap A_5| + |A_1 \cap A_3 \cap A_4| + |A_1 \cap A_3 \cap A_5| + |A_1 \cap A_4 \cap A_5| + |A_2 \cap A_3 \cap A_4| + |A_2 \cap A_3 \cap A_5| + |A_2 \cap A_4 \cap A_5| + |A_3 \cap A_4 \cap A_5| - |A_1 \cap A_2 \cap A_3 \cap A_4| - |A_1 \cap A_2 \cap A_3 \cap A_5| - |A_1 \cap A_2 \cap A_4 \cap A_5| - |A_1 \cap A_3 \cap A_4 \cap A_5| - |A_2 \cap A_3 \cap A_4 \cap A_5| + |A_1 \cap A_2 \cap A_3 \cap A_4 \cap A_5|$

**21.** Since no three of the sets have a common intersection, we need only carry our expression out as far as pairs. Thus we have $|A_1 \cup A_2 \cup A_3 \cup A_4 \cup A_5 \cup A_6| = |A_1| + |A_2| + |A_3| + |A_4| + |A_5| + |A_6| - |A_1 \cap A_2| - |A_1 \cap A_3| - |A_1 \cap A_4| - |A_1 \cap A_5| - |A_1 \cap A_6| - |A_2 \cap A_3| - |A_2 \cap A_4| - |A_2 \cap A_5| - |A_2 \cap A_6| - |A_3 \cap A_4| - |A_3 \cap A_5| - |A_3 \cap A_6| - |A_4 \cap A_5| - |A_4 \cap A_6| - |A_5 \cap A_6|$.

**23.** Since the probability of an event (i.e., a set) $E$ is proportional to the number of elements in the set $E$, this problem is just asking about cardinalities, and so inclusion-exclusion gives us the answer. Thus $p(E_1 \cup E_2 \cup E_3) = p(E_1) + p(E_2) + p(E_3) - p(E_1 \cap E_2) - p(E_1 \cap E_3) - p(E_2 \cap E_3) + p(E_1 \cap E_2 \cap E_3)$.

**25.** We can do this problem either by working directly with probabilities or by counting ways to satisfy the condition. We choose to do the former. First we need to determine the probability that all the numbers are odd. There are $C(100,4)$ ways to choose the numbers, and there are $C(50,4)$ ways to choose them all to be odd (since there are 50 odd numbers in the given interval). Therefore the probability that they are all odd is $C(50,4)/C(100,4)$. Similarly, since there are 33 multiples of 3 in the given interval, the probability of having all four numbers divisible by 3 is $C(33,4)/C(100,4)$. Finally, the probability that all four are divisible by 5 is $C(20,4)/C(100,4)$.

Next we need to know the probabilities that two of these events occur simultaneously. A number is both odd and divisible by 3 if and only if it is divisible by 3 by not by 6; therefore, since there are $\lfloor 100/6 \rfloor = 16$ multiples of 6 in the given interval, there are $33 - 16 = 17$ numbers that are both odd and divisible by 3. Thus the probability is $C(17,4)/C(100,4)$. Similarly there are 10 odd numbers divisible by 5, so the probability that all four numbers meet those conditions is $C(10,4)/C(100,4)$. Finally, the probability that all four numbers are divisible by both 3 and 5 is $C(6,4)/C(100,4)$, since there are only $\lfloor 100/15 \rfloor = 6$ such numbers.

Finally, the only numbers satisfying all three conditions are the odd multiples of 15, namely 15, 45, and 75. Since there are only 3 such numbers, it is impossible that all chosen four numbers are divisible by 2, 3, and 5; in other words, the probability of that event is 0. We are now ready to apply the result of Exercise 23 (i.e., inclusion-exclusion viewed in terms of probabilities). We get

$$\frac{C(50,4)}{C(100,4)} + \frac{C(33,4)}{C(100,4)} + \frac{C(20,4)}{C(100,4)} - \frac{C(17,4)}{C(100,4)} - \frac{C(10,4)}{C(100,4)} - \frac{C(6,4)}{C(100,4)} + 0$$

$$= \frac{230300 + 40920 + 4845 - 2380 - 210 - 15}{3921225}$$

$$= \frac{273460}{3921225} = \frac{4972}{71295} \approx 0.0697.$$

27. We are asked to write down inclusion-exclusion for five sets, just as in Exercise 19, except that intersections of more than three sets can be omitted. Furthermore, we are to use event notation, rather than set notation. Thus we have $p(E_1 \cup E_2 \cup E_3 \cup E_4 \cup E_5) = p(E_1) + p(E_2) + p(E_3) + p(E_4) + p(E_5) - p(E_1 \cap E_2) - p(E_1 \cap E_3) - p(E_1 \cap E_4) - p(E_1 \cap E_5) - p(E_2 \cap E_3) - p(E_2 \cap E_4) - p(E_2 \cap E_5) - p(E_3 \cap E_4) - p(E_3 \cap E_5) - p(E_4 \cap E_5) + p(E_1 \cap E_2 \cap E_3) + p(E_1 \cap E_2 \cap E_4) + p(E_1 \cap E_2 \cap E_5) + p(E_1 \cap E_3 \cap E_4) + p(E_1 \cap E_3 \cap E_5) + p(E_1 \cap E_4 \cap E_5) + p(E_2 \cap E_3 \cap E_4) + p(E_2 \cap E_3 \cap E_5) + p(E_2 \cap E_4 \cap E_5) + p(E_3 \cap E_4 \cap E_5)$.

29. We are simply asked to rephrase Theorem 1 in terms of probabilities of events. Thus we have

$$p(E_1 \cup E_2 \cup \cdots \cup E_n) = \sum_{1 \le i \le n} p(E_i) - \sum_{1 \le i < j \le n} p(E_i \cap E_j) + \sum_{1 \le i < j < k \le n} p(E_i \cap E_j \cap E_k)$$
$$\cdots + (-1)^{n+1} p(E_1 \cap E_2 \cap \cdots \cap E_n).$$

⇒ **SECTION 5.5**    **Applications of Inclusion-Exclusion**

*Some of these applications are quite subtle and not easy to understand on first encounter. They do point up the power of the inclusion-exclusion principle. Many of the exercises are closely tied to the examples, so additional study of the examples should be helpful in doing the exercises. It is often helpful, in organizing your work, to write down (in complete English sentences) exactly what the properties of interest are, calling them the $P_i$'s. To find the number of elements lacking all the properties (as you need to do in Exercise 2, for example), use the formula above Example 1.*

1. We want to find the number of apples that have neither of the properties of having worms or of having bruises. By inclusion-exclusion, we know that this is equal to the number of apples, minus the numbers with each of the properties, plus the number with both properties. In this case, this is $100 - 20 - 15 + 10 = 75$.

3. We need first to find the number of solutions with no restrictions. By the results of Section 4.5, there are $C(3 + 13 - 1, 13) = C(15, 13) = C(15, 2) = 105$. Next we need to find the number of solutions in which each restriction is violated. There are three variables that can fail to be less than 6, and the situation is symmetric, so the total number of solutions in which each restriction is violated is 3 times the number of solutions in which $x_1 \ge 6$. By the trick we used in Section 4.5, this is the same as the number of nonnegative integer solutions to $x_1' + x_2 + x_3 = 7$, where $x_1 = x_1' + 6$. This of course is $C(3 + 7 - 1, 7) = C(9, 7) = C(9, 2) = 36$. Therefore there are $3 \cdot 36 = 108$ solutions in which at least one of the restrictions is violated (with some of these counted more than once).

    Next we need to find the number of solutions with at least two of the restrictions violated. There are $C(3, 2) = 3$ ways to choose the pair to be violated, so the number we are seeking is 3 times the number of solutions in which $x_1 \ge 6$ and $x_2 \ge 6$. Again by the trick we used in Section 4.5, this is the same as the number of nonnegative integer solutions to $x_1' + x_2' + x_3 = 1$, where $x_1 = x_1' + 6$ and $x_2 = x_2' + 6$. This of course is $C(3 + 1 - 1, 1) = C(3, 1) = 3$. Therefore there are $3 \cdot 3 = 9$ solutions in which two of the restrictions are violated. Finally, we note that there are no solutions in which all three of the solutions are violated, since if each of the variables is at least 6, then their sum is at least 18, and hence cannot equal 13.

Thus by inclusion-exclusion, we see that there are $105 - 108 + 9 = 6$ solutions to the original problem. (We can check this on an ad hoc basis. The only way the sum of three numbers, not as big as 6, can be 13, is to have either two 5's and one 3, or else one 5 and two 4's. There are three variables that can be the "odd man out" in each case, for a total of 6 solutions.)

5. We follow the procedure described in the text. There are 198 positive integers less than 200 and greater than 1. The ones that are not prime are divisible by at least one of the primes in the set $\{2, 3, 5, 7, 11, 13\}$. The number of integers in the given range divisible by the prime $p$ is given by $\lfloor 199/p \rfloor$. Therefore we apply inclusion-exclusion and obtain the following number of integers from 2 to 199 that are not divisible by at least one of the primes in our set. (We have only listed those terms that contribute to the result, deleting all those that equal 0.)

$$198 - \left\lfloor \frac{199}{2} \right\rfloor - \left\lfloor \frac{199}{3} \right\rfloor - \left\lfloor \frac{199}{5} \right\rfloor - \left\lfloor \frac{199}{7} \right\rfloor - \left\lfloor \frac{199}{11} \right\rfloor - \left\lfloor \frac{199}{13} \right\rfloor + \left\lfloor \frac{199}{2 \cdot 3} \right\rfloor$$

$$+ \left\lfloor \frac{199}{2 \cdot 5} \right\rfloor + \left\lfloor \frac{199}{2 \cdot 7} \right\rfloor + \left\lfloor \frac{199}{2 \cdot 11} \right\rfloor + \left\lfloor \frac{199}{2 \cdot 13} \right\rfloor + \left\lfloor \frac{199}{3 \cdot 5} \right\rfloor + \left\lfloor \frac{199}{3 \cdot 7} \right\rfloor + \left\lfloor \frac{199}{3 \cdot 11} \right\rfloor$$

$$+ \left\lfloor \frac{199}{3 \cdot 13} \right\rfloor + \left\lfloor \frac{199}{5 \cdot 7} \right\rfloor + \left\lfloor \frac{199}{5 \cdot 11} \right\rfloor + \left\lfloor \frac{199}{5 \cdot 13} \right\rfloor + \left\lfloor \frac{199}{7 \cdot 11} \right\rfloor + \left\lfloor \frac{199}{7 \cdot 13} \right\rfloor + \left\lfloor \frac{199}{11 \cdot 13} \right\rfloor$$

$$- \left\lfloor \frac{199}{2 \cdot 3 \cdot 5} \right\rfloor - \left\lfloor \frac{199}{2 \cdot 3 \cdot 7} \right\rfloor - \left\lfloor \frac{199}{2 \cdot 3 \cdot 11} \right\rfloor - \left\lfloor \frac{199}{2 \cdot 3 \cdot 13} \right\rfloor - \left\lfloor \frac{199}{2 \cdot 5 \cdot 7} \right\rfloor - \left\lfloor \frac{199}{2 \cdot 5 \cdot 11} \right\rfloor$$

$$- \left\lfloor \frac{199}{2 \cdot 5 \cdot 13} \right\rfloor - \left\lfloor \frac{199}{2 \cdot 7 \cdot 11} \right\rfloor - \left\lfloor \frac{199}{2 \cdot 7 \cdot 13} \right\rfloor - \left\lfloor \frac{199}{3 \cdot 5 \cdot 7} \right\rfloor - \left\lfloor \frac{199}{3 \cdot 5 \cdot 11} \right\rfloor - \left\lfloor \frac{199}{3 \cdot 5 \cdot 13} \right\rfloor$$

$$= 198 - 99 - 66 - 39 - 28 - 18 - 15 + 33 + 19 + 14 + 9 + 7 + 13 + 9 + 6 + 5$$

$$+ 5 + 3 + 3 + 2 + 2 + 1 - 6 - 4 - 3 - 2 - 2 - 1 - 1 - 1 - 1 - 1 - 1 - 1 = 40.$$

These 40 numbers are therefore all prime, as are the 6 numbers in our set. Therefore there are exactly 46 prime numbers less than 200.

7. We can apply inclusion-exclusion if we reason as follows. First, we restrict ourselves to numbers greater than 1. If the number $N$ is the power of an integer, then it is certainly the prime power of an integer, since if $N = x^k$, where $k = mp$, with $p$ prime, then $N = (x^m)^p$. Thus we need to count the number of perfect second powers, the number of perfect third powers, the number of perfect fifth powers, etc., less than 10,000. Let us first determine how many positive integers greater than 1 and less than 10,000 are the square of an integer. Since $\lfloor \sqrt{9999} \rfloor = 99$, there must be $99 - 1 = 98$ such numbers (namely $2^2$ through $99^2$). Similarly, since $\lfloor \sqrt[3]{9999} \rfloor - 1 = 20$, there are 20 cubes of integers less than 10,000. Similarly, there are $\lfloor \sqrt[5]{9999} \rfloor - 1 = 5$ fifth powers, $\lfloor \sqrt[7]{9999} \rfloor - 1 = 2$ seventh powers, $\lfloor \sqrt[11]{9999} \rfloor - 1 = 1$ eleventh power, and $\lfloor \sqrt[13]{9999} \rfloor - 1 = 1$ thirteenth power. There are no higher prime powers, since $\lfloor \sqrt[17]{9999} \rfloor - 1 = 0$ (and indeed, $2^{17} = 131072 > 9999$).

Now we need to account for the double counting. There are $\lfloor \sqrt[6]{9999} \rfloor - 1 = 3$ sixth powers, and these were counted as both second powers and third powers. Similarly, there is $\lfloor \sqrt[10]{9999} \rfloor - 1 = 1$ tenth power ($10 = 2 \cdot 5$). These are the only two cases of double counting, since all other combinations give a count of 0. Therefore among the 9998 numbers from 2 to 9999, inclusive, we found that there were $98 + 20 + 5 + 2 + 1 + 1 - 3 - 1 = 123$ powers. Therefore there are $9998 - 123 = 9875$ numbers which are not powers.

9. This exercise is just asking for the number of onto functions from a set with 6 elements (the toys) to a set with 3 elements (the children), since each toy is assigned a unique child. By Theorem 1 there are $3^6 - C(3,1)2^6 + C(3,2)1^6 = 540$ such functions.

11. Here is one approach. Let us ignore temporarily the stipulation about the most difficult job being assigned to the best employee (we assume that this language uniquely specifies a job and an employee). Then we are looking for the number of onto functions from the set of 7 jobs to the set of 4 employees. By Theorem 1 there are $4^7 - C(4,1)3^7 + C(4,2)2^7 - C(4,1)1^7 = 8400$ such functions. Now by symmetry, in exactly one fourth of those assignments should the most difficult job be given to the best employee, as opposed to one of the other three employees. Therefore the answer is $8400/4 = 2100$.

13. We simply apply Theorem 2:

$$D_7 = 7! \left(1 - \frac{1}{1!} + \frac{1}{2!} - \frac{1}{3!} + \frac{1}{4!} - \frac{1}{5!} + \frac{1}{6!} - \frac{1}{7!}\right)$$
$$= 5040 - 5040 + 2520 - 840 + 210 - 42 + 7 - 1 = 1854.$$

15. **a)** An arrangement in which no letter is put into the correct envelope is a derangement. There are by definition $D_{100}$ derangements. Since there are $P(100,100) = 100!$ equally likely permutations altogether, the probability of a derangement is $D_{100}/100!$. Numerically, this is almost exactly equal to $1/e$, which is about $0.368$.

   **b)** We need to count the number of ways to put exactly one letter into the correct envelope. First, there are $C(100,1) = 100$ ways to choose the letter that is to be correctly stuffed. Then there are $D_{99}$ ways to insert the remaining 99 letters so that none of them go into their correct envelopes. By the product rule, there are $100D_{99}$ such arrangements. As in part **(a)** the denominator is $P(100,100) = 100!$. Therefore the answer is $100D_{99}/100! = D_{99}/99!$. Again this is almost exactly $1/e \approx 0.368$.

   **c)** This time, to count the number of ways that exactly 98 letters can be put into their correct envelopes, we need simply to choose the two letters that are to be misplaced, since there is only one way to misplace them. There are of course $C(100,2) = 4950$ ways to do this. As in part **(a)** the denominator is $P(100,100) = 100!$. Therefore the answer is $4950/100!$. This is substantially less than $10^{-100}$, so for all practical purposes, the answer is $0$.

   **d)** There is no way that exactly 99 letters can be inserted into their correct envelopes, since as soon as 99 letters have been correctly inserted, there is only one envelope left for the remaining letter, and it is the correct one. Therefore the answer is exactly $0$. (The probability of an event which cannot happen is $0$.)

   **e)** Only one of the 100! permutations is the correct stuffing, so the answer is $1/100!$. As in part **(c)** this is 0 for all practical purposes.

17. We can derive this answer by mimicking the derivation of the formula for the number of derangements, but worrying only about the even digits. There are 10! permutations altogether. Let $e$ be one of the 5 even digits. The number of permutations in which $e$ is in its original position is 9! (the other 9 digits need to be permuted). Therefore we need to subtract from 10! the $5 \cdot 9!$ ways in which the even digits can end up in their original positions. However, we have overcounted, since there are $C(5,2)8!$ ways in which 2 of the even digits can end up in their original positions, $C(5,3)7!$ ways in which 3 of them can, $C(5,4)6!$ ways in which 4 of them can, and $C(5,5)5!$ ways in which they can all retain their original positions. Applying inclusion-exclusion, we therefore have the answer

$$10! - 5 \cdot 9! + 10 \cdot 8! - 10 \cdot 7! + 5 \cdot 6! - 5! = 2,170,680.$$

**19.** We want to show that $D_n - nD_{n-1} = (-1)^n$. We will use an iterative approach, taking advantage of the result of Exercise 18, which can be rewritten algebraically as $D_k - kD_{k-1} = -(D_{k-1} - (k-1)D_{k-2})$ for all $k \geq 2$. We have

$$D_n - nD_{n-1} = -(D_{n-1} - (n-1)D_{n-2})$$
$$= -(-(D_{n-2} - (n-2)D_{n-3}))$$
$$= (-1)^2(D_{n-2} - (n-2)D_{n-3})$$
$$\vdots$$
$$= (-1)^{n-2}(D_2 - 2D_1)$$
$$= (-1)^n$$

since $D_2 = 1$ and $D_1 = 0$, and since $(-1)^{n-2} = (-1)^n$.

**21.** We can solve this problem by looking at the explicit formula we have for $D_n$ from Theorem 2 (multiplying through by $n!$):

$$D_n = n! - n! + \frac{n!}{2} - \frac{n!}{3!} + \cdots + (-1)^{n-1}\frac{n!}{(n-1)!} + (-1)^n\frac{n!}{n!}.$$

Now all of these terms are even except possibly for the last two, since they all contain the factors $n$ and $n - 1$, at least one of which must be even. Therefore to determine whether $D_n$ is even or odd, we need only look at these last two terms, which are $\pm n \mp 1$. If $n$ is even, then this difference is odd; but if $n$ is odd, then this difference is even. Therefore $D_n$ is even precisely when $n$ is odd.

**23.** Recall that $\phi(n)$, for a positive integer $n > 1$, denotes the number of positive integers less than (or, vacuously, equal to) $n$ and relatively prime to $n$ (in other words, that have no common prime factors with $n$). We will derive a formula for $\phi(n)$ using inclusion-exclusion. We are given that the prime factorization of $n$ is $n = p_1^{a_1} p_2^{a_2} \cdots p_m^{a_m}$. Let $P_i$ be the property that a positive integer less than or equal to $n$ has $p_i$ as a factor. Then $\phi(n)$ is precisely the number of positive integers less than or equal to $n$ which have none of the properties $P_i$. By the alternative form of the principle of inclusion-exclusion, we have the following formula for this quantity:

$$N(P_1'P_2' \cdots P_m') = n - \sum_{1 \leq i \leq m} N(P_i) + \sum_{1 \leq i < j \leq m} N(P_iP_j) - \sum_{1 \leq i < j < k \leq m} N(P_iP_jP_k)$$
$$+ \cdots + (-1)^m N(P_1P_2 \cdots P_m).$$

Our only remaining task is to find a formula for each of these sums. This is not hard. First $N(P_i)$, the number of positive integers less than or equal to $n$ divisible by $p_i$, is equal to $n/p_i$, just as in the discussion of the sieve of Eratosthenes (we need no floor function symbols since $n/p_i$ is necessarily an integer). Similarly, $N(P_iP_j)$, the number of positive integers less than or equal to $n$ divisible by both $p_i$ and $p_j$, i.e., by the product $p_ip_j$, is equal to $n/(p_ip_j)$, and so on. Making these substitutions, we can rewrite the formula displayed above as

$$N(P_1'P_2' \cdots P_m') = n - \sum_{1 \leq i \leq m} \frac{n}{p_i} + \sum_{1 \leq i < j \leq m} \frac{n}{p_ip_j} - \sum_{1 \leq i < j < k \leq m} \frac{n}{p_ip_jp_k}$$
$$+ \cdots + (-1)^m \frac{n}{p_1p_2 \cdots p_m}.$$

This formula can be written in a more useful form. If we factor out the $n$ from every term, then it is not hard to see that what remains is the product $(1 - 1/p_1)(1 - 1/p_2) \cdots (1 - 1/p_m)$. Therefore our answer is

$$n \prod_{i=1}^{m} \left(1 - \frac{1}{p_i}\right).$$

**25.** A permutation meeting these conditions must be a derangement of 123 followed by a derangement of 456 in positions 4, 5, and 6. Since there are $D_3 = 2$ derangements of the first 3 elements to choose from for the first half of our permutation and $D_3 = 2$ derangements of the last 3 elements to choose from for the second half, there are, by the product rule, $2 \cdot 2 = 4$ derangements satisfying the given conditions. Indeed, these 4 derangements are 231564, 231645, 312564, and 312645.

**27.** Let $P_i$ be the property that a function from a set with $m$ elements to a set with $n$ elements does not have the $i^{\text{th}}$ element of the codomain included in its range. We want to compute $N(P_1' P_2' \cdots P_n')$. In order to use the principle of inclusion-exclusion we need to determine $\sum N(P_i)$, $\sum N(P_i P_j)$, etc. By the product rule, there are $n^m$ functions from the set with $m$ elements to the set with $n$ elements. If we want the function not to have the $i^{\text{th}}$ element of the codomain in its range, then there are only $n - 1$ choices at each stage, rather than $n$, to assign to each element of the domain; therefore $N(P_i) = (n - 1)^m$, for each $i$. Furthermore, there are $C(n, 1)$ different $i$'s. Therefore $\sum N(P_i) = C(n, 1)(n - 1)^m$. Similarly, to compute $\sum N(P_i P_j)$, we note that there are $C(n, 2)$ ways to specify $i$ and $j$, and that once we have determined which 2 elements are to be omitted from the codomain, there are $(n - 2)^m$ different functions with this smaller codomain. Therefore $\sum N(P_i P_j) = C(n, 2)(n - 2)^m$. We continue in this way, until finally we need to find $N(P_1 P_2 \cdots P_n)$, which is clearly equal to 0, since the function must have at least one element in its range. The formula given in the statement of Theorem 1 therefore follows from the inclusion-exclusion principle.

⇒ **SUPPLEMENTARY EXERCISES FOR CHAPTER 5**

**1.** Let $L_n$ be the number of chain letters sent at the $n^{\text{th}}$ stage.

**a)** Since each person receiving a letter sends it to 4 new people, there will be 4 times as many letters sent at the $n^{\text{th}}$ stage as were sent at the $(n - 1)^{\text{th}}$ stage. Therefore the recurrence relation is $L_n = 4L_{n-1}$.

**b)** The initial condition is that at the first stage 40 letters are sent (each of the original 10 people sent it to 4 others), i.e., $L_1 = 40$.

**c)** We need to solve this recurrence relation. We do so easily by iteration, since $L_n = 4L_{n-1} = 4^2 L_{n-2} = \cdots = 4^{n-1} L_1 = 4^{n-1} \cdot 40$, or more simply $L_n = 10 \cdot 4^n$.

**3.** Let $M_n$ be the amount of money (in dollars) that the government prints in the $n^{\text{th}}$ hour.

**a)** According to the given information, the additional amount of money printed in the $n^{\text{th}}$ hour is $10,000 in $1 bills, $20,000 in $5 bills, $30,000 in $10 bills, $50,000 in $20 bills, and $50,000 in $50 bills, for a total of $160,000 additional money. Therefore our recurrence relation is $m_n = m_{n-1} + 160000$.

**b)** Since 1000 of each bill was produced in the first hour, we know that $M_1 = 1000(1 + 5 + 10 + 20 + 50 + 100) = 186000$.

**c)** We solve the recurrence relation by iteration:

$$
\begin{aligned}
M_n &= 160000 + M_{n-1} \\
&= 160000 + 160000 + M_{n-2} = 2 \cdot 160000 + M_{n-2} \\
&\phantom{=} \vdots \\
&= (n - 1) \cdot 160000 + M_1 \\
&= 160000(n - 1) + 186000 = 160000n + 26000.
\end{aligned}
$$

**d)** Let $T_n$ be the total amount of money produced in the first $n$ hours. Then $T_n = T_{n-1} + M_n$, since the total amount of money produced in the first $n$ hours is the same as the total amount of money produced in the first $n-1$ hours, plus the amount of money produced in the $n^{\text{th}}$ hour. Thus, from our result in part **(c)**, the recurrence relation is $T_n = T_{n-1} + 160000n + 26000$, with initial condition $T_0 = 0$ (no money is produced in 0 hours).

**e)** We solve the recurrence relation from part **(d)** by iteration:

$$
\begin{aligned}
T_n &= 26000 + 160000n + T_{n-1} \\
&= 26000 + 160000n + 26000 + 160000(n-1) + T_{n-2} \\
&= 2 \cdot 26000 + \big(n + (n-1)\big) \cdot 160000 + T_{n-2} \\
&\;\;\vdots \\
&= n \cdot 26000 + 160000 \cdot \big(n + (n-1) + \cdots + 1\big) + T_0 \\
&= 26000n + 160000 \cdot \frac{n(n+1)}{2} = 80000n^2 + 106000n \,.
\end{aligned}
$$

5. This problem is similar to Exercise 23 in Section 5.1. Let $m_n$ be the number of messages that can be sent in $n$ milliseconds.

   **a)** A message must begin with either the two-millisecond signal or the three-millisecond signal. If it begins with the two-millisecond signal, then the rest of the message is of length $n-2$; if it begins with the three-millisecond signal, then the message continues as a message of length $n-3$. Therefore the recurrence relation is $m_n = m_{n-2} + m_{n-3}$.

   **b)** We need initial conditions for $n = 0$, 1, and 2, since the recurrence relation has degree 3. Clearly $m_0 = 1$, since the empty message is the one and only message of length 0. Also $m_1 = 0$, since every nonempty message contains at least one signal, and the shortest signal has length 2. Finally $m_2 = 1$, since there is only one message of length 2, namely the one that uses one of the shorter signals and none of the longer signals.

   **c)** There are two approaches here. One is to solve the recurrence relation, using the methods of Section 5.2. Unfortunately, the characteristic equation is $r^3 - r - 1 = 0$, and it has no rational roots. It is possible to find real roots, but the formula for solving third degree equations is messy, and the algebra in completing the solution this way would not be pleasant. (Alternatively, one could get approximations to the roots, then get approximations to the coefficients in the solution, plug in $n = 12$, and round to the nearest integer; again the calculation involved would be unpleasant.)

   The other approach is simply to use the recurrence relation to compute $m_3, m_4, \ldots, m_{12}$. First $m_3 = m_1 + m_0 = 0 + 1 = 1$; then $m_4 = m_2 + m_1 = 1 + 0 = 1$, then $m_5 = m_3 + m_2 = 1 + 1 = 2$, and so on. Starting with $m_6$, the sequence continues 2, 3, 4, 5, 7, 9, 12. Therefore there are 12 different messages that can be sent in exactly 12 milliseconds. (If we wanted to find the number of nonempty messages that could be sent in at most 12 milliseconds—which is certainly one interpretation of the question—then we would add $m_1$ through $m_{12}$, obtaining 47 as our answer.)

7. The recurrence relation found in Exercise 6 is of degree 10, namely $a_n = a_{n-4} + a_{n-6} + a_{n-10}$. It needs 10 initial conditions, namely $a_0 = 1$, $a_1 = a_2 = a_3 = a_5 = a_7 = a_9 = 0$, and $a_4 = a_6 = a_8 = 1$.

   **a)** $a_{12} = a_8 + a_6 + a_2 = 1 + 1 + 0 = 2$ (Indeed, the 2 ways to affix 12 cents postage is either to use 3 4-cent stamps or to use 2 6-cent stamps.)

   **b)** First we need to compute $a_{10} = a_6 + a_4 + a_0 = 1 + 1 + 1 = 3$. Then $a_{14} = a_{10} + a_8 + a_4 = 3 + 1 + 1 = 5$.

**c)** We use the results of previous parts here: $a_{18} = a_{14} + a_{12} + a_8 = 5 + 2 + 1 = 8$.

**d)** First we need to compute $a_{16} = a_{12} + a_{10} + a_6 = 2 + 3 + 1 = 6$. Using this (and previous parts), we have $a_{22} = a_{18} + a_{16} + a_{12} = 8 + 6 + 2 = 16$.

9. Following the hint, let $b_n = \log a_n$ (remember that we mean log base 2). Then using the property that the log of a quotient is the difference of the logs and the log of a power is the multiple of the log, we take the logarithm of both sides of the recurrence relation for $a_n$ to obtain $b_n = 2b_{n-1} - b_{n-2}$. The initial conditions translate into $b_0 = \log a_0 = \log 1 = 0$ and $b_1 = \log a_1 = \log 2 = 1$. Thus we have transformed our problem into a linear, homogeneous, second degree recurrence relation with constant coefficients.

To solve $b_n = 2b_{n-1} - b_{n-2}$, we form the characteristic equation $r^2 - 2r + 1 = 0$, which has the repeated root $r = 1$. By Theorem 2 in Section 5.2, the general solution is $b_n = \alpha_1 1^n + \alpha_2 n 1^n = \alpha_1 + \alpha_2 n$. Plugging in the initial conditions gives the equations $\alpha_1 = 0$ and $\alpha_1 + \alpha_2 = 1$, whence $\alpha_2 = 1$. Therefore the solution is $b_n = n$. Finally, $b_n = \log a_n$ implies that $a_n = 2^{b_n}$. Therefore our solution to the original problem is $a_n = 2^n$.

11. Suppose that the roots of the characteristic equation are $r_1, r_2, \ldots, r_t$, and suppose that root $r_i$ has multiplicity $m_i$ (in other words, $(r - r_i)^{m_i}$ is a factor of the characteristic polynomial, but $(r - r_i)^{m_i + 1}$ is not). Then the general solution to the recurrence relation is

$$\alpha_{1,0} r_1^n + \alpha_{1,1} n r_1^n + \cdots + \alpha_{1,m_1-1} n^{m_1-1} r_1^n + \alpha_{2,0} r_2^n + \alpha_{2,1} n r_2^n + \cdots + \alpha_{2,m_2-1} n^{m_2-1} r_2^n$$
$$+ \cdots + \alpha_{t,0} r_t^n + \alpha_{t,1} n r_t^n + \cdots + \alpha_{t,m_t-1} n^{m_t-1} r_t^n$$

where the $\alpha_{i,j}$'s are constants. (A proof is not requested in this exercise, but the interested reader might consult Chapter 3 of C. L. Liu, *Introduction to Combinatorial Mathematics*, McGraw-Hill, 1968.)

13. One way to approach this problem is by temporarily using three variables. We assume that rabbits are born at the beginning of the month. Let $a_n$ be the number of $\frac{1}{2}$-month-old rabbits present in the middle of the $n^{\text{th}}$ month, let $b_n$ be the number of $1\frac{1}{2}$-month-old rabbits present in the middle of the $n^{\text{th}}$ month, and let $c_n$ be the number of $2\frac{1}{2}$-month-old rabbits present in the middle of the $n^{\text{th}}$ month. All the older rabbits have left the island, by the conditions of the exercise. Let us see how each of these depends on previous values. First note that $b_n = a_{n-1}$, since these rabbits are one month older. Similarly $c_n = b_{n-1}$. Combining these two equations gives $c_n = a_{n-2}$. Finally, $a_n = b_{n-1} + c_{n-1}$, since newborns come from these two groups of rabbits. Writing this last equation totally in terms of $a_n$ (using the previous equations) gives $a_n = a_{n-2} + a_{n-3}$.

Now we are interested in $T_n = a_n + b_n + c_n$, the total number of rabbits in the middle of the $n^{\text{th}}$ month. Since we have seen that the sequences $\{b_n\}$ and $\{c_n\}$ are the same as the sequence $\{a_n\}$, just shifted by one or two months, they must satisfy the same recurrence relation, so we have $b_n = b_{n-2} + b_{n-3}$ and $c_n = c_{n-2} + c_{n-3}$. If we add these three recurrence relations, we obtain $T_n = T_{n-2} + T_{n-3}$. We can take as the initial conditions $T_1 = T_2 = 1$ and $T_3 = 2$.

(We are not asked to solve this recurrence relation, and fortunately so. The characteristic equation, $r^3 - r - 1 = 0$ has no nice roots—one is irrational and two are complex. The roots are distinct, however, so let us call them $r_1$, $r_2$, and $r_3$. Then the general solution to the recurrence relation is $T_n = \alpha_1 r_1^n + \alpha_2 r_2^n + \alpha_3 r_3^n$. We could in principle determine the values of the $\alpha$'s by plugging in the initial conditions, thereby obtaining an explicit solution. We will not do this.)

15. We use Theorem 2 in Section 5.3, with $a = 3$, $b = 5$, $c = 2$ and $d = 4$. Since $a < b^d$, we have $f(n) = O(n^d) = O(n^4)$.

17. In the algorithm in Exercise 16, we need 2 comparisons to determine the largest and second largest elements of the sequence, knowing the largest and second largest elements of the first half and the second half. Thus letting $f(n)$ be the number of comparisons needed for a list with $n$ elements, and assuming that $n$ is even, we have $f(n) = 2f(n/2) + 2$. Now by Theorem 2 in Section 5.3, with $a = 2$, $b = 2$, $c = 2$ and $d = 0$, we know $f(n) = O(n^{\log_b a}) = O(n^1) = O(n)$.

19. First we have to find $\Delta a_n$. By definition we have $\Delta a_n = a_{n+1} - a_n = 3(n+1)^3 + (n+1) + 2 - (3n^3 + n + 2) = 9n^2 + 9n + 4$.
    a) By definition $\Delta^2 a_n = \Delta a_{n+1} - \Delta a_n = 9(n+1)^2 + 9(n+1) + 4 - (9n^2 + 9n + 4) = 18n + 18$.
    b) By definition $\Delta^3 a_n = \Delta^2 a_{n+1} - \Delta^2 a_n = 18(n+1) + 18 - (18n + 18) = 18$.
    c) By definition $\Delta^4 a_n = \Delta^3 a_{n+1} - \Delta^3 a_n = 18 - 18 = 0$.

21. We apply the definition, starting with the right-hand side:
$$a_{n+1}(\Delta b_n) + b_n(\Delta a_n) = a_{n+1}(b_{n+1} - b_n) + b_n(a_{n+1} - a_n)$$
$$= a_{n+1}b_{n+1} - a_n b_n \quad \text{(by algebra)}$$
$$= \Delta(a_n b_n) \quad \text{(by definition)}.$$

23. Let $H$, $C$, and $S$ stand for the sets of farms that have horses, cows, and sheep, respectively. We are told that $|H \cup C \cup S| = 323$, $|H| = 224$, $|C| = 85$, $|S| = 57$, and $|H \cap C \cap S| = 18$. We are asked to find $|H \cap C| + |H \cap S| + |C \cap S| - 3|H \cap C \cap S|$ (the reason for the subtraction is that the indicated sum counts the farms with all three animals 3 times, and we wish to count it no times). By the principle of inclusion-exclusion we know that $|H \cup C \cup S| = |H| + |C| + |S| - |H \cap C| - |H \cap S| - |C \cap S| + |H \cap C \cap S|$. Solving for the expression we are interested in, we get $|H \cap C| + |H \cap S| + |C \cap S| - 3|H \cap C \cap S| = |H| + |C| + |S| - |H \cup C \cup S| - 2|H \cap C \cap S| = 224 + 85 + 57 - 323 - 2 \cdot 18 = 7$. Thus 7 farms have exactly two of the three types of animals.

25. We apply the principle of inclusion-exclusion: $|AM \cup PM \cup OR \cup CS| = 23 + 17 + 44 + 63 - 5 - 8 - 4 - 6 - 5 - 14 + 2 + 2 + 1 + 1 - 1 = 110$.

27. Since the largest possible value for $x_1 + x_2 + x_3$ under these constraints is $5 + 9 + 4 = 18$, there are no solutions to the given equation.

29. a) We solve this problem in the same manner as we solved Exercise 7 in Section 5.5. As explained in our solution there, we need only look at prime powers. Let us restrict ourselves to integers greater than 1, and add 1 at the end. There are $\lfloor \sqrt{199} \rfloor - 1 = 13$ perfect second powers in the given range, namely $2^2$ through $14^2$. There are $\lfloor \sqrt[3]{199} \rfloor - 1 = 4$ perfect third powers, $\lfloor \sqrt[5]{199} \rfloor - 1 = 1$ perfect fifth power, and $\lfloor \sqrt[7]{199} \rfloor - 1 = 1$ perfect seventh power. Furthermore, there is $\lfloor \sqrt[6]{199} \rfloor - 1 = 1$ perfect sixth power, which is both a perfect square and a perfect cube. Therefore by inclusion-exclusion, the number of numbers between 2 and 199 inclusive that are powers greater than the first power of an integer is $13 + 4 + 1 + 1 - 1 = 18$; adding on the number 1 itself (since $1 = 1^2$), we get the answer 19.

**b)** We saw in Exercise 5 in Section 5.5 that there are 46 primes less than 200, and we just saw above that there are 19 powers. Since these two sets are disjoint, we just add the cardinalities, obtaining $19 + 46 = 65$.

**c)** Solving this problem is like counting prime numbers, except that the squares of primes play the role of the primes themselves. The squares of primes relevant to the problem are 4, 9, 25, 49, 121, and 169. The number of positive integers less than 200 divisible by $p^2$ is $\lfloor 199/p^2 \rfloor$. There is overcounting, however, since a number divisible by a number like $36 = 2^2 \cdot 3^2$ is counted in both $\lfloor 199/2^2 \rfloor$ and $\lfloor 199/3^2 \rfloor$; hence we need to subtract $\lfloor 199/6^2 \rfloor$. The number of numbers divisible by squares of primes is therefore

$$\left\lfloor \frac{199}{2^2} \right\rfloor + \left\lfloor \frac{199}{3^2} \right\rfloor + \left\lfloor \frac{199}{5^2} \right\rfloor + \left\lfloor \frac{199}{7^2} \right\rfloor + \left\lfloor \frac{199}{11^2} \right\rfloor + \left\lfloor \frac{199}{13^2} \right\rfloor - \left\lfloor \frac{199}{6^2} \right\rfloor - \left\lfloor \frac{199}{10^2} \right\rfloor - \left\lfloor \frac{199}{14^2} \right\rfloor,$$

which is just $49 + 22 + 7 + 4 + 1 + 1 - 5 - 1 - 1 = 77$. Therefore there are $199 - 77 = 122$ positive integers less than 200 that are not divisible by the square of an integer greater than 1.

**d)** This is similar to part **(c)**, with cubes in place of squares. Reasoning the same way, we get

$$199 - \left( \left\lfloor \frac{199}{2^3} \right\rfloor + \left\lfloor \frac{199}{3^3} \right\rfloor + \left\lfloor \frac{199}{5^3} \right\rfloor \right) = 199 - (24 + 7 + 1) = 167.$$

**e)** For each set of three prime numbers $\{p, q, r\}$, the number of positive integers less than 200 divisible by $p$, $q$, and $r$ is given by $\lfloor 200/(pqr) \rfloor$. There is no overcounting to worry about in this problem, since no number less than 200 is divisible by four primes (the smallest such number is $2 \cdot 3 \cdot 5 \cdot 7 = 210$). Therefore the number of positive integers less than 200 divisible by three primes is the sum of $\lfloor 200/(pqr) \rfloor$ over all triples of distinct primes whose product is at most 200. A tedious listing shows that there are 19 such triples, and when we form the sum we get 31. Therefore there are $199 - 31 = 168$ positive integers less than 200 which are not divisible by three or more primes.

**31.** There are $n$ ways to choose which person is to receive the correct hat, and there are $D_{n-1}$ ways to have the remaining hats returned totally incorrectly (where $D_{n-1}$ is the number of derangements of $n - 1$ objects). On the other hand there are $n!$ possible ways to return the hats. Therefore the probability is $nD_{n-1}/n! = D_{n-1}/(n-1)!$. Note that this happens to be the same as the probability that none of $n - 1$ people is given the correct hat; therefore it is approximately $1/e \approx 0.368$ for large $n$.

**33.** There are $2^6 = 64$ bit strings of length 6. We need to find the number that contain at least 4 1's. The number that contain exactly $i$ 1's is $C(6, i)$, since such a string is determined by choosing $i$ of the 6 positions to contain the 1's. Therefore there are $C(6, 4) + C(6, 5) + C(6, 6) = C(6, 2) + C(6, 1) + C(6, 0) = 15 + 6 + 1 = 22$ strings with at least 4 1's. Hence the probability in question is $22/64 = 11/32$.

# CHAPTER 6
## Relations

⇒ **SECTION 6.1    Relations and Their Properties**

*This chapter is one of the most important in the book. Many structures in mathematics and computer science are formulated in terms of relations. Not only is the terminology worth learning, but the experience to be gained by working with various relations will prepare the student for the more advanced structures that he or she is sure to encounter in future work.*

*This section gives the basic terminology, especially the important notions of reflexivity, symmetry, antisymmetry, and transitivity. If we are given a relation as a set of ordered pairs, then reflexivity is easy to check for: we make sure that each element is related to itself. Symmetry is also fairly easy to test for: we make sure that no pair $(a, b)$ is in the relation without its opposite $(b, a)$ being present as well. To check for antisymmetry we make sure that no pair $(a, b)$ with $a \neq b$ and its opposite are both in the relation. Transitivity is much harder to verify, since there are many triples of elements to check. A common mistake to try to avoid is forgetting that a relation which has pairs $(a, b)$ and $(b, a)$ must also include $(a, a)$ and $(b, b)$ if it is to be transitive.*

*More importantly, we can be given a relation as a rule as to when elements are related. Exercise 4 through Exercise 6 are particularly useful in helping to understand the notions of reflexivity, symmetry, antisymmetry, and transitivity for relations given in this manner. Here you have to ask yourself the appropriate questions in order to determine whether the properties hold. Is every element related to itself? If so, the relation is reflexive. Are the roles of the variables in the definition parallel? If so, then the relation is symmetric. Does the definition preclude two different elements from each being related to the other? If so, then the relation is antisymmetric. Does the fact that one element is related to a second, which is in turn related to a third, mean that the first is related to the third? If so, then the relation is transitive.*

*In general, try to think of a relation in these two ways at the same time: as a set of ordered pairs and as a propositional function describing a relationship among objects.*

1. In each case, we need to find all the pairs $(a, b)$ with $a \in A$ and $b \in B$ such that the condition is satisfied. This is straightforward.

   **a)** $\{(0,0), (1,1), (2,2), (3,3)\}$

   **b)** $\{(1,3), (2,2), (3,1), (4,0)\}$

   **c)** $\{(1,0), (2,0), (2,1), (3,0), (3,1), (3,2), (4,0), (4,1), (4,2), (4,3)\}$

   **d)** Recall that $a \mid b$ means that $b$ is a multiple of $a$ ($a$ is not allowed to be 0). Thus the answer is $\{(1,0), (1,1), (1,2), (1,3), (2,0), (2,2), (3,0), (3,3), (4,0)\}$.

   **e)** We need to look for pairs whose greatest common divisor is 1—in other words, pairs which are relatively prime. Thus the answer is $\{(0,1), (1,1), (1,2), (1,3), (2,1), (2,3), (3,1), (3,2), (4,1), (4,3)\}$

   **f)** There are not very many pairs of numbers (by definition only positive integers are considered) whose least common multiple is 2: only 1 and 2, and 2 and 2. Thus the answer is $\{(1,2), (2,1), (2,2)\}$

**3. a)** This relation is not reflexive, since it does not include, for instance $(1,1)$. It is not symmetric, since it includes, for instance, $(2,4)$ but not $(4,2)$. It is not antisymmetric since it includes both $(2,3)$ and $(3,2)$, but $2 \neq 3$. It is transitive. To see this we have to check that *whenever* it includes $(a,b)$ and $(b,c)$, then it also includes $(a,c)$. We can ignore the element 1 since it never appears. If $(a,b)$ is in this relation, then by inspection we see that $a$ must be either 2 or 3. But $(2,c)$ and $(3,c)$ are in the relation for all $c \neq 1$; thus $(a,c)$ has to be in this relation whenever $(a,b)$ and $(b,c)$ are. This proves that the relation is transitive. Note that it is very tedious to prove transitivity for an arbitrary list of ordered pairs.

**b)** This relation is reflexive, since all the pairs $(1,1)$, $(2,2)$, $(3,3)$, and $(4,4)$ are in it. It is clearly symmetric, the only nontrivial case to note being that both $(1,2)$ and $(2,1)$ are in the relation. It is not antisymmetric because both $(1,2)$ and $(2,1)$ are in the relation. It is transitive; the only nontrivial cases to note are that since both $(1,2)$ and $(2,1)$ are in the relation, we need to have (and do have) both $(1,1)$ and $(2,2)$ included as well.

**c)** This relation clearly is not reflexive and clearly is symmetric. It is not antisymmetric since both $(2,4)$ and $(4,2)$ are in the relation. It is not transitive, since although $(2,4)$ and $(4,2)$ are in the relation, $(2,2)$ is not.

**d)** This relation is clearly not reflexive. It is not symmetric, since, for instance, $(1,2)$ is included but $(2,1)$ is not. It is antisymmetric, since there are no cases of $(a,b)$ and $(b,a)$ both being in the relation. It is not transitive, since although $(1,2)$ and $(2,3)$ are in the relation, $(1,3)$ is not.

**e)** This relation is clearly reflexive and symmetric. It is trivially antisymmetric since there are no pairs $(a,b)$ in the relation with $a \neq b$. It is trivially transitive, since the only time the hypothesis $(a,b) \in R \wedge (b,c) \in R$ is met is when $a = b = c$.

**f)** This relation is clearly not reflexive. The presence of $(1,4)$ and absence of $(4,1)$ shows that it is not symmetric. The presence of both $(1,3)$ and $(3,1)$ shows that it is not antisymmetric. It is not transitive; both $(2,3)$ and $(3,1)$ are in the relation, but $(2,1)$ is not, for instance.

**5. a)** This relation is not reflexive since it is not the case that $1 \neq 1$, for instance. It is symmetric: if $x \neq y$, then of course $y \neq x$. It is not antisymmetric, since, for instance, $1 \neq 2$ and also $2 \neq 1$. It is not transitive, since $1 \neq 2$ and $2 \neq 1$, for instance, but it is not the case that $1 \neq 1$.

**b)** This relation is not reflexive, since $(0,0)$ is not included. It is symmetric, because the commutative property of multiplication tells us that $xy = yx$, so that one of these quantities is greater than or equal to 1 if and only if the other is. It is not antisymmetric, since, for instance, $(2,3)$ and $(3,2)$ are both included. It is transitive. To see this, note that the relation holds between $x$ and $y$ if and only if either $x$ and $y$ are both positive or $x$ and $y$ are both negative. So assume that $(a,b)$ and $(b,c)$ are both in the relation. There are two cases, nearly identical. If $a$ is positive, then so is $b$, since $(a,b) \in R$; therefore so is $c$, and hence $(a,c) \in R$. If $a$ is negative, then so is $b$, since $(a,b) \in R$; therefore so is $c$, and hence $(a,c) \in R$.

**c)** This relation is not reflexive, since $(1,1)$ is not included, for instance. It is symmetric: the equation $x = y - 1$ is equivalent to the equation $y = x + 1$, which is the same as the equation $x = y + 1$ with the roles of $x$ and $y$ reversed. (A more formal proof of symmetry would be by cases. If $x$ is related to $y$ then either $x = y + 1$ or $x = y - 1$. In the former case, $y = x - 1$, so $y$ is related to $x$; in the latter case $y = x + 1$, so $y$ is related to $x$.) It is not antisymmetric, since, for instance, both $(1,2)$ and $(2,1)$ are in the relation. It is not transitive, since, for instance, although both $(1,2)$ and $(2,1)$ are in the relation, $(1,1)$ is not.

**d)** Recall that $x \equiv y \pmod 7$ means that $x - y$ is a multiple of 7, i.e., that $x - y = 7t$ for some integer $t$. This relation is reflexive, since $x - x = 7 \cdot 0$ for all $x$. It is symmetric, since if $x \equiv y \pmod 7$, then $x - y = 7t$ for some $t$; therefore $y - x = 7(-t)$, so $y \equiv x \pmod 7$. It is not antisymmetric, since, for instance, we have both $2 \equiv 9$ and $9 \equiv 2 \pmod 7$. It is transitive. Suppose $x \equiv y$ and $y \equiv z \pmod 7$. This means that $x - y = 7s$ and $y - z = 7t$ for some integers $s$ and $t$. The trick is to add these two equations and note that the $y$ disappears; we get $x - z = 7s + 7t = 7(s + t)$. By definition, this means that $x \equiv z \pmod 7$, as desired.

**e)** Every number is a multiple of itself (namely 1 times itself), so this relation is reflexive. (There is one bit of controversy here; we assume that 0 is to be considered a multiple of 0, even though we do not consider that 0 is a divisor of 0.) It is clearly not symmetric, since, for instance, 6 is a multiple of 2, but 2 is not a multiple of 6. The relation is not antisymmetric either; we have that 2 is a multiple of $-2$, for instance, and $-2$ is a multiple of 2, but $2 \neq -2$. The relation is transitive, however. If $x$ is a multiple of $y$ (say $x = ty$), and $y$ is a multiple of $z$ (say $y = sz$), then we have $x = t(sz) = (ts)z$, so we know that $x$ is a multiple of $z$.

**f)** This relation is the same relation as in part **(b)**. Therefore the same answer applies (it is symmetric and transitive).

**g)** This relation is not reflexive, since, for instance, $17 \neq 17^2$. It is not symmetric, since although $289 = 17^2$, it is not the case that $17 = 289^2$. To see whether it is antisymmetric, suppose we have both $(x, y)$ and $(y, x)$ in the relation. Then $x = y^2$ and $y = x^2$. To solve this system of equations, plug the second into the first, to obtain $x = x^4$, which is equivalent to $x - x^4 = 0$. The left-hand side factors as $x(1 - x^3) = x(1 - x)(1 + x + x^2)$, so the solutions for $x$ are 0 and 1 (and a pair of irrelevant complex numbers). The corresponding solutions for $y$ are therefore also 0 and 1. Thus the only time we have both $x = y^2$ and $y = x^2$ is when $x = y$; this means that the relation is antisymmetric. It is not transitive, since, for example, $16 = 4^2$ and $4 = 2^2$, but $16 \neq 2^2$.

**h)** This relation is not reflexive, since, for instance, $17 \not\geq 17^2$. It is not symmetric, since although $289 \geq 17^2$, it is not the case that $17 \geq 289^2$. To see whether it is antisymmetric, we assume that both $(x, y)$ and $(y, x)$ are in the relation. Then $x \geq y^2$ and $y \geq x^2$. Since both sides of the second inequality are nonnegative, we can square both sides to get $y^2 \geq x^4$. Combining this with the first inequality, we have $x \geq x^4$, which is equivalent to $x - x^4 \geq 0$. The left-hand side factors as $x(1 - x^3) = x(1 - x)(1 + x + x^2)$. The last factor is always positive, so we can divide the original inequality by it to obtain the equivalent inequality $x(1 - x) \geq 0$. Now if $x > 1$ or $x < 0$, then the factors have different signs, so the inequality does not hold. Thus the only solutions are $x = 0$ and $x = 1$. The corresponding solutions for $y$ are therefore also 0 and 1. Thus the only time we have both $x \geq y^2$ and $y \geq x^2$ is when $x = y$; this means that the relation is antisymmetric. It is transitive. Suppose $x \geq y^2$ and $y \geq z^2$. Again the second inequality implies that both sides are nonnegative, so we can square both sides to obtain $y^2 \geq z^4$. Combining these inequalities gives $x \geq z^4$. Now we claim that it is always the case that $z^4 \geq z^2$; if so, then we combine this fact with the last inequality to obtain $x \geq z^2$, so $x$ is related to $z$. To verify the claim, note that since we are working with integers, it is always the case that $z^2 \geq |z|$ (equality for $z = 0$ and $z = 1$, strict inequality for other $z$). Squaring both sides gives the desired inequality.

**7.** The relations in parts **(a)**, **(b)**, and **(e)** all have at least one pair of the form $(x, x)$ in them, so they are not irreflexive. The relations in parts **(c)**, **(d)**, and **(f)** do not, so they are irreflexive.

**9.** The relation in Exercise 3a is neither reflexive nor irreflexive.

**11.** The relation in part **(a)** is asymmetric, since if $a$ is taller than $b$, then certainly $b$ cannot be taller than $a$. The relation in part **(b)** is not asymmetric, since there are many instances of $a$ and $b$ born on the same day (both cases in which $a = b$ and cases in which $a \neq b$), and in all such cases, it is also the case that $b$ and $a$ were born on the same day. The relations in part **(c)** and part **(d)** are just like that in part **(b)**, so they, too, are not asymmetric.

13. There are $mn$ elements of the set $A \times B$, if $A$ is a set with $m$ elements and $B$ is a set with $n$ elements. A relation from $A$ to $B$ is a subset of $A \times B$. Thus the question asks for the number of subsets of the set $A \times B$, which has $mn$ elements. By the product rule, it is $2^{mn}$.

15. **a)** By definition the answer is $\{ (b, a) \mid a \text{ divides } b \}$, which, by changing the names of the dummy variables, can also be written $\{ (a, b) \mid b \text{ divides } a \}$. (The universal set is still the set of positive integers.)
    **b)** By definition the answer is $\{ (a, b) \mid a \text{ does not divide } b \}$. (The universal set is still the set of positive integers.)

17. The inverse relation is just the graph of the inverse function. Somewhat more formally, we have $R^{-1} = \{ (f(a), a) \mid a \in A \} = \{ (b, f^{-1}(b)) \mid b \in B \}$, since we can index this collection just as easily by elements of $B$ as by elements of $A$ (using the correspondence $b = f(a)$).

19. This exercise is just a matter of the definitions of the set operations.
    **a)** the set of pairs $(a, b)$ where $a$ is required to read $b$ in a course or has read $b$
    **b)** the set of pairs $(a, b)$ where $a$ is required to read $b$ in a course and has read $b$
    **c)** the set of pairs $(a, b)$ where $a$ is required to read $b$ in a course or has read $b$, but not both; equivalently, the set of pairs $(a, b)$ where $a$ is required to read $b$ in a course but has not done so, or has read $b$ although not required to do so in a course
    **d)** the set of pairs $(a, b)$ where $a$ is required to read $b$ in a course but has not done so
    **e)** the set of pairs $(a, b)$ where $a$ has read $b$ although not required to do so in a course

21. To find $S \circ R$ we want to find the set of pairs $(a, c)$ such that for some person $b$, $a$ is a parent of $b$, and $b$ is a sibling of $c$. Since brothers and sisters have the same parents, this means that $a$ is also the parent of $c$. Thus $S \circ R$ is contained in the relation $R$. More specifically, $(a, c) \in S \circ R$ if and only if $a$ is the parent of $c$, and $c$ has a sibling (who is necessarily also a child of $a$). To find $R \circ S$ we want to find the set of pairs $(a, c)$ such that for some person $b$, $a$ is a sibling of $b$, and $b$ is a parent of $c$. This is the same as the condition that $a$ is the aunt or uncle of $c$ (by blood, not marriage).

23. A relation is just a subset. A subset can either contain a specified element or not; half of them do and half of them do not. Therefore 8 of the 16 relations on $\{0, 1\}$ contain the pair $(0, 1)$.

25. These are combinatorics problems, some harder than others. Let $A$ be the set with $n$ elements on which the relations are defined.
    **a)** To specify a symmetric relation, we need to decide, for each unordered pair $\{a, b\}$ of distinct elements of $A$, whether to include the pairs $(a, b)$ and $(b, a)$ or leave them out; this can be done in 2 ways for each such unordered pair. Also, for each element $a \in A$, we need to decide whether to include $(a, a)$ or not, again 2 possibilities. We can think of these two parts as one by considering an element to be an unordered pair with repetition allowed. Thus we need to make this 2-fold choice

$C(n+1,2)$ times, since there are $C(n+2-1,2)$ ways to choose an unordered pair with repetition allowed. Therefore the answer is $2^{C(n+1,2)} = 2^{n(n+1)/2}$.

**b)** This is somewhat similar to part **(a)**. For each unordered pair $\{a,b\}$ of distinct elements of $A$, we have a 3-way choice—either include $(a,b)$ only, include $(b,a)$ only, or include neither. For each element of $A$ we have a 2-way choice. Therefore the answer is $3^{C(n,2)}2^n = 3^{n(n-1)/2}2^n$.

**c)** As in part **(b)** we have a 3-way choice for $a \neq b$. There is no choice about including $(a,a)$ in the relation—the definition prohibits it. Therefore the answer is $3^{C(n,2)} = 3^{n(n-1)/2}$.

**d)** For each ordered pair $(a,b)$, with $a \neq b$ (and there are $P(n,2)$ such pairs), we can choose to include $(a,b)$ or to leave it out. There is no choice for pairs $(a,a)$. Therefore the answer is $2^{P(n,2)} = 2^{n(n-1)}$.

**e)** This is just like part **(a)**, except that there is no choice about including $(a,a)$. For each unordered pair of distinct elements of $A$, we can choose to include neither or both of the corresponding ordered pairs. Therefore the answer is $2^{C(n,2)} = 2^{n(n-1)/2}$.

**f)** We have complete freedom with the ordered pairs $(a,b)$ with $a \neq b$, so that part of the choice gives us $2^{P(n,2)}$ possibilities, just as in part **(d)**. For the decision as to whether to include $(a,a)$, two of the $2^n$ possibilities are prohibited: we cannot include all such pairs, and we cannot leave them all out. Therefore the answer is $2^{P(n,2)}(2^n - 2) = 2^{n^2-n}(2^n - 2) = 2^{n^2} - 2^{n^2-n+1}$.

27. The second sentence of the proof asks us to "take an element $b \in A$ such that $(a,b) \in R$." There is no guarantee that such an element exists for the taking. This is the only mistake in the proof. If one could be guaranteed that each element in $A$ is related to at least one other element, then symmetry and transitivity would indeed imply reflexivity. Without this assumption, however, the proof and the proposition are wrong. As a simple example, take the relation $\emptyset$ on any nonempty set. This relation is vacuously symmetric and transitive, but not reflexive. Here is another counterexample: the relation $\{(1,1),(1,2),(2,1),(2,2)\}$ on the set $\{1,2,3\}$.

29. We need to show two things. First, we need to show that if a relation $R$ is symmetric, then $R = R^{-1}$, which means we must show that $R \subseteq R^{-1}$ and $R^{-1} \subseteq R$. To do this, let $(a,b) \in R$. Since $R$ is symmetric, this implies that $(b,a) \in R$. But since $R^{-1}$ consists of all pairs $(a,b)$ such that $(b,a) \in R$, this means that $(a,b) \in R^{-1}$. Thus we have shown that $R \subseteq R^{-1}$. Next let $(a,b) \in R^{-1}$. By definition this means that $(b,a) \in R$. Since $R$ is symmetric, this implies that $(a,b) \in R$ as well. Thus we have shown that $R^{-1} \subseteq R$.

Second we need to show that $R = R^{-1}$ implies that $R$ is symmetric. To this end we let $(a,b) \in R$ and try to show that $(b,a)$ is also necessarily an element of $R$. Since $(a,b) \in R$, the definition tells us that $(b,a) \in R^{-1}$. But since we are under the hypothesis that $R = R^{-1}$, this tells us that $(b,a) \in R$, exactly as desired.

31. Suppose $R$ is reflexive. We must show that $R^{-1}$ is reflexive, i.e., that $(a,a) \in R^{-1}$ for each $a \in A$. Now since $R$ is reflexive, we know that $(a,a) \in R$ for each $a \in R$. By definition, this tells us that $(a,a) \in R^{-1}$, as desired. (Interchanging the two $a$'s in the pair $(a,a)$ leaves it as it was.) Conversely, if $R^{-1}$ is reflexive, then $(a,a) \in R^{-1}$ for each $a \in A$. By definition this means that $(a,a) \in R$ (again we interchanged the two $a$'s).

33. We prove this by induction on $n$. The case $n = 1$ is trivial, since it is the statement $R = R$. Assume the inductive hypothesis that $R^n = R$. We must show that $R^{n+1} = R$. By definition $R^{n+1} = R^n \circ R$. Thus our task is to show that $R^n \circ R \subseteq R$ and $R \subseteq R^n \circ R$. The first uses the transitivity of $R$, as follows. Suppose $(a,c) \in R^n \circ R$. This means that there is an element $b$ such that $(a,b) \in R$ and

$(b, c) \in R^n$. By the inductive hypothesis, the latter statement implies that $(b, c) \in R$. Thus by the transitivity of $R$, we know that $(a, c) \in R$, as desired.

Next assume that $(a, b) \in R$. We must show that $(a, b) \in R^n \circ R$. By the inductive hypothesis, $R^n = R$, and therefore $R^n$ is reflexive by assumption. Thus $(b, b) \in R^n$. Since we have $(a, b) \in R$ and $(b, b) \in R^n$, we have by definition that $(a, b)$ is an element of $R^n \circ R$, exactly as desired. (The first half of this proof was not really necessary, since Theorem 1 in this section already told us that $R^n \subseteq R$ for all $n$.)

35. We use induction on $n$, the result being trivially true for $n = 1$. Assume that $R^n$ is reflexive; we must show that $R^{n+1}$ is reflexive. Let $a \in A$, where $A$ is the set on which $R$ is defined. By definition $R^{n+1} = R^n \circ R$. By the inductive hypothesis, $R^n$ is reflexive, so $(a, a) \in R^n$. Also, since $R$ is reflexive by assumption, $(a, a) \in R$. Therefore by the definition of composition, $(a, a) \in R^n \circ R$, as desired.

37. It is not necessarily true that $R^2$ is irreflexive when $R$ is. We might have pairs $(a, b)$ and $(b, a)$ both in $R$, with $a \neq b$; then it would follow that $(a, a) \in R^2$, preventing $R^2$ from being irreflexive. As the simplest example, let $A = \{1, 2\}$ and let $R = \{(1, 2), (2, 1)\}$. Then $R$ is clearly irreflexive. In this case $R^2 = \{(1, 1), (2, 2)\}$, which is not irreflexive.

⇒ **SECTION 6.2   *n*-ary Relations and Their Applications**

*This section is a very brief introduction to relational models for data bases. The exercises are straightforward and similar to the examples. Projections are formed by omitting certain columns, and then eliminating duplicate rows. Joins are analogous to compositions of relations.*

1. We simply need to find solutions of the inequality, which we can do by common sense. The set is $\{(1, 2, 3), (1, 2, 4), (1, 3, 4), (2, 3, 4)\}$.

3. The 5-tuples are just the lines of the table. Thus the relation is $\{(\text{Nadir}, 122, 34, \text{Detroit}, 08:10),$ $(\text{Acme}, 221, 22, \text{Denver}, 08:17),$ $(\text{Acme}, 122, 33, \text{Anchorage}, 08:22),$ $(\text{Acme}, 322, 34, \text{Honolulu}, 08:30),$ $(\text{Nadir}, 199, 13, \text{Detroit}, 08:47),$ $(\text{Acme}, 222, 22, \text{Denver}, 09:10), (\text{Nadir}, 322, 34, \text{Detroit}, 09:44)\}$.

5. We need to find a field which, when used along with the *Airline* field uniquely specifies a row of the table. Certainly *Flight Number* is one such field, since there is only one line of the table for each pair (*Airline*, *Flight Number*); no airline has the same flight number for two different flights. *Gate* and *Destination* do not qualify, however, since Nadir has two flights leaving from Gate 34 going to Detroit. Finally, *Departure Time* is a key by itself (no two flights leave at the same time), so it and *Airline* form a composite key as well.

7. The subscripts on the projection mapping notation indicate which columns are to be retained. Thus if we want to delete columns 1, 2, and 4 from a 6-tuple, we need to use the projection $P_{3,5,6}$.

**9.** The table uses columns 1 and 4 of Table 8. We start by deleting columns 2, 3, and 5 from Table 8. At this point, rows 5, 6 and 7 are duplicates of earlier rows, so they are omitted (rather than being listed twice). Therefore the answer is as follows.

| *Airline* | *Destination* |
|-----------|---------------|
| Nadir | Detroit |
| Acme | Denver |
| Acme | Anchorage |
| Acme | Honolulu |

**11.** We need to find rows of Table 9 the last two entries of which are identical to the first two entries of rows of Table 10. We combine each such pair of rows into one row of our new table. For instance, the last two entries in the first row of Table 9 are 1092 and 1. The first two entries in the second row of Table 10 are also 1092 and 1. Therefore we combine them into the row $23, 1092, 1, 2, 2$ of our new table, whose columns represent *Supplier*, *Part Number*, *Project*, *Quantity*, and *Color Code*. The new table consists of all pairs found in this way.

| *Supplier* | *Part Number* | *Project* | *Quantity* | *Color Code* |
|------------|---------------|-----------|------------|--------------|
| 23 | 1092 | 1 | 2 | 2 |
| 23 | 1101 | 3 | 1 | 1 |
| 23 | 9048 | 4 | 12 | 2 |
| 31 | 4975 | 3 | 6 | 2 |
| 31 | 3477 | 2 | 25 | 2 |
| 32 | 6984 | 4 | 10 | 1 |
| 32 | 9191 | 2 | 80 | 4 |
| 33 | 1001 | 1 | 14 | 8 |

⇒ **SECTION 6.3   Representing Relations**

*Matrices and directed graphs provide useful ways for computers and humans to represent relations and manipulate them. In addition to getting some familiarity in working with these representations and the operations on them (especially the matrix operation for forming composition), the reader should look at Exercise 3 through Exercise 7, Exercise 14, and Exercise 15 to see how properties of a relation can be found from these representations.*

**1.** In each case we use a $3 \times 3$ matrix, putting a 1 in position $(i, j)$ if the pair $(i, j)$ is in the relation and a 0 in position $(i, j)$ if the pair $(i, j)$ is not in the relation. For instance, in part **(a)** there are 1's in the first row, since each of the pairs $(1, 1)$, $(1, 2)$, and $(1, 3)$ are in the relation, and there are 0's elsewhere.

**a)** $\begin{bmatrix} 1 & 1 & 1 \\ 0 & 0 & 0 \\ 0 & 0 & 0 \end{bmatrix}$  **b)** $\begin{bmatrix} 0 & 1 & 0 \\ 1 & 1 & 0 \\ 0 & 0 & 1 \end{bmatrix}$  **c)** $\begin{bmatrix} 1 & 1 & 1 \\ 0 & 1 & 1 \\ 0 & 0 & 1 \end{bmatrix}$  **d)** $\begin{bmatrix} 0 & 0 & 1 \\ 0 & 0 & 0 \\ 1 & 0 & 0 \end{bmatrix}$

**3.** Just as a reflexive relation is one whose matrix has all 1's on the main diagonal (to indicate that each pair $(a, a)$ is in the relation), an irreflexive relation is one whose matrix has all 0's on the main diagonal (to indicate that each pair $(a, a)$ is not in the relation).

**5.** Since the relation $\overline{R}$ is the relation which contains the pair $(a, b)$ (where $a$ and $b$ are elements of the appropriate sets) if and only if $R$ does not contain that pair, we can form the matrix for $\overline{R}$ simply by changing all the 1's to 0's and 0's to 1's in the matrix for $R$.

**7.** Exercise 6 tells us how to do part **(a)** (we take the transpose of the given matrix $\mathbf{M}_R$, which in this case happens to be the matrix itself). Exercise 5 tells us how to do part **(b)** (we change 1's to 0's and 0's to 1's in $\mathbf{M}_R$). For part **(c)** we take the Boolean product of $\mathbf{M}_R$ with itself (see the discussion surrounding Examples 7 and 8).

**a)** $\begin{bmatrix} 0 & 1 & 1 \\ 1 & 1 & 0 \\ 1 & 0 & 1 \end{bmatrix}$ **b)** $\begin{bmatrix} 1 & 0 & 0 \\ 0 & 0 & 1 \\ 0 & 1 & 0 \end{bmatrix}$ **c)** $\begin{bmatrix} 1 & 1 & 1 \\ 1 & 1 & 1 \\ 1 & 1 & 1 \end{bmatrix}$

**9.** According to the discussion surrounding Examples 7 and 8, we simply compute the Boolean powers of $\mathbf{M}_R$; thus $\mathbf{M}_{R^2} = \mathbf{M}_R^{[2]}$, $\mathbf{M}_{R^3} = \mathbf{M}_R^{[3]}$, and $\mathbf{M}_{R^4} = \mathbf{M}_R^{[4]}$.

**a)** $\begin{bmatrix} 0 & 0 & 1 \\ 1 & 1 & 0 \\ 0 & 1 & 1 \end{bmatrix}$ **b)** $\begin{bmatrix} 1 & 1 & 0 \\ 0 & 1 & 1 \\ 1 & 1 & 1 \end{bmatrix}$ **c)** $\begin{bmatrix} 0 & 1 & 1 \\ 1 & 1 & 1 \\ 1 & 1 & 1 \end{bmatrix}$

**11.** In each case we draw a directed graph on three vertices with an edge from $a$ to $b$ for each pair $(a, b)$ in the relation, i.e., whenever there is a 1 in position $(a, b)$ in the matrix. In part **(a)**, for instance, we need an edge from 1 to itself since there is a 1 in position $(1, 1)$ in the matrix, and an edge from 1 to 3, but no edge from 1 to 2.

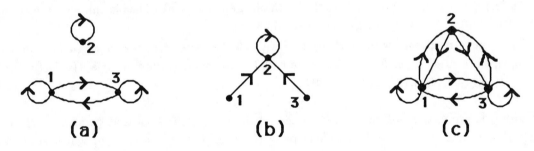

**13.** In each case we list all the pairs $(x, y)$ for which there is an edge from $x$ to $y$ in the directed graph.
**a)** $\{(a, b), (a, c), (b, c), (c, b)\}$
**b)** $\{(a, a), (a, b), (b, a), (b, b), (c, a), (c, c), (c, d), (d, d)\}$
**c)** $\{(a, a), (a, b), (a, c), (b, a), (b, b), (b, c), (c, a), (c, b), (d, d)\}$

**15.** Recall that the relation is reflexive if there is a loop at each vertex; irreflexive if there are no loops at all; symmetric if edges appear only in pairs; antisymmetric if there is no pair of **antiparallel edges** (edges from one vertex to a second vertex and from the second to the first); and transitive if all paths of length 2 (a pair of edges $(x, y)$ and $(y, z)$) are accompanied by the corresponding path of length 1 (the edge $(x, z)$).

**a)** This relation is not reflexive but is irreflexive since there are no loops. It is not symmetric, since, for instance, the edge $(a, b)$ is present but not the edge $(b, a)$. It is not antisymmetric, since both edges $(b, c)$ and $(c, b)$ are present. It is not transitive, since the path $(b, c), (c, b)$ from $b$ to $b$ is not accompanied by the edge $(b, b)$.

**b)** This relation is reflexive and not irreflexive since there are loops at each vertex. It is not symmetric, since, for instance, the edge $(c, a)$ is present but not the edge $(a, c)$. It is not antisymmetric, since both edges $(a, b)$ and $(b, a)$ are present. It is not transitive, since the path of $(c, a), (a, b)$ from $c$ to $b$ is not accompanied by the edge $(c, b)$.

**c)** This relation is neither reflexive nor irreflexive, since there are loops at some, but not all, of the vertices. It is symmetric, since all the edges which are not loops appear in antiparallel pairs. It is certainly not antisymmetric because of the existence of these antiparallel pairs of edges ($(a, b)$ and $(b, a)$, for example). It is also not transitive, since the path of $(c, a), (a, c)$ from $c$ to $c$ is not accompanied by the edge $(c, c)$.

**17.** We prove this statement by induction on $n$. The base case $n = 1$ is tautologically true, since $\mathbf{M}_R^{[1]} = \mathbf{M}_R$. Assume the inductive hypothesis that $\mathbf{M}_R^{[n]}$ is the matrix representing $R^n$. Now $\mathbf{M}_R^{[n+1]} = \mathbf{M}_R \odot \mathbf{M}_R^{[n]}$. By the inductive hypothesis and the assertion made before Example 5, that $\mathbf{M}_{S \circ R} = \mathbf{M}_R \odot \mathbf{M}_S$, the right-hand side is the matrix representing $R^n \circ R$. But $R^n \circ R = R^{n+1}$, so our proof is complete.

⇒ **SECTION 6.4    Closures of Relations**

*This section is harder than the previous ones in this section. Warshall's algorithm, in particular, is fairly tricky, and Exercise 25 should be worked carefully, following Example 8. It is easy to forget to include the loops $(a, a)$ when forming transitive closures "by hand."*

**1. a)** The reflexive closure of $R$ is $R$ together with all the pairs $(a, a)$. Thus in this case the closure of $R$ is $\{(0, 0), (0, 1), (1, 1), (1, 2), (2, 0), (2, 2), (3, 0), (3, 3)\}$.

**b)** The symmetric closure of $R$ is $R$ together with all the pairs $(b, a)$ for which $(a, b)$ is in $R$. For example, since $(1, 2)$ is in $R$, we need to add $(2, 1)$. Thus the closure of $R$ is $\{(0, 1), (0, 2), (0, 3), (1, 0), (1, 1), (1, 2), (2, 0), (2, 1), (2, 2), (3, 0)\}$.

**3.** To form the symmetric closure we need to add all the pairs $(b, a)$ such that $(a, b)$ is in $R$. In this case, that means that we need to include pairs $(b, a)$ such that $a$ divides $b$, which is equivalent to saying that we need to include all the pairs $(a, b)$ such that $b$ divides $a$. Thus the closure is $\{(a, b) \mid a \text{ divides } b \text{ or } b \text{ divides } a\}$.

**5.** We form the reflexive closure by taking the given directed graph and appending loops at all vertices at which there are not already loops.

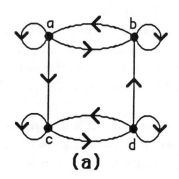

**(a)**

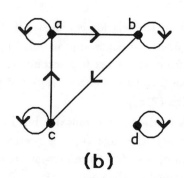

**(b)**

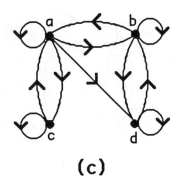

## (c)

7. We form the symmetric closure by taking the given directed graph and appending an edge pointing in the opposite direction for every edge already in the directed graph (unless it is already there); in other words, we append the edge $(b,a)$ whenever we see the edge $(a,b)$.

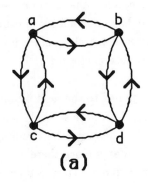
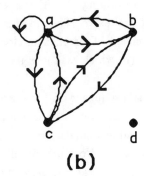
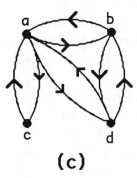

**(a)**                      **(b)**                      **(c)**

9. We are asked for the symmetric and reflexive closure of the given relation. We form it by taking the given directed graph and appending (1) a loop at each vertex at which there is not already a loop and (2) an edge pointing in the opposite direction for every edge already in the directed graph (unless it is already there).

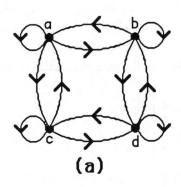
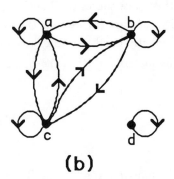

**(a)**                                          **(b)**

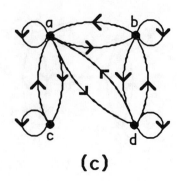

**(c)**

**11.** The symmetric closure of $R$ is $R \cup R^{-1}$. The matrix for $R^{-1}$ is $\mathbf{M}_R^t$, as we saw in Exercise 6 in Section 6.3. The matrix for the union of two relations is the join of the matrices for the two relations, as we saw in Section 6.3. Therefore the matrix representing the symmetric closure of $R$ is indeed $\mathbf{M}_R \vee \mathbf{M}_R^t$.

**13.** If $R$ is already irreflexive, then it is clearly its own irreflexive closure. On the other hand if $R$ is not irreflexive, then there is no relation containing $R$ which is irreflexive, since the loop or loops in $R$ prevent any such relation from being irreflexive. Thus in this case $R$ has no irreflexive closure. This exercise shows essentially that the concept of "irreflexive closure" is rather useless, since no relation has one unless it is already irreflexive (in which case it is its own "irreflexive closure").

**15.** A circuit of length 3 can be written as a sequence of 4 vertices, each joined to the next by an edge of the given directed graph, ending at the same vertex at which it began. There are several such circuits here, and we just have to be careful and systematically list them all. There are the circuits formed entirely by the loops: $aaaa$, $cccc$, and $eeee$. No other circuit can begin at $a$ since there are no other edges coming into $a$. The only circuit starting at $b$ is $bccb$. There are two more circuits starting at $c$, namely $ccbc$ and $cbcc$. Similarly there are the circuits $deed$, $eede$ and $edee$.

**17.** The way to form these powers is first to form the matrix representing $R$, namely

$$\mathbf{M}_R = \begin{bmatrix} 0 & 0 & 1 & 0 & 0 \\ 0 & 0 & 0 & 1 & 0 \\ 1 & 0 & 0 & 0 & 1 \\ 0 & 0 & 1 & 0 & 0 \\ 1 & 1 & 0 & 1 & 0 \end{bmatrix},$$

and then take successive Boolean powers of it to get the matrices representing $R^2$, $R^3$, and so on. Finally, for part (**f**) we take the join of the matrices representing $R$, $R^2$, ..., $R^5$. Since the matrix is a perfectly good way to express the relation, we will not list the ordered pairs.

**a)** The matrix for $R^2$ is the Boolean product of the matrix displayed above with itself, namely

$$\mathbf{M}_{R^2} = \mathbf{M}_R^{[2]} = \begin{bmatrix} 1 & 0 & 0 & 0 & 1 \\ 0 & 0 & 1 & 0 & 0 \\ 1 & 1 & 1 & 1 & 0 \\ 1 & 0 & 0 & 0 & 1 \\ 0 & 0 & 1 & 1 & 0 \end{bmatrix}.$$

**b)** The matrix for $R^3$ is the Boolean product of the first matrix displayed above with the answer to part **(a)**, namely

$$\mathbf{M}_{R^3} = \mathbf{M}_R^{[3]} = \begin{bmatrix} 1 & 1 & 1 & 1 & 0 \\ 1 & 0 & 0 & 0 & 1 \\ 1 & 0 & 1 & 1 & 1 \\ 1 & 1 & 1 & 1 & 0 \\ 1 & 0 & 1 & 0 & 1 \end{bmatrix}.$$

**c)** The matrix for $R^4$ is the Boolean product of the first matrix displayed above with the answer to part **(b)**, namely

$$\mathbf{M}_{R^4} = \mathbf{M}_R^{[4]} = \begin{bmatrix} 1 & 0 & 1 & 1 & 1 \\ 1 & 1 & 1 & 1 & 0 \\ 1 & 1 & 1 & 1 & 1 \\ 1 & 0 & 1 & 1 & 1 \\ 1 & 1 & 1 & 1 & 1 \end{bmatrix}.$$

**d)** The matrix for $R^5$ is the Boolean product of the first matrix displayed above with the answer to part **(c)**, namely

$$\mathbf{M}_{R^5} = \mathbf{M}_R^{[5]} = \begin{bmatrix} 1 & 1 & 1 & 1 & 1 \\ 1 & 0 & 1 & 1 & 1 \\ 1 & 1 & 1 & 1 & 1 \\ 1 & 1 & 1 & 1 & 1 \\ 1 & 1 & 1 & 1 & 1 \end{bmatrix}.$$

**e)** The matrix for $R^6$ is the Boolean product of the first matrix displayed above with the answer to part **(d)**, namely

$$\mathbf{M}_{R^6} = \mathbf{M}_R^{[6]} = \begin{bmatrix} 1 & 1 & 1 & 1 & 1 \\ 1 & 1 & 1 & 1 & 1 \\ 1 & 1 & 1 & 1 & 1 \\ 1 & 1 & 1 & 1 & 1 \\ 1 & 1 & 1 & 1 & 1 \end{bmatrix}.$$

**f)** The matrix for $R^*$ is the join of the first matrix displayed above and the answers to parts **(a)** through **(d)**, namely

$$\mathbf{M}_{R^*} = \mathbf{M}_R \vee \mathbf{M}_R^{[2]} \vee \mathbf{M}_R^{[3]} \vee \mathbf{M}_R^{[4]} \vee \mathbf{M}_R^{[5]} = \begin{bmatrix} 1 & 1 & 1 & 1 & 1 \\ 1 & 1 & 1 & 1 & 1 \\ 1 & 1 & 1 & 1 & 1 \\ 1 & 1 & 1 & 1 & 1 \\ 1 & 1 & 1 & 1 & 1 \end{bmatrix}.$$

**19. a)** The pair $(a, b)$ is in $R^2$ if there is a person $c$ who is in a class with $a$ and a class with $b$. Note that it is almost certain that $(a, a)$ is in $R^2$, since as long as $a$ is taking a class that has at least one other person in it, that person serves as the "$c$."

**b)** The pair $(a, b)$ is in $R^3$ if there are persons $c$ and $d$ such that $c$ is in a class with $a$, $c$ is in a class with $d$, and $d$ is in a class with $b$.

**c)** The pair $(a, b)$ is in $R^*$ if there is a sequence of persons, $c_0, c_1, c_2, \ldots, c_n$, with $n \geq 1$, such that $c_0 = a$, $c_n = b$, and for each $i$ from 1 to $n$, $c_{i-1}$ is in at least one class with $c_i$.

**21.** Suppose $(a, b) \in R^*$; then there is a path from $a$ to $b$ in $R$. Given such a path, if $R$ is symmetric, then the reverse of every edge in the path is also in $R$; therefore there is a path from $b$ to $a$ in $R$ (following the given path backwards). This means that $(b, a)$ is in $R^*$ whenever $(a, b)$ is, exactly what we needed to prove.

**23.** Algorithm 1 finds the transitive closure by computing the successive powers and taking their join. We exhibit our answers in matrix form as $M_R \vee M_R^{[2]} \vee \ldots \vee M_R^{[n]} = M_{R^*}$.

a)
$$\begin{bmatrix} 0 & 1 & 0 & 0 \\ 1 & 0 & 1 & 0 \\ 0 & 0 & 0 & 1 \\ 1 & 0 & 0 & 0 \end{bmatrix} \vee \begin{bmatrix} 1 & 0 & 1 & 0 \\ 0 & 1 & 0 & 1 \\ 1 & 0 & 0 & 0 \\ 0 & 1 & 0 & 0 \end{bmatrix} \vee \begin{bmatrix} 0 & 1 & 0 & 1 \\ 1 & 0 & 1 & 0 \\ 0 & 1 & 0 & 0 \\ 1 & 0 & 1 & 0 \end{bmatrix} \vee \begin{bmatrix} 1 & 0 & 1 & 0 \\ 0 & 1 & 0 & 1 \\ 1 & 0 & 1 & 0 \\ 0 & 1 & 0 & 1 \end{bmatrix} = \begin{bmatrix} 1 & 1 & 1 & 1 \\ 1 & 1 & 1 & 1 \\ 1 & 1 & 1 & 1 \\ 1 & 1 & 1 & 1 \end{bmatrix}$$

b)
$$\begin{bmatrix} 0 & 0 & 0 & 0 \\ 1 & 0 & 1 & 0 \\ 1 & 0 & 0 & 1 \\ 1 & 0 & 1 & 0 \end{bmatrix} \vee \begin{bmatrix} 0 & 0 & 0 & 0 \\ 1 & 0 & 0 & 1 \\ 1 & 0 & 1 & 0 \\ 1 & 0 & 0 & 1 \end{bmatrix} \vee \begin{bmatrix} 0 & 0 & 0 & 0 \\ 1 & 0 & 1 & 0 \\ 1 & 0 & 0 & 1 \\ 1 & 0 & 1 & 0 \end{bmatrix} \vee \begin{bmatrix} 0 & 0 & 0 & 0 \\ 1 & 0 & 0 & 1 \\ 1 & 0 & 1 & 0 \\ 1 & 0 & 0 & 1 \end{bmatrix} = \begin{bmatrix} 0 & 0 & 0 & 0 \\ 1 & 0 & 1 & 1 \\ 1 & 0 & 1 & 1 \\ 1 & 0 & 1 & 1 \end{bmatrix}$$

c)
$$\begin{bmatrix} 0 & 1 & 1 & 1 \\ 0 & 0 & 1 & 1 \\ 0 & 0 & 0 & 1 \\ 0 & 0 & 0 & 0 \end{bmatrix} \vee \begin{bmatrix} 0 & 0 & 1 & 1 \\ 0 & 0 & 0 & 1 \\ 0 & 0 & 0 & 0 \\ 0 & 0 & 0 & 0 \end{bmatrix} \vee \begin{bmatrix} 0 & 0 & 0 & 1 \\ 0 & 0 & 0 & 0 \\ 0 & 0 & 0 & 0 \\ 0 & 0 & 0 & 0 \end{bmatrix} \vee \begin{bmatrix} 0 & 0 & 0 & 0 \\ 0 & 0 & 0 & 0 \\ 0 & 0 & 0 & 0 \\ 0 & 0 & 0 & 0 \end{bmatrix} = \begin{bmatrix} 0 & 1 & 1 & 1 \\ 0 & 0 & 1 & 1 \\ 0 & 0 & 0 & 1 \\ 0 & 0 & 0 & 0 \end{bmatrix}$$

Note that the relation was already transitive, so its transitive closure is itself.

d)
$$\begin{bmatrix} 1 & 0 & 0 & 1 \\ 1 & 0 & 1 & 0 \\ 1 & 1 & 0 & 1 \\ 0 & 1 & 0 & 0 \end{bmatrix} \vee \begin{bmatrix} 1 & 1 & 0 & 1 \\ 1 & 1 & 0 & 1 \\ 1 & 1 & 1 & 1 \\ 1 & 0 & 1 & 0 \end{bmatrix} \vee \begin{bmatrix} 1 & 1 & 1 & 1 \\ 1 & 1 & 1 & 1 \\ 1 & 1 & 1 & 1 \\ 1 & 1 & 0 & 1 \end{bmatrix} \vee \begin{bmatrix} 1 & 1 & 1 & 1 \\ 1 & 1 & 1 & 1 \\ 1 & 1 & 1 & 1 \\ 1 & 1 & 1 & 1 \end{bmatrix} = \begin{bmatrix} 1 & 1 & 1 & 1 \\ 1 & 1 & 1 & 1 \\ 1 & 1 & 1 & 1 \\ 1 & 1 & 1 & 1 \end{bmatrix}$$

**25.** In Warshall's algorithm (Algorithm 2 in this section), we compute a sequence of matrices $W_0$ (the matrix representing $R$), $W_1$, $W_2$, ..., $W_n$, the last of which represents the transitive closure of $R$. Each matrix $W_k$ comes from the matrix $W_{k-1}$ in the following way. The $(i, j)^{\text{th}}$ entry of $W_k$ is the "$\vee$" of the $(i, j)^{\text{th}}$ entry of $W_{k-1}$ with the "$\wedge$" of the $(i, k)^{\text{th}}$ entry and the $(k, j)^{\text{th}}$ entry of $W_{k-1}$. We will exhibit our solution by listing the matrices $W_0$, $W_1$, $W_2$, $W_3$, $W_4$, in that order; $W_4$ represents the answer. In each case $W_0$ is the matrix of the given relation. To compute the next matrix in the solution, we need to compute it one entry at a time, using the equation just discussed (the "$\vee$" of the corresponding entry in the previous matrix with the "$\wedge$" of two entries in the old matrix), i.e., as $i$ and $j$ each go from 1 to 4, we need to write down the $(i, j)^{\text{th}}$ entry using this formula. Note that in computing $W_k$ the $k^{\text{th}}$ row and the $k^{\text{th}}$ column are unchanged, but some of the entries in other rows and columns may change.

a)
$$\begin{bmatrix} 0 & 1 & 0 & 0 \\ 1 & 0 & 1 & 0 \\ 0 & 0 & 0 & 1 \\ 1 & 0 & 0 & 0 \end{bmatrix} \begin{bmatrix} 0 & 1 & 0 & 0 \\ 1 & 1 & 1 & 0 \\ 0 & 0 & 0 & 1 \\ 1 & 1 & 0 & 0 \end{bmatrix} \begin{bmatrix} 1 & 1 & 1 & 0 \\ 1 & 1 & 1 & 0 \\ 0 & 0 & 0 & 1 \\ 1 & 1 & 1 & 0 \end{bmatrix} \begin{bmatrix} 1 & 1 & 1 & 1 \\ 1 & 1 & 1 & 1 \\ 0 & 0 & 0 & 1 \\ 1 & 1 & 1 & 1 \end{bmatrix} \begin{bmatrix} 1 & 1 & 1 & 1 \\ 1 & 1 & 1 & 1 \\ 1 & 1 & 1 & 1 \\ 1 & 1 & 1 & 1 \end{bmatrix}$$

b)
$$\begin{bmatrix} 0 & 0 & 0 & 0 \\ 1 & 0 & 1 & 0 \\ 1 & 0 & 0 & 1 \\ 1 & 0 & 1 & 0 \end{bmatrix} \begin{bmatrix} 0 & 0 & 0 & 0 \\ 1 & 0 & 1 & 0 \\ 1 & 0 & 0 & 1 \\ 1 & 0 & 1 & 0 \end{bmatrix} \begin{bmatrix} 0 & 0 & 0 & 0 \\ 1 & 0 & 1 & 0 \\ 1 & 0 & 0 & 1 \\ 1 & 0 & 1 & 0 \end{bmatrix} \begin{bmatrix} 0 & 0 & 0 & 0 \\ 1 & 0 & 1 & 1 \\ 1 & 0 & 0 & 1 \\ 1 & 0 & 1 & 1 \end{bmatrix} \begin{bmatrix} 0 & 0 & 0 & 0 \\ 1 & 0 & 1 & 1 \\ 1 & 0 & 1 & 1 \\ 1 & 0 & 1 & 1 \end{bmatrix}$$

c)
$$\begin{bmatrix} 0 & 1 & 1 & 1 \\ 0 & 0 & 1 & 1 \\ 0 & 0 & 0 & 1 \\ 0 & 0 & 0 & 0 \end{bmatrix} \begin{bmatrix} 0 & 1 & 1 & 1 \\ 0 & 0 & 1 & 1 \\ 0 & 0 & 0 & 1 \\ 0 & 0 & 0 & 0 \end{bmatrix} \begin{bmatrix} 0 & 1 & 1 & 1 \\ 0 & 0 & 1 & 1 \\ 0 & 0 & 0 & 1 \\ 0 & 0 & 0 & 0 \end{bmatrix} \begin{bmatrix} 0 & 1 & 1 & 1 \\ 0 & 0 & 1 & 1 \\ 0 & 0 & 0 & 1 \\ 0 & 0 & 0 & 0 \end{bmatrix} \begin{bmatrix} 0 & 1 & 1 & 1 \\ 0 & 0 & 1 & 1 \\ 0 & 0 & 0 & 1 \\ 0 & 0 & 0 & 0 \end{bmatrix}$$

Note that the relation was already transitive, so each matrix in the sequence was the same.

d)
$$\begin{bmatrix} 1 & 0 & 0 & 1 \\ 1 & 0 & 1 & 0 \\ 1 & 1 & 0 & 1 \\ 0 & 1 & 0 & 0 \end{bmatrix} \begin{bmatrix} 1 & 0 & 0 & 1 \\ 1 & 0 & 1 & 1 \\ 1 & 1 & 0 & 1 \\ 0 & 1 & 0 & 0 \end{bmatrix} \begin{bmatrix} 1 & 0 & 0 & 1 \\ 1 & 0 & 1 & 1 \\ 1 & 1 & 1 & 1 \\ 1 & 1 & 1 & 1 \end{bmatrix} \begin{bmatrix} 1 & 0 & 0 & 1 \\ 1 & 1 & 1 & 1 \\ 1 & 1 & 1 & 1 \\ 1 & 1 & 1 & 1 \end{bmatrix} \begin{bmatrix} 1 & 1 & 1 & 1 \\ 1 & 1 & 1 & 1 \\ 1 & 1 & 1 & 1 \\ 1 & 1 & 1 & 1 \end{bmatrix}$$

**27. a)** We need to include at least the transitive closure, which we can compute by Algorithm 1 or Algorithm 2 to be (in matrix form) $\begin{bmatrix} 1 & 1 & 0 & 1 \\ 0 & 0 & 0 & 0 \\ 0 & 0 & 1 & 0 \\ 1 & 1 & 0 & 1 \end{bmatrix}$. All we need in addition is the pair $(2,2)$ in order to make the relation reflexive. Note that the result is still transitive (the addition of a pair $(a,a)$ cannot make a transitive relation no longer transitive), so our answer is $\begin{bmatrix} 1 & 1 & 0 & 1 \\ 0 & 1 & 0 & 0 \\ 0 & 0 & 1 & 0 \\ 1 & 1 & 0 & 1 \end{bmatrix}$.

**b)** The symmetric closure of the original relation is represented by $\begin{bmatrix} 0 & 1 & 0 & 1 \\ 1 & 0 & 0 & 0 \\ 0 & 0 & 1 & 0 \\ 1 & 0 & 0 & 0 \end{bmatrix}$. We need at least the transitive closure of this relation, namely $\begin{bmatrix} 1 & 1 & 0 & 1 \\ 1 & 1 & 0 & 1 \\ 0 & 0 & 1 & 0 \\ 1 & 1 & 0 & 1 \end{bmatrix}$. Since it is also symmetric, we are done.

Note that it would not have been correct to find first the transitive closure of the original matrix and then make it symmetric, since the pair $(2,2)$ would be missing. What is going on here is that the transitive closure of a symmetric relation is still symmetric, but the symmetric closure of a transitive relation may not be transitive.

**c)** Since the answer to part **(b)** was already reflexive, it must be the answer to this part as well.

**29.** Algorithm 1 has a loop executed $O(n)$ times in which the primary operation is the Boolean product computation (the join operation is fast by comparison). If we can do the product in $O(n^{2.8})$ bit operations, then the number of bit operations in the entire algorithm is $O(n \cdot n^{2.8}) = O(n^{3.8})$. Since Algorithm 2 does not use the Boolean product, a fast Boolean product algorithm is irrelevant, so Algorithm 2 still requires $O(n^3)$ bit operations.

**31.** There are two ways to go. One approach is to take the output of Algorithm 1 as it stands and then make sure that all the pairs $(a,a)$ are included by forming the join with the identity matrix (specifically set $\mathbf{B} := \mathbf{B} \vee \mathbf{I}_n$). See the discussion in Exercise 27a for the justification. The other approach is to insure the reflexivity at the beginning by initializing $\mathbf{A} := \mathbf{M}_r \vee \mathbf{I}_n$; if we do this, then only paths of length strictly less than $n$ need to be looked at, so we can change the $n$ in the loop to $n-1$.

**33. a)** No relation which contains $R$ is not reflexive, since $R$ already contains all the pairs $(0,0)$, $(1,1)$, and $(2,2)$. Therefore there is no "nonreflexive" closure of $R$.

**b)** Suppose $S$ were the closure of $R$ with respect to this property. Since $R$ does not have an odd number of elements, $S \neq R$, so $S$ must be a proper superset of $R$. Clearly $S$ cannot have more than 5 elements, for if it did, then any subset of $S$ consisting of $R$ and one element of $S - R$ would be a proper subset of $S$ with the property; this would violate the requirement that $S$ be a subset of every superset of $R$ with the property. Thus $S$ must have exactly 5 elements. Let $T$ be another superset of $R$ with 5 elements (there are $9 - 4 = 5$ such sets in all). Thus $T$ has the property, but $S$ is not a subset of $T$. This contradicts the definition. Therefore our original assumption was faulty, and the closure does not exist.

⇒ **SECTION 6.5   Equivalence Relations**

*This section is extremely important. If you do nothing else, do Exercise 5 and understand it, for it deals with the most common instances of equivalence relations. Exercise 10 is interesting—it hints at what fractions really are (if understood properly) and perhaps helps to explain why children (and adults) usually have so much trouble with fractions: they really involve equivalence relations. Spend some time thinking about fractions in this context.*

*It is usually easier to understand equivalence relations in terms of the associated partition—it's a more concrete visual image. Thus make sure you understand exactly what Theorem 2 says. Look at Exercise 35 for the relationship between equivalence relations and closures.*

1. In each case we need to check for reflexivity, symmetry, and transitivity.

   **a)** This is an equivalence relation; it is easily seen to have all three properties. The equivalence classes all have just one element.

   **b)** This relation is not reflexive since the pair $(1,1)$ is missing. It is also not transitive, since the pairs $(0,2)$ and $(2,3)$ are there, but not $(0,3)$.

   **c)** This is an equivalence relation. The elements 1 and 2 are in the same equivalence class; 0 and 3 are each in their own equivalence class.

   **d)** This relation is reflexive and symmetric, but it is not transitive. The pairs $(1,3)$ and $(3,2)$ are present, but not $(1,2)$.

   **e)** This relation would be an equivalence relation were the pair $(2,1)$ present. As it is, its absence makes the relation neither symmetric nor transitive.

3. As in Exercise 1, we need to check for reflexivity, symmetry, and transitivity.

   **a)** This is an equivalence relation, one of the general form that two things are considered equivalent if they have the same "something" (see Exercise 5 for a formalization of this idea). In this case the "something" is the value at 1.

   **b)** This is not an equivalence relation because it is not transitive. Let $f(x) = 0$, $g(x) = x$, and $h(x) = 1$. Then $f$ is related to $g$ since $f(0) = g(0)$, and $g$ is related to $h$ since $g(1) = h(1)$, but $f$ is not related to $h$ since they have no values in common. By inspection we see that this relation is reflexive and symmetric.

   **c)** This relation has none of the three properties. It is not reflexive, since $f(x) - f(x) = 0 \neq 1$. It is not symmetric, since if $f(x) - g(x) = 1$, then $g(x) - f(x) = -1 \neq 1$. It is not transitive, since if $f(x) - g(x) = 1$ and $g(x) - h(x) = 1$, then $f(x) - h(x) = 2 \neq 1$.

   **d)** This is an equivalence relation. Two functions are related here if they differ by a constant. It is clearly reflexive (the constant is 0). It is symmetric, since if $f(x) - g(x) = C$, then $g(x) - f(x) = -C$. It is symmetric, since if $f(x) - g(x) = C_1$ and $g(x) - h(x) = C_2$, then $f(x) - h(x) = C_3$, where $C_3 = C_1 + C_2$ (add the first two equations).

   **e)** This relation is not reflexive, since there are lots of functions $f$ (for instance, $f(x) = x$) which do not have the property that $f(0) = f(1)$. It is symmetric by inspection (the roles of $f$ and $g$ are the same). It is not transitive. For instance, let $f(0) = g(1) = h(0) = 7$, and let $f(1) = g(0) = h(1) = 3$; fill in the remaining values arbitrarily. Then $f$ and $g$ are related, as are $g$ and $h$, but $f$ is not related to $h$ since $7 \neq 3$.

5. This is an important exercise, since very many equivalence relations are of this form.

   **a)** This relation is reflexive, since obviously $f(x) = f(x)$ for all $x \in A$. It is symmetric, since if $f(x) = f(y)$, then $f(y) = f(x)$ (this is one of the fundamental properties of equality). It is transitive, since if $f(x) = f(y)$ and $f(y) = f(z)$, then $f(x) = f(z)$ (this is another fundamental property of equality).

b) The equivalence class of $x$ is the set of all $y \in A$ such that $f(y) = f(x)$. This is by definition just the inverse image of $f(x)$. Thus the equivalence classes are precisely the sets $f^{-1}(b)$ for every $b$ in the range of $f$.

7. This follows from Exercise 5, where $f$ is the function which takes a bit string of length 3 or more to its first 3 bits.

9. Two propositions are equivalent if their truth tables are identical. This relation is reflexive, since the truth table of a proposition is identical to itself. It is symmetric, since if $p$ and $q$ have the same truth table, then $q$ and $p$ have the same truth table. There is one technical point about transitivity that should be noted. We need to assume that the truth tables, as we consider them for three propositions $p$, $q$, and $r$, have the same atomic variables in them. If we make this assumption (and it cannot hurt to do so, since adding information about extra variables which do not appear in a pair of propositions does not change the truth value of the propositions), then we argue in the usual way: if $p$ and $q$ have identical truth tables, and if $q$ and $r$ have identical truth tables, then $p$ and $r$ have that same common truth table.

11. We need to observe whether the relations are reflexive (there is a loop at each vertex), symmetric (every edge that appears is accompanied by its antiparallel mate—an edge involving the same two vertices but pointing in the opposite direction), and transitive (paths of length 2 are accompanied by the path of length 1—i.e., edge—between the same two vertices in the same direction).

a) This relation is not transitive, since the edges $(c,d)$ and $(d,c)$ are missing.

b) This is an equivalence relation. The equivalence classes are $\{a,d\}$ and $\{b,c\}$.

c) This relation is not transitive, since several required edges are missing (such as $(a,c)$).

13. This follows from Exercise 5, with $f$ being the function from bit strings to nonnegative integers given by $f(s) =$ the number of 1's in $s$.

15. Only parts (a) and (b) are relevant here, since the others are not equivalence relations.

a) An equivalence class is the set of all people who are the same age. (To really identify the equivalence class and the equivalence relation itself, one would need to specify exactly what one meant by "the same age." For example, we could define two people to be the same age if their official dates of birth were identical. In that case, everybody born on April 25, 1948, for example, would constitute one equivalence class.)

b) For each pair $(m,f)$ of a man and a woman, the set of offspring of their union, if nonempty, is an equivalence class. In many cases, then, an equivalence class consists of all the children in a nuclear family with children. (In real life, of course, this is complicated by such things as divorce and remarriage.)

17. The equivalence class of 011 is the set of all bit strings that are related to 011, namely the set of all bit strings that have the same number of 1's as 011. In other words, it is the (infinite) set of all bit strings with exactly 2 1's.

19. Since two strings are related if they agree beyond their first 3 bits, the equivalence class of a bit string $xyzt$, where $x$, $y$, and $z$ are bits, and $t$ is a bit string, is the set of all bit strings of the form $x'y'z't$, where $x'$, $y'$, and $z'$ are any bits.

   a) the set of all bit strings of length 3 (take $t = \lambda$ in the formulation given above)

   b) the set of all bit strings of length 4 that end with a 1

   c) the set of all bit strings of length 5 that end 11

   d) the set of all bit strings of length 8 that end 10101

21. This is very similar to Example 8. There are 6 equivalence classes, namely

$$[0]_6 = \{\ldots, -12, -6, 0, 6, 12, \ldots\},$$
$$[1]_6 = \{\ldots, -11, -5, 1, 7, 13, \ldots\},$$
$$[2]_6 = \{\ldots, -10, -4, 2, 8, 14, \ldots\},$$
$$[3]_6 = \{\ldots, -9, -3, 3, 9, 15, \ldots\},$$
$$[4]_6 = \{\ldots, -8, -2, 4, 10, 16, \ldots\},$$
$$[5]_6 = \{\ldots, -7, -1, 5, 11, 17, \ldots\}.$$

Another way to describe this collection is to say that it is the collection of sets $\{6n + k \mid n \in \mathbf{Z}\}$ for $k = 0, 1, 2, 3, 4, 5$.

23. The sets in a partition must be nonempty, pairwise disjoint, and have as their union all of the underlying set.

   a) This is not a partition, since the sets are not pairwise disjoint (the elements 2 and 4 each appear in two of the sets).

   b) This is a partition.

   c) This is a partition.

   d) This is not a partition, since none of the sets includes the element 3.

25. We need to show that every equivalence class modulo 6 is contained in an equivalence class modulo 3. We claim that in fact, for each $n \in \mathbf{Z}$, $[n]_6 \subseteq [n]_3$. To see this suppose $m \in [n]_6$. This means that $m \equiv n \pmod 6$, i.e., that $m - n$ is a multiple of 6. Then perforce $m - n$ is a multiple of 3, so $m \equiv n \pmod 3$, which means that $m \in [n]_3$.

27. We need first to make the relation symmetric, so we add the pairs $(b, a)$, $(c, a)$, and $(e, d)$. Then we need to make it transitive, so we add the pairs $(b, c)$, $(c, b)$, $(a, a)$, $(b, b)$, $(c, c)$, $(d, d)$, and $(e, e)$. (In other words, we formed the transitive closure of the symmetric closure of the original relation.) It happens that we have already achieved reflexivity, so we are done; if there had been some pairs $(x, x)$ missing at this point, we would have added them as well. Thus the desired equivalence relation is the one consisting of the original 3 pairs and the 10 we have added. There are two equivalence classes, $\{a, b, c\}$, and $\{d, e\}$.

29. a) The equivalence class of 1 is the set of all real numbers that differ from 1 by an integer. Obviously this is the set of all integers.

   b) The equivalence class of 1/2 is the set of all real number that differ from 1/2 by an integer, namely 1/2, 3/2, 5/2, etc., and −1/2, −3/2, etc. These are often called **half-integers**. We could write this set as $\{(2n + 1)/2 \mid n \in \mathbf{Z}\}$, among other ways.

**31.** We do get an equivalence relation. The issue is whether the relation formed in this way is reflexive, transitive and symmetric. It is clearly reflexive, since we included all the pairs $(a, a)$ at the outset. It is clearly transitive, since the last thing we did was to form the transitive closure. It is symmetric by Exercise 21 in Section 6.4.

**33.** We end up with the relation $R$ that we started with. Two elements are related if they are in the same set of the partition, but the partition is made up of the equivalence classes of $R$, so two elements are related precisely if they are related in $R$.

**35.** We make use of Exercise 31. Given the relation $R$, we first form the reflexive closure $R'$ of $R$ by adding to $R$ each pair $(a, a)$ that is not already there. Next we form the symmetric closure $R''$ of $R'$, by adding, for each pair $(a, b) \in R'$ the pair $(b, a)$ if it is not already there. Finally we apply Warshall's algorithm (or Algorithm 1) from Section 6.4 to form the transitive closure of $R''$. This is the smallest equivalence relation containing $R$.

$\Rightarrow$ **SECTION 6.6    Partial Orderings**

*Partial orders rival equivalence relations in importance in mathematics and computer science. Again, try to concentrate on the visual image—in this case the Hasse diagram. Play around with different posets to become familiar with the different possibilities; not all posets have to look like the less than or equal relation on the integers. Exercise 16 and Exercise 17 are important, and they are not difficult if you pay careful attention to the definitions.*

**1.** The question in each case is whether the relation is reflexive, antisymmetric, and transitive.
 **a)** The equality relation on any set satisfies all three conditions and is therefore a partial order. (It is the smallest partial order; reflexivity insures that any partial order contain at least all the pairs $(a, a)$.)
 **b)** This is not a poset, since the relation is not reflexive, not antisymmetric, and not transitive (the absence of one of these would have been enough).
 **c)** This is a poset, as explained in Example 1.
 **d)** This is not a poset. The relation is not reflexive, since it is not true, for instance, that $2 \nmid 2$. (It also is not antisymmetric and not transitive.)

**3.** We need to check for reflexivity, antisymmetry, and transitivity.
 **a)** This relation is not transitive (there is no arrow from $a$ to $d$), so it is not a partial order.
 **b)** This relation is not transitive (there is no arrow from $c$ to $b$), so it is not a partial order.
 **c)** This relation is a partial order, since it has all three properties.

**5.** The dual of a poset is the poset with the same underlying set and with the relation defined by declaring $a$ related to $b$ if and only if $b \preceq a$ in the given poset.
 **a)** The dual relation to $\leq$ is $\geq$, so the dual poset is $(\{0, 1, 2\}, \geq)$. Explicitly it is the set $\{(0, 0), (1, 0), (1, 1), (2, 0), (2, 1), (2, 2)\}$.
 **b)** The dual relation to $\geq$ is $\leq$, so the dual poset is $(\mathbf{Z}, \leq)$.
 **c)** The dual relation to $\supseteq$ is $\subseteq$, so the dual poset is $(P(\mathbf{Z}), \subseteq)$.
 **d)** There is no symbol generally used for the "is a multiple of" relation, which is the dual to the "divides" relation in this part of the exercise. If we let $R$ be the relation such that $aRb$ if and only if $b \mid a$, then the answer can be written $(\mathbf{Z}^+, R)$.

7. We need to find elements such that the relation holds in neither direction between them. The answers we give are not the only ones possible.

a) One such pair is $\{1\}$ and $\{2\}$. These are both subsets of $\{0, 1, 2\}$, so they are in the poset, but neither is a subset of the other.

b) Neither 6 nor 8 divides the other, so they are incomparable.

9. We find the first coordinate (from left to right) at which the tuples differ and place first the tuple with the smaller value in that coordinate.

a) Since $1 = 1$ in the first coordinate, but $1 < 2$ in the second coordinate, $(1, 1, 2) < (1, 2, 1)$.

b) The first two coordinates agree, but $2 < 3$ in the third, so $(0, 1, 2, 3) < (0, 1, 3, 2)$.

c) Since $0 < 1$ in the first coordinate, $(0, 1, 1, 1, 0) < (1, 0, 1, 0, 1)$.

11. All the strings that begin with 0 precede all those that begin with 1. The 0 comes first. Next comes 0001, which begins with three 0's, then 001, which begins with two 0's. Among the strings that begin 01, the order is $01 < 010 < 0101 < 011$. Putting this all together, we have $0 < 0001 < 001 < 01 < 010 < 0101 < 011 < 11$.

13. We put $x$ above $y$ if $y$ divides $x$. We draw a line between $x$ and $y$, where $y$ divides $x$, if there is no number $z$ in our set such that $y \,|\, z \wedge z \,|\, x$. Note that in part (b) the numbers other than 1 are all (relatively) prime, so the Hasse diagram is very short, whereas in part (d) the numbers all divide one another, so the Hasse diagram is very narrow.

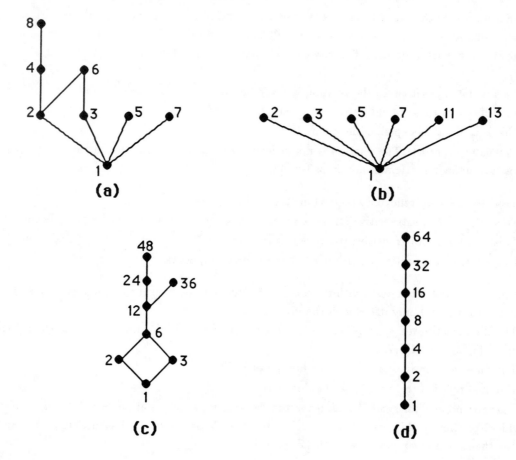

**15.** We need to include every pair $(x, y)$ for which we can find a path going upward in the diagram from $x$ to $y$. We also need to include all the reflexive pairs $(x, x)$.

    **a)** $\{(a,a),(a,b),(a,c),(a,d),(b,b),(b,c),(b,d),(c,c),(d,d)\}$

    **b)** $\{(a,a),(a,b),(a,c),(a,d),(a,e),(b,b),(b,d),(b,e),(c,c),(c,d),(d,d),(e,e)\}$

    **c)** $\{(a,a),(a,d),(a,e),(a,f),(a,g),(b,b),(b,d),(b,e),(b,f),(b,g),(c,c),(c,d),(c,e),(c,f),(c,g),(d,d),$
$(e,e),(f,f),(g,d),(g,e),(g,f),(g,g)\}$

**17.** **a)** Maximal elements are those that do not divide any other elements of the set. In this case 24 and 45 are the only numbers that meet that requirement.

    **b)** Minimal elements are those that are not divisible by any other elements of the set. In this case 3 and 5 are the only numbers that meet that requirement.

    **c)** A greatest element would be one that all the other elements divide. The only two candidates are 24 and 45, and since neither divides the other, we conclude that there is no greatest element.

    **d)** A least element would be one that divides all the other elements. The only two candidates are 3 and 5, and since neither divides the other, we conclude that there is no least element.

    **e)** We want to find all elements that both 3 and 5 divide. Clearly only 15 and 45 meet this requirement.

    **f)** The least upper bound is 15 since it divides 45 (see part (**e**)).

    **g)** We want to find all elements that divide both 15 and 45. Clearly only 3, 5, and 15 meet this requirement.

    **h)** The number 15 is the greatest lower bound, since both 3 and 5 divide it (see part (**g**)).

**19.** First we need to show that lexicographic order is reflexive, i.e., that $(a, b) \preceq (a, b)$; this is true by fiat, since we defined $\preceq$ by adding equality to $\prec$. Next we need to show antisymmetry: if $(a, b) \preceq (c, d)$ and $(a, b) \neq (c, d)$, then $(c, d) \not\preceq (a, b)$. By definition $(a, b) \prec (c, d)$ if and only if either $a \prec c$, or $a = c$ and $b \prec d$. In the first case, by the antisymmetry of the underlying relation, we know that $c \not\prec a$, and similarly in the second case we know that $d \not\prec d$. Thus there is no way that we could have $(c, d) \prec (a, b)$. Finally, for transitivity, let $(a, b) \preceq (c, d) \preceq (e, f)$. We want to show that $(a, b) \preceq (e, f)$. If one of the given inequalities is an equality, then there is nothing to prove, so we may assume that $(a, b) \prec (c, d) \prec (e, f)$. If $a \prec c$, then by the transitivity of the underlying relation, we know that $a \prec e$ and so $(a, b) \prec (e, f)$. Similarly, if $c \prec e$, then again $a \prec e$ and so $(a, b) \prec (e, f)$. The only other way for the given inequalities to hold is if $a = c = e$ and $b \prec d \prec f$. In this case the latter string of inequalities implies that $b \prec f$ and so again by definition $(a, b) \prec (e, f)$.

**21.** First we must show that $\preceq$ is reflexive. Since $s \preceq_1 s$ and $t \preceq_2 t$ by the reflexivity of these underlying partial orders, $(s, t) \preceq (s, t)$ by definition. For antisymmetry, assume that $(s, t) \preceq (u, v)$ and $(u, v) \preceq (s, t)$. Then by definition $s \preceq_1 u$ and $t \preceq_2 v$, and $u \preceq_1 s$ and $v \preceq_2 t$. By the antisymmetry of the underlying relations, we conclude that $s = u$ and $t = v$, whence $(s, t) = (u, v)$. Finally, for transitivity, suppose that $(s, t) \preceq (u, v) \preceq (w, x)$. This means that $s \preceq_1 u \preceq_1 w$ and $t \preceq_2 v \preceq_2 x$. The transitivity of the underlying partial orders tells us that $s \preceq_1 w$ and $t \preceq_2 x$, whence by definition $(s, t) \preceq (w, x)$.

**23.** **a)** We argue essentially by contradiction. Suppose $m_1$ and $m_2$ are two maximal elements in a poset which has a greatest element $g$; we will show that $m_1 = m_2$. Now since $g$ is greatest, we know that $m_1 \preceq g$, and similarly for $m_2$. But since each $m_i$ is maximal, it cannot be that $m_i \prec g$; hence $m_1 = g = m_2$.

**b)** The proof is exactly dual to the proof in part (**a**), so we just copy over that proof, making the appropriate changes in wording. To wit: we argue essentially by contradiction. Suppose $m_1$ and $m_2$ are two minimal elements in a poset which has a least element $l$; we will show that $m_1 = m_2$. Now since $l$ is least, we know that $l \preceq m_1$, and similarly for $m_2$. But since each $m_i$ is minimal, it cannot be that $l \prec m_i$; hence $m_1 = l = m_2$.

25. We need to show that every nonempty subset of $\mathbf{Z}^+ \times \mathbf{Z}^+$ has a least element under lexicographic order. Given such a subset $S$, look at the set of positive integers $S_1$ which occur as first coordinates in elements of $S$. Let $m_1$ be the least element of $S_1$, which exists since $\mathbf{Z}^+$ is well-ordered under $\leq$. Let $S'$ be the subset of $S$ consisting of those pairs which have $m_1$ as their first coordinate. Thus $S'$ is clearly nonempty, and by the definition of lexicographic order, every element of $S'$ is less than every element in $S - S'$. Now let $S_2$ be the set of positive integers which occur as second coordinates in elements of $S'$, and let $m_2$ be the least element of $S_2$. Then clearly the element $(m_1, m_2)$ is the least element of $S'$ and hence is the least element of $S$.

27. We need to peel elements off the bottom of the Hasse diagram. We can begin with $a$, $b$, or $c$. Suppose we decide to start with $a$. Next we may choose any minimal element of what remains after we have removed $a$; only $b$ and $c$ meet this requirement. Suppose we choose $b$ next. Then $c$, $d$, and $e$ are minimal elements in what remains, so any of those can come next. We continue in this manner until we have listed and removed all the elements. One possible order, then, is $a \prec b \prec d \prec e \prec c \prec f \prec g \prec h \prec i \prec j \prec k \prec m \prec l$.

29. We follow the same reasoning as in Exercise 27. We can start with $E$, for instance (and this will make our answer different from the one obtained in Example 21). One such order is $E \prec C \prec A \prec B \prec F \prec D \prec G$.

$\Rightarrow$ **SUPPLEMENTARY EXERCISES FOR CHAPTER 6**

1. **a)** This relation is not reflexive, since most strings have many letters in common with themselves. Whether it is irreflexive depends on whether we mean to include the empty string; the empty string is the only string $s$ such that $(s, s) \in R_1$ (the empty string has no letters in common with itself, since it has no letters). Thus if we mean not to include the empty string in the underlying set, then the relation is irreflexive; otherwise it is not. The relation is symmetric by inspection (the roles of $a$ and $b$ in the sentence are symmetric). It is not antisymmetric, since there are many pairs of strings such that $(a, b) \in R_1 \wedge (b, a) \in R_1$; for instance $a = bullfinch$ and $b = parrot$. The relation is not transitive, since, for example, although *bullfinch* and *parrot* are related, and *parrot* and *chicken* are related, *bullfinch* and *chicken* do have letters in common and so are not related.
**b)** This relation is very similar to the relation $R_1$. For no string is $(a, a) \in R_2$, so the relation is irreflexive and not reflexive. It is symmetric by inspection, and not antisymmetric (same example as above). It is also not transitive, since, for instance, *finch* is related to *parrot*, which is related to *chicken*, but *finch* is not related to *chicken*.
**c)** No string is longer than itself, so $R_3$ is irreflexive and not reflexive. It is not symmetric, since, for instance, *robin* is longer than *wren*, but *wren* is not longer than *robin*. It is antisymmetric: there is no way for both $a$ to be longer than $b$ and $b$ to be longer than $a$. Finally, it is clearly transitive, since if $a$ is longer than $b$ which is longer than $c$, then $a$ is longer than $c$.

3. By algebra, the given condition is the same as the condition that $f((a,b)) = f((c,d))$, where $f((x,y)) = x - y$. Therefore by Exercise 5 in Section 6.5, this is an equivalence relation.

5. Suppose $(a,b) \in R$. We must show that $(a,b) \in R^2$. By reflexivity, we know that $(b,b) \in R$. Therefore by the definition of $R^2$, we combine the facts that $(a,b) \in R$ and $(b,b) \in R$ to conclude that $(a,b) \in R^2$.

7. Both of these conclusions are valid. Since each pair $(a,a)$ is in both $R_1$ and $R_2$, we can conclude that each pair $(a,a)$ is in $R_1 \cap R_2$ and $R_1 \cup R_2$.

9. Both of these conclusions are valid. For the first, suppose $(a,b) \in R_1 \cap R_2$. This means that $(a,b) \in R_1$ and $(a,b) \in R_2$. By the symmetry of $R_1$ and $R_2$, we conclude that $(b,a) \in R_1$ and $(b,a) \in R_2$. Therefore $(b,a)$ is in their intersection, as desired. For the second part, suppose $(a,b) \in R_1 \cup R_2$. This means that $(a,b) \in R_1$ or $(a,b) \in R_2$. By the symmetry of $R_1$ and $R_2$, we conclude either that $(b,a) \in R_1$ or $(b,a) \in R_2$. Therefore $(b,a)$ is in their union, as desired.

11. A primary key is one for which there are no two different rows with the same value in this field. If there were two different rows with the same value after projection, then there certainly would have been two different rows with the same value before projection.

13. The key point is that $\Delta^{-1} = \Delta$, where $\Delta$ consists of all the pairs $(a,a)$. Thus it does not matter whether we add the pairs in $\Delta$ before or after we add the reverse of every pair in the original relation.

15. **a)** We observed in Exercise 27b in Section 6.4 that we need to take the symmetric closure first in order to insure that the result is symmetric. The relation given in that exercise provides an example. An even simpler one is the relation $\{(0,1),(2,1)\}$; the symmetric closure of the transitive closure is $\{(0,1), (1,0),(1,2),(2,1)\}$, but the transitive closure of the symmetric closure is all of $\{0,1,2\} \times \{0,1,2\}$.
    **b)** Suppose $(a,b)$ is in the symmetric closure of the transitive closure of $R$. We must show that $(a,b)$ is also in the transitive closure of the symmetric closure of $R$. Now either $(a,b)$ or $(b,a)$ is in the transitive closure of $R$. This means that either there is a path from $a$ to $b$ or a path from $b$ to $a$ in $R$. In the former case, there is perforce a path from $a$ to $b$ in the symmetric closure of $R$. In the latter case, the path from $b$ to $a$ can be followed backwards in the symmetric closure of $R$, since the symmetric closure adds the reverses of all the edges in $R$. Therefore in either case $(a,b)$ is in the transitive closure of the symmetric closure of $R$. (See also the related Exercise 21 in Section 6.4.)

17. The closure of $S$ with respect to **P** is a relation $S'$ which contains $S$ as a subset and has property **P**. Since $R \subseteq S$, we conclude that $R \subseteq S'$. By definition of closure, then, the closure of $R$ must be a subset of $S'$, as desired.

19. We use the basic idea of Warshall's algorithm, except that $w_{ij}^{[k]}$ will be a numerical variable (taking values from 0 to $\infty$, inclusive) representing the length of the longest path from $v_i$ to $v_j$ all of whose interior vertices are labeled less than or equal to $k$, rather than simply a Boolean variable indicating whether such a path exists. A value of 0 for $w_{ij}^{[k]}$ will mean that there is no path from $v_i$ to $v_j$ all of whose interior vertices are labeled less than or equal to $k$. To compute $w_{ij}^{[k]}$ from the matrix $\mathbf{W}_{k-1}$, we determine, for each pair $(i,j)$, whether there are paths from $v_i$ to $v_k$ and from $v_k$ to $v_j$ using no interior vertices labeled greater than $k-1$. If either of $w_{ik}^{[k-1]}$ or $w_{kj}^{[k-1]}$ equals 0, then such a pair

of paths does not exist, so we set $w_{ij}^{[k]}$ equal to $w_{ij}^{[k-1]}$. Otherwise (if such a pair of paths does exist), then there are two possibilities. If $w_{kk}^{[k-1]} > 0$, then we now know that there are paths of arbitrary length from $v_i$ to $v_j$, since we can loop around $v_k$ as long as we please; in this case we set $w_{ij}^{[k]}$ to $\infty$. If $w_{kk}^{[k-1]} = 0$, then we do not yet have such looping, so we set $w_{ij}^{[k]}$ to the larger of $w_{ij}^{[k-1]}$ and $w_{ik}^{[k-1]} + w_{kj}^{[k-1]}$. (Initially we set $\mathbf{W}_0$ equal to the matrix representing the relation.)

**21.** There are 52 of them, and we have to be fairly careful to count them all. Let us organize the count by the cardinalities of the sets in the partition induced by the equivalence relation (it is easier to visualize partitions, and counting them is, by Theorem 2 in Section 6.5, the same as counting equivalence relations). There is only 1 partition into one set with 5 elements. There are $C(5,4) = 5$ partitions into one set with 4 elements and a singleton set. There are $C(5,3) = 10$ partitions into one set with 3 elements and another set with 2 elements. Similarly, there are $C(5,3) = 10$ partitions into one set with 3 elements and the other two sets of 1 element each. There are $C(5,2)C(3,2)/2 = 15$ ways to partition our set into sets of size 2, 2, and 1; we need to choose the 2 elements for the first set of size 2, then we need to choose the 2 elements from the 3 remaining for the second set of size 2, except that we have overcounted by a factor of 2, since we could choose these two 2-sets in either order. There are $C(5,2) = 10$ ways to partition our set into sets of sizes 2, 1, 1, and 1. Finally, there is only 1 way to partition our set totally into singleton sets. Adding these numbers gives the total of 52. An alternative approach is to develop a recurrence relation for the number of partitions of a set with $n$ elements and use it to compute the desired value.

**23.** There is no question that the collection defined here is a refinement of each of the given partitions, since each set $A_i \cap B_j$ is a subset of $A_i$ and of $B_j$. We must show that it is actually a partition. By construction, each of the sets in this collection is nonempty. To see that their union is all of $S$, let $s \in S$. Since $P_1$ and $P_2$ are partitions of $S$, there are sets $A_i$ and $B_j$ such that $s \in A_i$ and $s \in B_j$. Therefore $s \in A_i \cap B_j$, which shows that $s$ is in one of the sets in our collection. Finally, to see that these sets are pairwise disjoint, simply note that unless $i = i'$ and $j = j'$, then $(A_i \cap B_j) \cap (A_{i'} \cap B_{j'}) = (A_i \cap A_{i'}) \cap (B_j \cap B_{j'})$ is empty, since either $(A_i \cap A_{i'})$ or $(B_j \cap B_{j'})$ is empty.

**25.** The subset relation is a partial order on any collection of sets, since it is reflexive, antisymmetric, and transitive. Here the collection of sets happens to be $\mathbf{R}(S)$.

**27.** We need to find a total order compatible with this partial order. We work from the bottom up, writing down a task (vertex in the diagram) and removing it from the diagram, so that at each stage we choose a vertex with no vertices below it. One such order is: determine user needs $\prec$ write functional requirements $\prec$ set up test sites $\prec$ develop system requirements $\prec$ develop module $A$ $\prec$ develop module $C$ $\prec$ develop module $B$ $\prec$ write documentation $\prec$ integrate modules $\prec$ $\alpha$ test $\prec$ $\beta$ test $\prec$ completion.

**29.** Since any subset of an antichain is clearly an antichain, we will list only the maximal antichains; the actual answers will be everything we list together with all the subsets of them.
**a)** Here every two elements are comparable except $c$ and $d$. Thus the maximal antichains are $\{c,d\}$, $\{a\}$, and $\{b\}$. (There are three more antichains which are subsets of these: $\{c\}$, $\{d\}$, and $\varnothing$.)
**b)** Here the maximal antichains are $\{a\}$, $\{b,c\}$, $\{c,e\}$, and $\{d,e\}$.
**c)** In this case there are only three maximal antichains: $\{a,b,c\}$, $\{d,e,f\}$, and $\{g\}$.

**31.** Let $C$ be a maximal chain. We must show that $C$ contains a minimal element of $S$. Since $C$ can itself be viewed as a finite poset (being a subset of a poset), it contains a minimal element $m$. We need to show that $m$ is also a minimal element of $S$. If it were not, then there would be another element $a \in S$ such that $a \prec m$. Now we claim that $C \cup \{a\}$ is a chain, which will contradict the maximality of $C$. We need to show that $a$ is comparable to every element of $C$. We already know that $a$ is comparable to $m$. Let $x$ be any other element of $C$. Since $m$ is minimal in $C$, it cannot be that $x \prec m$; thus since $x$ and $m$ have to be comparable (they are both in $C$), it must be that $m \prec x$. Now by transitivity we have $a \prec x$, and we are done.

**33.** Consider the relation $R$ on the set of $mn+1$ people given by $(a, b) \in R$ if and only if $a$ is a descendant of or equal to $b$. This makes the collection into a poset. In the notation of Exercise 32, if there is not a subset of $n + 1$ people none of whom is a descendant of any other, then $k \leq n$, since such a subset is certainly an antichain. Therefore the poset can be partitioned into $k \leq n$ chains. Now by the generalized pigeonhole principle, at least one of these chains must contain at least $m+1$ elements, and this is the desired list of descendants.

**35.** The least element of our set is $(0, 0)$. By definition we have $a_{0,0} = 0$, and that equals $[0 \cdot (0+1)/2] + 0$. Thus the proposition holds for the basis case. Now suppose (this is the inductive hypothesis) that $a_{i,j} = [j(j + 1)/2] + i$ for all $(i, j) \prec (m, n)$; we need to show that $a_{m,n} = [n(n + 1)/2] + m$. We look at the recursive definition. If $n = 0$, then the first line applies, so $a_{m,n} = a_{m-1,n} + 1$. Since $(m - 1, n) < (m, n)$ in lexicographic order, we know by the inductive hypothesis that $a_{m-1,n} = [n(n+1)/2] + (m-1)$; adding 1 to both sides gives the desired equality. On the other hand, if $n \neq 0$, then the second line in the recursive definition applies, so $a_{m,n} = a_{m,n-1} + n$. Since $(m, n-1) < (m, n)$ in lexicographic order, we know by the inductive hypothesis that $a_{m,n-1} = [(n - 1)n/2] + m$; adding $n$ to both sides and doing a bit of algebra on the right-hand side gives the desired equality.

# CHAPTER 7
# Graphs

⇒ **SECTION 7.1    Introduction to Graphs**

*The examples and exercises give a good picture of the ways in which graphs can model various real world applications. In constructing graph models you need to determine what the vertices will represent, what the edges will represent, whether the edges will be directed or undirected, whether loops should be allowed, and whether a simple graph or multigraph is more appropriate.*

1. In part (**a**) we have a simple graph, with undirected edges, no loops or multiple edges. In part (**b**) we have a multigraph, since there are multiple edges (making the figure somewhat less than ideal visually).

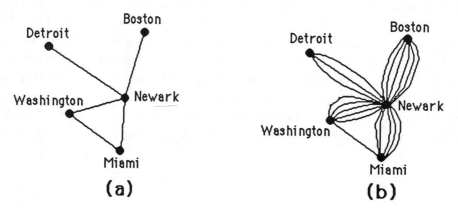

In part (**c**) we have the same picture as in part (**b**) except that there is now a loop at one vertex; thus this is a pseudograph.

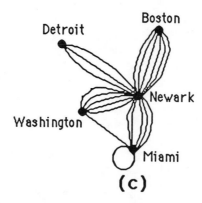

In part (**d**) we have a directed graph, the directions of the edges telling the directions of the flights; note that the **antiparallel edges** (pairs of the form $(u, v)$ and $(v, u)$) are not parallel. In part (**e**) we have a directed multigraph, since there are parallel edges.

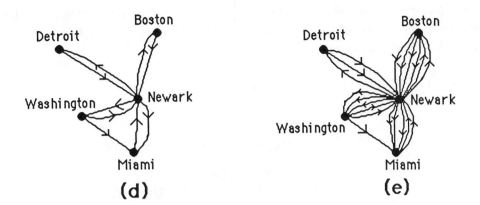

3. a) This is a simple graph; the edges are undirected, and there are no parallel edges or loops.

   b) This is a multigraph; the edges are undirected, and there are no loops, but there are parallel edges.

   c) This is a pseudograph; the edges are undirected, but there are loops and parallel edges.

   d) This is a multigraph; the edges are undirected, and there are no loops, but there are parallel edges.

   e) This is a directed graph; the edges are directed, but there are no parallel edges. (Loops and antiparallel edges are allowed in a directed graph.)

   f) This is a directed multigraph; the edges are directed, and there are parallel edges.

5. In each case we draw a picture of the graph in question. All are simple graphs. An edge is drawn between two vertices if the sets for the two vertices have at least one element in common. For example, in part (a) there is an edge between vertices $A_1$ and $A_2$ because there is at least one element common to $A_1$ and $A_2$ (in fact there are three such elements). There is no edge between $A_1$ and $A_3$ since $A_1 \cap A_3 = \emptyset$.

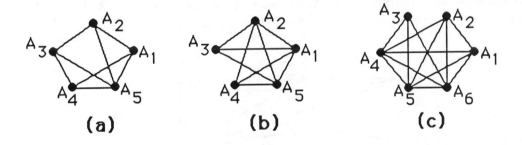

7. We draw a picture of the graph in question, which is a simple graph. Two vertices are joined by an edge if we are told that the species compete (such as robin and mockingbird) but there is no edge between pairs of species which are not given as competitors (such as robin and blue jay).

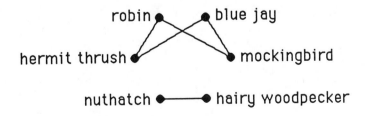

9. We draw a picture of the graph in question, which is a directed graph. We draw an edge from $u$ to $v$ if we are told that $u$ can influence $v$. For instance the Chief Financial Officer is an isolated vertex since she can influence no one and influences no one.

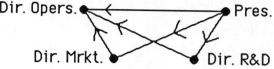

11. We draw a picture of the graph in question, which is a directed graph. We draw an edge from $u$ to $v$ if we are told that $u$ beat $v$.

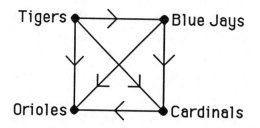

13. We draw a picture of the directed graph in question. There is an edge from $u$ to $v$ if the assignment made in $u$ can possibly influence the assignment made in $v$. For example, there is an edge from $S_3$ to $S_6$, since the assignment in $S_3$ changes the value of $y$, which then influences the value of $z$ (in $S_4$) and hence has a bearing on $S_6$. We assume that the statements are to be executed in the given order, so, for example, we do not draw an edge from $S_5$ to $S_2$.

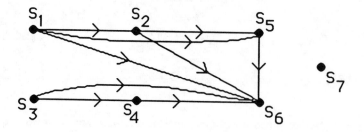

⇒ **SECTION 7.2    Graph Terminology**

*Graph theory is sometimes jokingly called the "theory of definitions," because so many terms can be—and have been—defined for graphs. A few of the most important concepts are given in this section; others appear in the rest of this chapter and the next, in the exposition and in the exercises. As usual with definitions, it is important to understand exactly what they are saying. You should construct some examples for each definition you encounter—examples both of the thing being defined and of its absence. Some students find it useful to build a dictionary as they read, including their examples along with the formal definitions.*

*The handshake theorem (that the sum of the degrees of the vertices in a graph equals twice the number of edges), although trivial to prove, is quite handy, as Exercise 19, for example, illustrates. Be sure to look at Exercise 13, which deals with the problem of when a sequence of numbers can possibly be the degrees of the vertices of a simple graph. Some interesting subtleties arise there, as you will discover when you try to draw the graphs. Many arguments in graph theory tend to be rather ad hoc, really getting down to the nitty gritty, and Exercise 13c is a good example. Exercise 15 is really a combinatorial problem; such problems abound in graph theory, and entire books have been written on counting graphs of various types. The notion of* **complementary graph***, introduced in Exercise 21, will appear again later in this chapter, so it would be wise to look at the exercises dealing with it.*

1.  **a)** There are 6 vertices here, and 6 edges. The degree of each vertex is the number of edges incident to it. Thus $\deg(a) = 2$, $\deg(b) = 4$, $\deg(c) = 1$ (and hence $c$ is pendant), $\deg(d) = 0$ (and hence $d$ is isolated), $\deg(e) = 2$, and $\deg(f) = 3$. Note that the sum of the degrees is $2+4+1+0+2+3 = 12$, which is twice the number of edges.
    **b)** In this pseudograph there are 5 vertices and 13 edges. The degree of vertex $a$ is 6, since in addition to the 4 nonloops incident to $a$, there is a loop contributing 2 to the degree. The degrees of the other vertices are $\deg(b) = 6$, $\deg(c) = 6$, $\deg(d) = 5$, and $\deg(e) = 3$. There are no pendant or isolated vertices in this pseudograph. Again the sum of the degrees equals twice the number of edges: $6+6+6+5+3 = 26 = 2 \cdot 13$.

3.  By Theorem 2, the number of vertices of odd degree must be even. Hence there cannot be a graph with 15 vertices of odd degree 5.

5.  **a)** This directed graph has 4 vertices and 7 edges. The in-degree of vertex $a$ is $\deg^-(a) = 3$ since there are 3 edges with $a$ as their terminal vertex; its out-degree is $\deg^+(a) = 1$ since only the loop has $a$ as its initial vertex. Similarly we have $\deg^-(b) = 1$, $\deg^+(b) = 2$, $\deg^-(c) = 2$, $\deg^+(c) = 1$, $\deg^-(d) = 1$, and $\deg^+(d) = 3$. As a check we see that the sum of the in-degrees and the sum of the out-degrees are equal (both are equal to 7).
    **b)** In this directed multigraph there are 4 vertices and 8 edges. The degrees are $\deg^-(a) = 2$, $\deg^+(a) = 2$, $\deg^-(b) = 3$, $\deg^+(b) = 4$, $\deg^-(c) = 2$, $\deg^+(c) = 1$, $\deg^-(d) = 1$, and $\deg^+(d) = 1$. The sum of the in-degrees and the sum of the out-degrees are both 8.

7.  To form the underlying undirected graph we simply take all the arrows off the edges. Thus, for example, the edges from $c$ to $d$ and from $d$ to $c$ become a pair of parallel edges between $c$ and $d$.

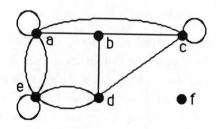

9. To show that a graph is bipartite we can exhibit the parts and note that indeed every edge joins vertices in different parts. To show that a graph is not bipartite we must give a proof that there is no possible way to specify the parts. (There is a good way to characterize nonbipartite graphs, but it takes some notions not introduced until the Section 7.4.)

**a)** This graph is bipartite: we can take $\{e\}$ to be one part and $\{a, b, c, d\}$ to be the other (in fact there is no choice in the matter). Each edge joins a vertex in one part to a vertex in the other. This graph is the complete bipartite graph $K_{1,4}$.

**b)** This graph is also bipartite, with **bipartition** (as it is called) $\{a, c\}$ and $\{b, d, e\}$. Again this is in fact a complete bipartite graph, $K_{2,3}$. If this graph were missing the edge between $a$ and $d$, then it would still be bipartite on the same sets, but not a complete bipartite graph.

**c)** We can show that this graph is not bipartite by the pigeonhole principle. Consider the vertices $b$, $c$, and $f$. They form a triangle—each is joined by an edge to the other two. By the pigeonhole principle, at least two of them must be in the same part of any proposed bipartition. Therefore there would be an edge joining two vertices in the same part, a contradiction to the definition of a bipartite graph. Thus this graph is not bipartite.

11. **a)** Obviously $K_n$ has $n$ vertices. It has $C(n, 2) = n(n-1)/2$ edges, since each unordered pair of distinct vertices is an edge.

**b)** Obviously $C_n$ has $n$ vertices. Just as obviously it has $n$ edges.

**c)** The wheel $W_n$ is the same as $C_n$ with an extra vertex and $n$ extra edges incident to that vertex added. Therefore it has $n + 1$ vertices and $n + n = 2n$ edges.

**d)** By definition $K_{m,n}$ has $m + n$ vertices. Since it has one edge for each choice of a vertex in the one part and a vertex in the other part, it has $mn$ edges.

**e)** Since the vertices of $Q_n$ are the bit strings of length $n$, there are $2^n$ vertices. Each vertex has degree $n$, since there are $n$ strings that differ from any given string in exactly one bit (any one of the $n$ different bits can be changed). Thus the sum of the degrees is $n2^n$. Since this must equal twice the number of edges (by the handshake theorem), we know that there are $n2^n/2 = n2^{n-1}$ edges.

13. There is no such graph in part (**b**), since the sum of the degrees is odd (and also because a simple graph with 5 vertices cannot have any degrees greater than 4). Similarly, the odd degree sum prohibits the existence of graphs with the degree sequences given in part (**d**) and part (**f**). There is no such graph in part (**c**), since the existence of two vertices of degree 4 implies that there are two vertices each joined by an edge to every other vertex. This means that the degree of each vertex has to be at least 2, and there can be no vertex of degree 1. The graphs for part (**a**) and part (**e**) are shown below; one can draw them after just a little trial and error.

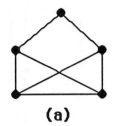  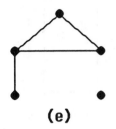

**(a)**                          **(e)**

**15.** This graph has a lot of subgraphs. First of all, any nonempty subset of the vertex set can be the vertex set for a subgraph, and there are 15 such subsets. If the set of vertices of the subgraph does not contain vertex $a$, then the subgraph can of course have no edges. If it does contain vertex $a$, then it can contain or fail to contain each edge from $a$ to whichever other vertices are included. A careful enumeration of all the possibilities gives the 34 graphs shown below.

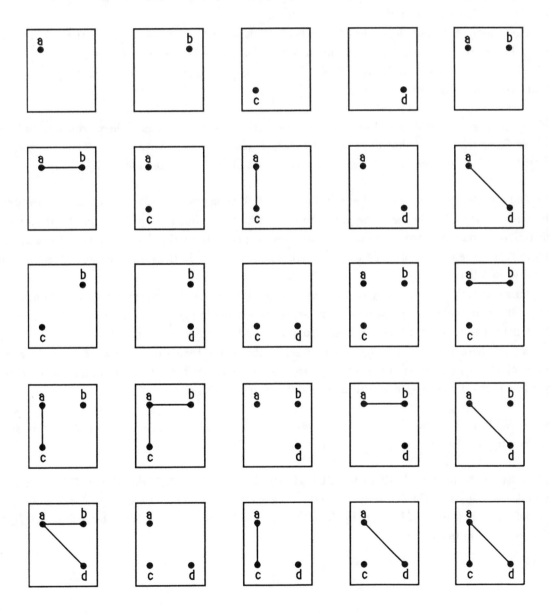

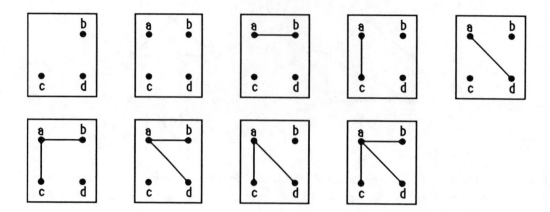

**17. a)** The complete graph $K_n$ is regular for all values of $n \geq 1$, since the degree of each vertex is $n-1$.

**b)** The degree of each vertex of $C_n$ is 2 for all $n$ for which $C_n$ is defined, namely $n \geq 3$, so $C_n$ is regular for all these values of $n$.

**c)** The degree of the middle vertex of the wheel $W_n$ is $n$, and the degree of the vertices on the "rim" is 3. Therefore $W_n$ is regular if and only if $n = 3$. Of course $W_3$ is the same as $K_4$.

**d)** The cube $Q_n$ is regular for all values of $n \geq 0$, since the degree of each vertex in $Q_n$ is $n$. (Note that $Q_0$ is the graph with 1 vertex.)

**19.** If a graph is regular of degree 4 and has $n$ vertices, then by the handshake theorem it has $4n/2 = 2n$ edges. Since we are told that there are 10 edges, we just need to solve $2n = 10$. Thus the graph has 5 vertices. The complete graph $K_5$ is one such graph (and the only simple one).

**21. a)** The complement of a complete graph is a graph with no edges. It is often called the **trivial graph**.

**b)** Since all the edges between the parts are present in $K_{m,n}$, but none of the edges between vertices in the same part are, the complement must consist precisely of the disjoint union of a $K_m$ and a $K_n$, i.e., the graph containing all the edges joining two vertices in the same part and no edges joining vertices in different parts.

**c)** There is really no better way to describe this graph than simply by saying it is the complement of $C_n$. One representation would be to take as vertex set the integers from 1 to $n$, inclusive, with an edge between distinct vertices $i$ and $j$ as long as $i$ and $j$ do not differ by $\pm 1$, modulo $n$.

**d)** Again, there is really no better way to describe this graph than simply by saying it is the complement of $Q_n$. One representation would be to take as vertex set the bit strings of length $n$, with two vertices joined by an edge if the bit strings differ in more than one bit.

**23.** Since $K_v$ has $C(v, 2) = v(v-1)/2$ edges, and since $\overline{G}$ has all the edges of $K_v$ that $G$ is missing, it is clear that $\overline{G}$ has $v(v-1)/2 - e$ edges.

**25.** Consider the graph $G \cup \overline{G}$. Its vertex set is clearly the vertex set of $G$; therefore it has $n$ vertices. If $u$ and $v$ are any two distinct vertices of $G \cup \overline{G}$, then either the edge between $u$ and $v$ is in $G$, or else by definition it is in $\overline{G}$. Therefore by definition of union, it is in $G \cup \overline{G}$. Thus by definition $G \cup \overline{G}$ is the complete graph $K_n$.

⇒ **SECTION 7.3    Representing Graphs**

*Human beings can get a good feeling for a small graph by looking at a picture of it drawn with points in the plane and lines or curves joining pairs of these points. If a graph is at all large (say with more than a dozen vertices, or so), then the picture soon becomes too crowded to be useful. A computer has little use for nice pictures, no matter how small the vertex set. Thus people and machines need more precise—more discrete—representations of graphs. In this section we learned about some useful representations. They are for the most part exactly what any intelligent person would come up with, given the assignment to do so.*

*The only tricky idea in this section is the concept of graph isomorphism. It is a special case of a larger notion of isomorphism, or sameness, of mathematical objects in various settings. Isomorphism tries to capture the idea that all that really matters in a graph is the adjacency structure. If we can find a way to superimpose the graphs so that the adjacency structures match, then the graphs are, for all purposes that matter, the same. In trying to show that two graphs are isomorphic, try moving the vertices around in your mind to see if you can make the graphs look the same. Of course there are often lots of things to help. For example, in any isomorphism, vertices which correspond must have the same degree.*

*A good general strategy for determining whether two graphs are isomorphic might go something like this. First check the degrees of the vertices to make sure there are the same number of each degree. See if vertices of corresponding degrees follow the same adjacency pattern (e.g., if there is a vertex of degree 1 adjacent to a vertex of degree 4 in one of the graphs, there must be the same pattern in the other, if the graphs are isomorphic). Then look for triangles in the graphs, and see if they correspond. Sometimes, if the graphs have lots of edges, it is easier to see if the complements are isomorphic (see Exercise 20). If you cannot find a good reason for the graphs not to be isomorphic (an invariant on which they differ), then try to write down a one-to-one and onto function which shows them to be isomorphic (there may be more than one such function); such a function has to have vertices of like degrees correspond, so often the function practically writes itself. Then check each edge of the first graph to make sure that it corresponds to an edge of the second graph under this correspondence.*

*Unfortunately, no one has yet discovered a really good algorithm for determining graph isomorphism that works on all pairs of graphs. Research in this subject has been quite active in recent years.*

1. Adjacency lists are lists of lists. The adjacency list of an undirected graph is simply a list of the vertices of the given graph, together with a list of the vertices adjacent to each. In the case of a directed graph, we list, for each vertex in the graph, the terminal vertex of each edge which has the given vertex as its initial vertex.

    **a)** The list is as follows. Since, for instance, $b$ is adjacent to $a$ and $d$, we list $a$ and $d$ in the row for $b$.

    | Vertex | Adjacent vertices |
    |--------|-------------------|
    | $a$    | $b, c, d$         |
    | $b$    | $a, d$            |
    | $c$    | $a, d$            |
    | $d$    | $a, b, c$         |

    **b)** The list is as follows.

| Vertex | Adjacent vertices |
|--------|-------------------|
| $a$ | $b, d$ |
| $b$ | $a, d, e$ |
| $c$ | $d, e$ |
| $d$ | $a, b, c$ |
| $e$ | $b, c$ |

**c)** The list is as follows. For example, since there are edges from $d$ to each of $b$, $c$, and $d$, we put those vertices in the row for $d$.

| Initial vertex | Terminal vertices |
|----------------|-------------------|
| $a$ | $a, b, c, d$ |
| $b$ | $d$ |
| $c$ | $a, b$ |
| $d$ | $b, c, d$ |

**d)** The list is as follows.

| Initial vertex | Terminal vertices |
|----------------|-------------------|
| $a$ | $b, d$ |
| $b$ | $a, c, d, e$ |
| $c$ | $b, c$ |
| $d$ | $a, e$ |
| $e$ | $c, e$ |

**3.** We can solve these problems by first drawing the graph, then labeling the vertices, and finally constructing the matrix by putting a 1 in position $(i, j)$ whenever vertices $i$ and $j$ are joined by an edge. It helps to choose a nice order, since then the matrix will have nice patterns in it.

**a)** The order of the vertices does not matter, since they all play the same role. The matrix has 0's on the diagonal, since there are no loops in the complete graph.

$$\begin{bmatrix} 0 & 1 & 1 & 1 \\ 1 & 0 & 1 & 1 \\ 1 & 1 & 0 & 1 \\ 1 & 1 & 1 & 0 \end{bmatrix}$$

**b)** We put the vertex in the part by itself first.

$$\begin{bmatrix} 0 & 1 & 1 & 1 & 1 \\ 1 & 0 & 0 & 0 & 0 \\ 1 & 0 & 0 & 0 & 0 \\ 1 & 0 & 0 & 0 & 0 \\ 1 & 0 & 0 & 0 & 0 \end{bmatrix}$$

**c)** We put the vertices in the part of size 2 first.

$$\begin{bmatrix} 0 & 0 & 1 & 1 & 1 \\ 0 & 0 & 1 & 1 & 1 \\ 1 & 1 & 0 & 0 & 0 \\ 1 & 1 & 0 & 0 & 0 \\ 1 & 1 & 0 & 0 & 0 \end{bmatrix}$$

**d)** We put the vertices in the same order in the matrix as they are around the cycle.

$$\begin{bmatrix} 0 & 1 & 0 & 1 \\ 1 & 0 & 1 & 0 \\ 0 & 1 & 0 & 1 \\ 1 & 0 & 1 & 0 \end{bmatrix}$$

**e)** We put the center vertex first. Note that the last four columns of the last four rows represent a $C_4$.

$$\begin{bmatrix} 0 & 1 & 1 & 1 & 1 \\ 1 & 0 & 1 & 0 & 1 \\ 1 & 1 & 0 & 1 & 0 \\ 1 & 0 & 1 & 0 & 1 \\ 1 & 1 & 0 & 1 & 0 \end{bmatrix}$$

**f)** We can label the vertices by the binary numbers from 0 to 7. Thus the first row (also the first column) of this matrix corresponds to the string 000, the second to the string 001, and so on. Since $Q_3$ has 8 vertices, this is an $8 \times 8$ matrix.

$$\begin{bmatrix} 0 & 1 & 1 & 0 & 1 & 0 & 0 & 0 \\ 1 & 0 & 0 & 1 & 0 & 1 & 0 & 0 \\ 1 & 0 & 0 & 1 & 0 & 0 & 1 & 0 \\ 0 & 1 & 1 & 0 & 0 & 0 & 0 & 1 \\ 1 & 0 & 0 & 0 & 0 & 1 & 1 & 0 \\ 0 & 1 & 0 & 0 & 1 & 0 & 0 & 1 \\ 0 & 0 & 1 & 0 & 1 & 0 & 0 & 1 \\ 0 & 0 & 0 & 1 & 0 & 1 & 1 & 0 \end{bmatrix}$$

**5.** We use alphabetical order of the vertices. If there are $k$ parallel edges between vertices $i$ and $j$, then we put the number $k$ into the $(i,j)^{\text{th}}$ entry of the matrix. In particular, loops are represented by entries on the diagonal. For example, since there are 2 edges between $a$ and $c$ in part **(c)**, the $(1,3)^{\text{th}}$ entry of the adjacency matrix is 2; the loop at $c$ is shown by the 1 as the $(3,3)^{\text{th}}$ entry of that matrix.

**a)** $\begin{bmatrix} 0 & 0 & 1 & 0 \\ 0 & 0 & 1 & 2 \\ 1 & 1 & 0 & 1 \\ 0 & 2 & 1 & 0 \end{bmatrix}$    **b)** $\begin{bmatrix} 0 & 3 & 0 & 1 \\ 3 & 0 & 1 & 0 \\ 0 & 1 & 0 & 3 \\ 1 & 0 & 3 & 0 \end{bmatrix}$    **c)** $\begin{bmatrix} 1 & 0 & 2 & 1 \\ 0 & 1 & 1 & 2 \\ 2 & 1 & 1 & 0 \\ 1 & 2 & 0 & 1 \end{bmatrix}$

**7.** We use alphabetical order of the vertices. If there are $k$ parallel edges from vertex $i$ to vertex $j$, then we put the number $k$ into the $(i,j)^{\text{th}}$ entry of the matrix. In particular, loops are represented by entries on the diagonal. For example, since there are 2 edges from $a$ to $c$ in part **(c)**, the $(1,3)^{\text{th}}$ entry of the adjacency matrix is 2; the loop at $c$ is shown by the 1 as the $(3,3)^{\text{th}}$ entry of that matrix.

**a)** $\begin{bmatrix} 0 & 1 & 0 & 0 \\ 0 & 1 & 1 & 0 \\ 0 & 1 & 1 & 1 \\ 1 & 0 & 0 & 0 \end{bmatrix}$    **b)** $\begin{bmatrix} 1 & 1 & 1 & 1 \\ 0 & 1 & 0 & 1 \\ 1 & 0 & 1 & 0 \\ 1 & 1 & 1 & 1 \end{bmatrix}$    **c)** $\begin{bmatrix} 1 & 1 & 2 & 1 \\ 1 & 0 & 0 & 2 \\ 1 & 0 & 1 & 1 \\ 0 & 2 & 1 & 0 \end{bmatrix}$

**9.** Since the matrix is symmetric, it has to be square, so it represents a graph of some sort. In fact, such a matrix does represent a simple graph. The fact that it is a zero-one matrix means that there are no parallel edges. The fact that there are 0's on the diagonal means that there are no loops. The fact that the matrix is symmetric means that the edges can be assumed to be undirected. Note that such a matrix also represents a directed graph in which all the edges happen to appear in antiparallel pairs, but that is irrelevant to this question; the answer to the question asked is "yes."

11. In an incidence matrix we have one column for each edge. We use alphabetical order of the vertices. Loops are represented by columns with one 1; other edges are represented by columns with two 1's. The order in which the columns are listed is immaterial.

a) $$\begin{bmatrix} 1 & 0 & 0 & 0 & 0 \\ 0 & 1 & 1 & 1 & 0 \\ 1 & 1 & 0 & 0 & 1 \\ 0 & 0 & 1 & 1 & 1 \end{bmatrix}$$
   b) $$\begin{bmatrix} 1 & 1 & 1 & 1 & 0 & 0 & 0 & 0 \\ 1 & 1 & 1 & 0 & 1 & 0 & 0 & 0 \\ 0 & 0 & 0 & 0 & 1 & 1 & 1 & 1 \\ 0 & 0 & 0 & 1 & 0 & 1 & 1 & 1 \end{bmatrix}$$

c) $$\begin{bmatrix} 1 & 1 & 1 & 1 & 0 & 0 & 0 & 0 & 0 & 0 \\ 0 & 0 & 0 & 0 & 1 & 1 & 1 & 1 & 0 & 0 \\ 0 & 1 & 1 & 0 & 0 & 1 & 0 & 0 & 1 & 0 \\ 0 & 0 & 0 & 1 & 0 & 0 & 1 & 1 & 0 & 1 \end{bmatrix}$$

13. In an undirected graph, each edge incident to a vertex $j$ contributes 1 in the $j$th column; thus the sum of the entries in that column is just the number of edges incident to $j$. Another way to state the answer is that the sum of the entries is the degree of $j$ minus the number of loops at $j$, since each loop counts 2 toward the degree.

   In a directed graph, each edge whose terminal vertex is $j$ contributes 1 in the $j$th column; thus the sum of the entries in that column is just the number of edges which have $j$ as their terminal vertex. Another way to state the answer is that the sum of the entries is the in-degree of $j$.

15. Since each column represents an edge, the sum of the entries in the column is either 2, if the edge has 2 incident vertices (i.e., is not a loop), or 1 if it has only 1 incident vertex (i.e., is a loop).

17. a) The incidence matrix for $K_n$ has $n$ rows and $C(n,2)$ columns. For each $1 \le i < j \le n$, there is a column with 1's in rows $i$ and $j$ and 0's elsewhere.

   b) The matrix looks like this, with $n$ rows and $n$ columns.

$$\begin{bmatrix} 1 & 0 & \cdots & 0 & 1 \\ 1 & 1 & \cdots & 0 & 0 \\ 0 & 1 & \cdots & 0 & 0 \\ 0 & 0 & \cdots & 0 & 0 \\ \vdots & \vdots & \ddots & \vdots & \vdots \\ 0 & 0 & \cdots & 1 & 0 \\ 0 & 0 & \cdots & 1 & 1 \end{bmatrix}$$

   c) The matrix looks like the matrix for $C_n$, except with an extra row of 0's (which we have put at the end), since the vertex "in the middle" is not involved in the edges "around the outside," and $n$ more columns for the "spokes." We show some extra space between the rim edge columns and the spoke columns; this is for human convenience only and does not have any bearing on the matrix itself.

$$\begin{bmatrix} 1 & 0 & \cdots & 0 & 1 & 1 & 0 & \cdots & 0 \\ 1 & 1 & \cdots & 0 & 0 & 0 & 1 & \cdots & 0 \\ 0 & 1 & \cdots & 0 & 0 & 0 & 0 & \cdots & 0 \\ 0 & 0 & \cdots & 0 & 0 & 0 & 0 & \cdots & 0 \\ \vdots & \vdots & \ddots & \vdots & \vdots & \vdots & \vdots & \ddots & \vdots \\ 0 & 0 & \cdots & 1 & 0 & 0 & 0 & \cdots & 0 \\ 0 & 0 & \cdots & 1 & 1 & 0 & 0 & \cdots & 1 \\ 0 & 0 & \cdots & 0 & 0 & 1 & 1 & \cdots & 1 \end{bmatrix}$$

**d)** This matrix has $m + n$ rows and $mn$ columns, one column for each pair $(i, j)$ with $1 \leq i \leq m$ and $1 \leq j \leq n$. We have put in some extra spacing for readability of the pattern.

$$
\begin{bmatrix}
1 & 1 & \cdots & 1 & 0 & 0 & \cdots & 0 & \cdots & 0 & 0 & \cdots & 0 \\
0 & 0 & \cdots & 0 & 1 & 1 & \cdots & 1 & \cdots & 0 & 0 & \cdots & 0 \\
\vdots & \vdots & \ddots & \vdots & \vdots & \vdots & \ddots & \vdots & \ddots & \vdots & \vdots & \ddots & \vdots \\
0 & 0 & \cdots & 0 & 0 & 0 & \cdots & 0 & \cdots & 1 & 1 & \cdots & 1 \\
\\
1 & 0 & \cdots & 0 & 1 & 0 & \cdots & 0 & \cdots & 1 & 0 & \cdots & 0 \\
0 & 1 & \cdots & 0 & 0 & 1 & \cdots & 0 & \cdots & 0 & 1 & \cdots & 0 \\
\vdots & \vdots & \ddots & \vdots & \vdots & \vdots & \ddots & \vdots & \ddots & \vdots & \vdots & \ddots & \vdots \\
0 & 0 & \cdots & 1 & 0 & 0 & \cdots & 1 & \cdots & 0 & 0 & \cdots & 1
\end{bmatrix}
$$

**19.** We must show that being isomorphic is reflexive, symmetric, and transitive. It is reflexive since the identity function from a graph to itself provides the isomorphism (the one-to-one correspondence)—certainly the identity function preserves adjacency and nonadjacency. It is symmetric, since if $f$ is a one-to-one correspondence that makes $G_1$ isomorphic to $G_2$, then $f^{-1}$ is a one-to-one correspondence that makes $G_2$ isomorphic to $G_1$; that is, $f^{-1}$ is a one-to-one and onto function from $V_2$ to $V_1$ such that $c$ and $d$ are adjacent in $G_2$ if and only if $f^{-1}(c)$ and $f^{-1}(d)$ are adjacent in $G_1$. It is transitive, since if $f$ is a one-to-one correspondence that makes $G_1$ isomorphic to $G_2$, and $g$ is a one-to-one correspondence that makes $G_2$ isomorphic to $G_3$, then $g \circ f$ is a one-to-one correspondence that makes $G_1$ isomorphic to $G_3$.

**21.** If a vertex is isolated, then it has no adjacent vertices. Therefore in the adjacency matrix the row and column for that vertex must contain all 0's.

**23.** Let $V_1$ and $V_2$ be the two parts, say of sizes $m$ and $n$, respectively. We can number the vertices so that all the vertices in $V_1$ come before all the vertices in $V_2$. The adjacency matrix has $m + n$ rows and $m + n$ columns. Since there are no edges between two vertices in $V_1$, the first $m$ columns of the first $m$ rows must all be 0's. Similarly, since there are no edges between two vertices in $V_2$, the last $n$ columns of the last $n$ rows must all be 0's. This is what we were asked to prove.

**25.** There are two such graphs, which can be found by trial and error. (We need only look for graphs with 5 vertices and 5 edges, since a self-complementary graph with 5 vertices must have $C(5,2)/2 = 5$ edges. If nothing else, we can draw them all and find the complement of each. See the pictures for Exercise 27d in Section 7.4.) One such graph is $C_5$. The other consists of a triangle, together with an edge from one vertex of the triangle to the fourth vertex, and an edge from another vertex of the triangle to the fifth vertex.

**27.** If $C_n$ is to be self-complementary, then $C_n$ must have the same number of edges as its complement. We know that $C_n$ has $n$ edges. Its complement has the number of edges in $K_n$ minus the number of edges in $C_n$, namely $C(n,2) - n = n(n-1)/2 - n$. If we set these two quantities equal we obtain $n(n-1)/2 - n = n$, which has $n = 5$ as its only solution. Thus $C_5$ is the only $C_n$ which *might* be self-complementary—our argument just shows that it has the same number of edges as its complement, not that it is indeed isomorphic to its complement. However, it we draw $C_5$ and then draw its complement, then we see that the complement is again a copy of $C_5$. Thus $n = 5$ is the answer to the problem.

**29.** We need to enumerate these graphs carefully to make sure of getting them all—leaving none out and not duplicating any. Let us organize our catalog by the degrees of the vertices. Since there are only 3 edges, the largest the degree could be is 3, and the only graph with 5 vertices, 3 edges, and a vertex of degree 3 is a $K_{1,3}$ together with an isolated vertex. If all the vertices that are not isolated have degree 2, then the graph must consist of a $C_3$ and 2 isolated vertices. The only way for there to be two vertices of degree 2 (and therefore also 2 of degree 1) is for the graph to be three edges strung end to end, together with an isolated vertex. The only other possibility is for 2 of the edges to be adjacent and the third to be not adjacent to either of the others. All in all, then, we have the 4 possibilities shown below.

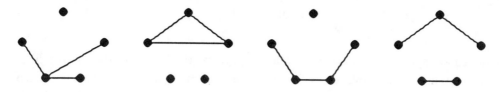

**31.** **a)** Both graphs consist of 2 sides of a triangle; they are clearly isomorphic.

**b)** The graphs are not isomorphic, since the first has 4 edges and the second has 5 edges.

**c)** The graphs are not isomorphic, since the first has 4 edges and the second has 3 edges.

**33.** There are at least two approaches we could take here. One approach is to have a correspondence not only of the vertices but also of the edges, with incidence (and nonincidence) preserved. In detail, we say that two pseudographs $G_1 = (V_1, E_1)$ and $G_2 = (V_2, E_2)$ are isomorphic if there are one-to-one and onto functions $f : V_1 \rightarrow V_2$ and $g : E_1 \rightarrow E_2$ such that for each vertex $v \in V_1$ and edge $e \in E_1$, $v$ is incident to $e$ if and only if $f(v)$ is incident to $g(e)$.

Another approach is simply to count the number of edges between pairs of vertices. Thus we can define $G_1 = (V_1, E_1)$ to be isomorphic to $G_2 = (V_2, E_2)$ if there is a one-to-one and onto function $f : V_1 \rightarrow V_2$ such that for every pair of (not necessarily distinct) vertices $u$ and $v$ in $V_1$, there are exactly the same number of edges in $E_1$ with $\{u, v\}$ as their set of endpoints as there are edges in $E_2$ with $\{f(u), f(v)\}$ as their set of endpoints.

**35.** **a)** We can tell by looking at the loop, the parallel edges, and the degrees of the vertices that if these directed graphs are to be isomorphic, then the isomorphism has to be $f(u_1) = v_3$, $f(u_2) = v_4$, $f(u_3) = v_2$, and $f(u_4) = v_1$. We then need to check that each directed edge $(u_i, u_j)$ corresponds to a directed edge $(f(u_i), f(u_j))$. We check that indeed it does for each of the 7 edges (and there are only 7 edges in the second graph). Therefore the two graphs are isomorphic.

**b)** These two graphs are not isomorphic. In the first there is no edge from the unique vertex of in-degree 0 ($u_1$) to the unique vertex of out-degree 0 ($u_2$), whereas in the second graph there is such an edge, namely $v_3v_4$.

**c)** If there is to be an isomorphism, the vertices with the same in-degree would have to correspond, and the edge between them would have to point in the same direction, so we would need $u_1$ to correspond to $v_3$, and $u_2$ to correspond to $v_1$. Similarly we would need $u_3$ to correspond to $v_4$, and $u_4$ to correspond to $v_2$. If we check all 6 edges under this correspondence, then we see that adjacencies are preserved (in the same direction), so the graphs are isomorphic.

**37.** Suppose the graph has $v$ vertices and $e$ edges. Then the incidence matrix is a $v \times e$ matrix, so its transpose is an $e \times v$ matrix. Therefore the product is a $v \times v$ matrix. Suppose we denote the typical entry of this product by $a_{ij}$. Let $t_{ik}$ be the typical entry of the incidence matrix; it is either a 0 or a 1. By definition

$$a_{ij} = \sum_{k=1}^{e} t_{ik} t_{jk} \, .$$

We can now read off the answer from this equation. If $i \neq j$, then $a_{ij}$ is just a count of the number of edges incident to both $i$ and $j$—in other words, the number of edges between $i$ and $j$. On the other hand $a_{ii}$ is equal to the number of edges incident to $i$.

⇒ **SECTION 7.4    Connectivity**

*Some of the most important uses of graphs deal with the notion of path, as the examples and exercises in this and subsequent sections show. It is important to understand the definitions, of course. Many of the exercises here are straightforward. The reader who wants to get a better feeling for what the arguments in more advanced graph theory are like should tackle exercises like Exercise 15 through Exercise 18.*

1. **a)** This is a path, but it is not simple, since edge $\{b, c\}$ is used twice. It is not a circuit, since it ends at a different vertex from the one at which it began.

   **b)** This is not a path, since there is no edge from $c$ to $a$.

   **c)** This is not a path, since there is no edge from $b$ to $a$.

   **d)** This is a path of length 5 (it has 5 edges in it). It is simple, since no edge is repeated. It is a circuit since it ends at the same vertex at which it began.

3. **a)** This graph is not connected—it has three components.

   **b)** This graph is connected—there is a path from every vertex to every other vertex.

   **c)** This graph is not connected. There is no path from the vertices in one of the triangles to the vertices in the other.

5. One approach here is simply to invoke Theorem 2 and take successive powers of the adjacency matrix

$$A = \begin{bmatrix} 0 & 1 & 1 & 1 \\ 1 & 0 & 1 & 1 \\ 1 & 1 & 0 & 1 \\ 1 & 1 & 1 & 0 \end{bmatrix} .$$

The answers are the off-diagonal elements of these powers. An alternative approach is to argue combinatorially as follows. Without loss of generality, we assume that the vertices are called $1, 2, 3, 4$, and the path is to run from 1 to 2. A path of length $n$ is determined by choosing the $n - 1$ intermediate vertices. Each vertex in the path must differ from the one immediately preceding it.

**a)** A path of length 2 requires the choice of 1 intermediate vertex, which must be different from both of the ends. Vertices 3 and 4 are the only ones available. Therefore the answer is 2.

**b)** Let the path be denoted $1, x, y, 2$. If $x = 2$, then there are 3 choices for $y$. If $x = 3$, then there are 2 choices for $y$; similarly if $x = 4$. Therefore there are $3 + 2 + 2 = 7$ possibilities in all.

**c)** Let the path be denoted $1, x, y, z, 2$. If $x = 3$, then by part (b) there are 7 choices for $y$ and $z$. Similarly if $x = 4$. If $x = 2$, then $y$ and $z$ can be any two distinct members of $\{1, 3, 4\}$, and there are $P(3, 2) = 6$ ways to choose them. Therefore there are $7 + 7 + 6 = 20$ possibilities in all.

**d)** Let the path be denoted $1, w, x, y, z, 2$. If $w = 3$, then by part (c) there are 20 choices for $x$, $y$, and $z$. Similarly if $w = 4$. If $w = 2$, then $x$ must be different from 2, and there are 3 choices for $x$.

For each of these there are by part **(b)** 7 choices for $y$ and $z$. This gives a total of 21 possibilities in this case. Therefore the answer is $20 + 20 + 21 = 61$.

7. As in Exercise 5, we could take powers of the adjacency matrix

$$A = \begin{bmatrix} 0 & 0 & 0 & 1 & 1 & 1 \\ 0 & 0 & 0 & 1 & 1 & 1 \\ 0 & 0 & 0 & 1 & 1 & 1 \\ 1 & 1 & 1 & 0 & 0 & 0 \\ 1 & 1 & 1 & 0 & 0 & 0 \\ 1 & 1 & 1 & 0 & 0 & 0 \end{bmatrix}.$$

The answers are found in location $(1, 2)$, for instance. Using the alternative approach is much easier than in Exercise 5. First of all, two nonadjacent vertices must lie in the same part, so only paths of even length can join them. Also, there are clearly 3 choices for each intermediate vertex in a path. Therefore we have the following answers.

a) $3^1 = 3$

b) $0$

c) $3^3 = 27$

d) $0$

9. There are two approaches here. We could use matrix multiplication on the adjacency matrix of this directed graph (by Theorem 2), which is

$$A = \begin{bmatrix} 0 & 1 & 0 & 1 & 0 \\ 1 & 0 & 0 & 0 & 1 \\ 0 & 1 & 0 & 0 & 0 \\ 1 & 0 & 0 & 0 & 0 \\ 0 & 0 & 1 & 1 & 0 \end{bmatrix}.$$

Thus we can compute $A^2$ for part **(a)**, $A^3$ for part **(b)**, and so on, and look at the $(1, 5)^{\text{th}}$ entry to determine the number of paths from $a$ to $e$. Alternately, we can argue in an ad hoc manner, as we do below.

a) There is just 1 path of length 2, namely $a, b, e$.

b) There are no paths of length 3, since after 3 steps, a path starting at $a$ must be at $b$, $c$, or $d$.

c) For a path of length 4 to end at $e$, it must be at $b$ after 3 steps. There are only 2 such paths, $a, b, a, b, e$ and $a, d, a, b, e$.

d) The only way for a path of length 5 to end at $e$ is for the path to go around the triangle $bec$. Therefore only the path $a, b, e, c, b, e$ is possible.

e) There are several possibilities for a path of length 6. Since the only way to get to $e$ is from $b$, we are asking for the number of paths of length 5 from $a$ to $b$. We can go around the square $(a, b, e, d, a, b)$, or else we can jog over to either $b$ or $d$ and back twice—there being 4 ways to choose where to do the jogging. Therefore there are 5 paths in all.

f) As in part **(d)**, it is clear that we have to use the triangle. We can either have $a, b, a, b, e, c, b, e$ or $a, d, a, b, e, c, b, e$ or $a, b, e, c, b, a, b, e$. Thus there are 3 paths.

11. The definition given here makes it clear that $u$ and $v$ are related if and only if they are in the same component—in other words $f(u) = f(v)$ where $f(x)$ is the component in which $x$ lies. Therefore by Exercise 5 in Section 6.5 this is an equivalence relation.

13. A cut vertex is one whose removal splits the graph into more components than it originally had (which is 1 in each case of this exercise).

    **a)** Only vertex $c$ is a cut vertex here.

    **b)** Vertices $c$ and $d$ are the cut vertices.

    **c)** There are several cut vertices here: $b$, $c$, $e$, and $i$.

15. Without loss of generality, we can restrict our attention to the component in which the cut edge lies; other components of the graph are irrelevant to this proposition. To fix notation, let the cut edge be $uv$. When the cut edge is removed, the graph has two components, one of which contains $v$ and the other of which contains $u$. If $v$ is pendant, then it is clear that the removal of $v$ results in exactly the component containing $u$—a connected graph. Therefore $v$ is not a cut vertex in this case. On the other hand, if $v$ is not pendant, then there are other vertices in the component containing $v$—at least one other vertex $w$ adjacent to $v$. (We are assuming that this proposition refers to a simple graph, so that there is no loop at $v$.) Therefore when $v$ is removed, there are at least two components, one containing $u$ and another containing $w$.

17. If every component of $G$ is a single vertex, then clearly no vertex is a cut vertex (the removal of any of them actually decreases the number of components rather than increasing it). Therefore we may as well assume that some component of $G$ has at least two vertices, and we can restrict our attention to that component; in other words, we can assume that $G$ is connected. One clever way to do this problem is as follows. Define the **distance** between two vertices $u$ and $v$, denoted $d(u,v)$, to be the length of the shortest path joining $u$ and $v$. Now choose $u$ and $v$ so that $d(u,v)$ is as large as possible. We claim that neither $u$ nor $v$ is a cut vertex. Suppose otherwise, say that $u$ is a cut vertex. Then $v$ is in one component that results after $u$ is removed, and some vertex $w$ is in another. Since there is no path from $w$ to $v$ in the graph with $u$ removed, every path from $w$ to $v$ must have passed through $u$. Therefore the distance between $w$ and $v$ must have been strictly greater than the distance between $u$ and $v$. This is a contradiction to the choice of $u$ and $v$, and our proof by contradiction is complete.

19. This problem is simply asking for the cut edges of these graphs.

    **a)** The link joining Denver and Chicago, and the link joining Boston and New York are the cut edges.

    **b)** The following links are the cut edges: Seattle–Portland, Portland–San Franciso, Salt Lake City–Denver, New York–Boston, Boston–Bangor, Boston–Burlington.

21. A vertex basis will be a set of people who collectively can influence everyone, at least indirectly. The set consisting of Deborah is a vertex basis, since she can influence everyone except Yvonne directly, and she can influence Yvonne indirectly through Brian.

23. Since there can be no edges between vertices in different components, the most edges $G$ could possibly have would occur when each of the components is a complete graph. Since $K_{n_i}$ has $C(n_i, 2)$ edges, the maximum number of edges is the sum given in the exercise.

25. Before we give a correct proof here, let us look at an incorrect proof that students often give for this exercise. It goes something like this. "Suppose the graph is not connected. Then no vertex can be adjacent to every other vertex, only to $n-2$ other vertices. One vertex joined to $n-2$ other vertices creates a component with $n-1$ vertices in it. To get the most edges possible, we must use all the edges

in this component. The number of edges in this component is thus $C(n-1,2) = (n-1)(n-2)/2$, and the other component (with only one vertex) has no edges. Thus we have shown that a disconnected graph has at most $(n-1)(n-2)/2$ edges, so any graph with more edges than that has to be connected." The fallacy here is in assuming—without justification—that the maximum number of edges is achieved when one component has $n-1$ vertices. What if, say, there were two components of roughly equal size? Might they not together contain more edges? We will see that the answer is "no," but it is important to realize that this requires proof—it is not obvious without some calculations.

Here is a correct proof, then. Suppose the graph is not connected. Then it has a component with $k$ vertices in it, for some $k$ between 1 and $n-1$, inclusive. The remaining $n-k$ vertices are in one or more other components. The maximum number of edges this graph could have is then $C(k,2)+C(n-k,2)$, which, after a bit of algebra, simplifies to $k^2-nk+(n^2-n)/2$. This is a quadratic function of $k$. It is minimized when $k=n/2$ (the $k$ coordinate of the vertex of the parabola which is the graph of this function) and maximized at the endpoints of the domain, namely $k=1$ and $k=n-1$. In the latter cases its value is $(n-1)(n-2)/2$. Therefore the largest number of edges that a disconnected graph can have is $(n-1)(n-2)/2$, so any graph with more edges than this must be connected.

27. We have to enumerate carefully all the possibilities.

**a)** There is obviously only 1, namely $K_2$, the graph consisting of two vertices and the edge between them.

**b)** There are clearly 2 connected graphs with 3 vertices, namely $K_3$ and $K_3$ with one edge deleted, as shown.

**c)** There are several connected graphs with $n=4$. If the graph has no circuits, then it must either be a path of length 3 or the "star" $K_{1,3}$. If it contains a triangle but no copy of $C_4$, then the other vertex must be pendant—only 1 possibility. If it contains a copy of $C_4$, then neither, one, or both of the other two edges may be present—3 possibilities. Therefore the answer is $2+1+3=6$. The graphs are shown below.

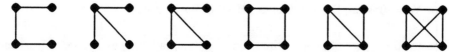

**d)** We need to enumerate the possibilities in some systematic way, such as by the largest cycle contained in the graph. There are 21 such graphs, as can be seen by such an enumeration, shown below. First we show those graphs with no circuits, then those with a triangle but no $C_4$ or $C_5$, then those with a $C_4$ but no $C_5$, and finally those with a $C_5$. In doing this problem we have to be careful not only not to leave out any graphs, but also not to list any twice.

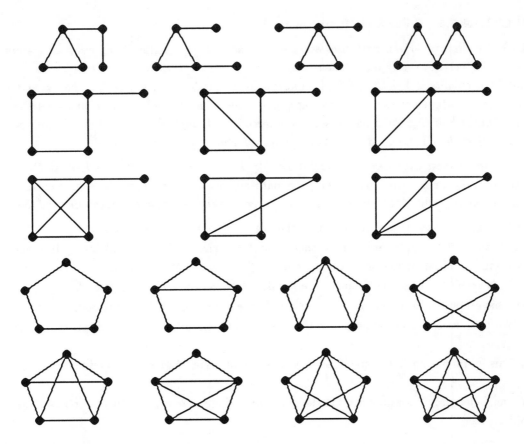

29. We need to look at successive powers of the adjacency matrix until we find one in which the $(1,6)^{\text{th}}$ entry is not $0$. Since the matrix is

$$A = \begin{bmatrix} 0 & 1 & 0 & 1 & 1 & 0 \\ 1 & 0 & 1 & 0 & 1 & 1 \\ 0 & 1 & 0 & 1 & 0 & 1 \\ 1 & 0 & 1 & 0 & 1 & 0 \\ 1 & 1 & 0 & 1 & 0 & 1 \\ 0 & 1 & 1 & 0 & 1 & 0 \end{bmatrix},$$

we see that the $(1,6)^{\text{th}}$ entry of $A^2$ is $2$. Thus there is a path of length $2$ from $a$ to $f$ (in fact $2$ of them). On the other hand there is no path of length $1$ from $a$ to $f$ (i.e., no edge), so the length of the shortest path is $2$.

31. Let the paths $P_1$ and $P_2$ be $u = x_0, x_1, \ldots, x_n = v$ and $u = y_0, y_1, \ldots, y_m = v$, respectively. The paths thus start out at the same vertex. Since the paths do not contain the same set of edges, they must diverge eventually. If they diverge only after one of them has ended, then the rest of the other path is a simple circuit from $v$ to $v$. Otherwise we can suppose that $x_0 = y_0$, $x_1 = y_1$, $\ldots$, $x_i = y_i$, but $x_{i+1} \neq y_{i+1}$. To form our simple circuit, we follow the path $y_i$, $y_{i+1}$, $y_{i+2}$, and so on, until it once again first encounters a vertex on $P_1$ (possibly as early as $y_{i+1}$, no later than $y_m$). Once we are back on $P_1$, we follow it along—forwards or backwards, as necessary—to return to $x_i$. Since $x_i = y_i$, this certainly forms a circuit. It must be a simple circuit, since no edge among the $x_k$'s or the $y_l$'s can be repeated ($P_1$ and $P_2$ are simple by hypothesis) and no edge among the $x_k$'s can equal one of the edges $y_l$ that we used, since we abandoned $P_2$ for $P_1$ as soon as we hit $P_1$.

⇒ **SECTION 7.5   Euler and Hamilton Paths**

*An Euler circuit or Euler path uses every edge exactly once. A Hamilton circuit or Hamilton path uses every vertex exactly once (not counting the circuit's return to its starting vertex). Euler and Hamilton circuits and paths have an important place in the history of graph theory, and as we see in this section they have some interesting applications. They provide a nice contrast—there are good algorithms for finding Euler paths (see also Exercise 24 through Exercise 27), but computer scientists believe that there is no good (efficient) algorithm for finding Hamilton paths.*

*Most of these exercises are straightforward. The reader should at least look at Exercise 8 and Exercise 9 to see how the concept of Euler path applies to directed graphs—these exercises are not hard if you understood the proof of Theorem 1 (given in the text before the statement of the theorem).*

1. **a)** This graph has no Euler circuit, since the degree of vertex $a$ (for one) is odd.

   **b)** All the vertex degrees are even, so there is an Euler circuit. We can find one by trial and error, or by using Algorithm 1. One such circuit is $a, b, c, f, i, h, g, d, e, h, f, e, b, d, a$.

   **c)** This graph has no Euler circuit, since the degree of vertex $a$ (for one) is odd.

   **d)** This graph has no Euler circuit, since the degree of vertex $c$ (for one) is odd.

   **e)** All the vertex degrees are even, so there is an Euler circuit. One such circuit is $a, b, c, d, c, e, d, b, e, a, e, a$.

   **f)** This graph has no Euler circuit, since the degree of vertex $b$ (for one) is odd.

3. No, an Euler circuit does not exist in the graph modeling the new city either. Vertices $A$ and $B$ have odd degree.

5. Assuming we have just one truck to do the painting, the truck must follow an Euler path through the streets in order to do the job without traveling a street twice. Therefore this can be done precisely when there is an Euler path or circuit in the graph, which means that either zero or two vertices (intersections) have odd degree (number of streets meeting there). We are assuming, of course, that the city is connected.

7. In order for the picture to be drawn under these conditions, the graph formed by the picture must have an Euler path or Euler circuit. Note that all of these graphs are connected.

   **a)** This graph has all vertices of even degree; therefore it has an Euler circuit and can be so traced.

   **b)** This graph has exactly two vertices of odd degree; therefore it has an Euler path and can be so traced.

   **c)** This graph has 4 vertices of odd degree; therefore it has no Euler path or circuit and cannot be so traced.

9. If there is an Euler path, then as we follow it through the graph, each vertex except the starting and ending vertex must have equal in-degree and out-degree, since whenever we come to the vertex along some edge, we leave it along some edge. The starting vertex must have out-degree 1 greater than its in-degree, since after we have started, using one edge leading out of this vertex, the same argument applies. Similarly, the ending vertex must have in-degree 1 greater than its out-degree, since until we end, using one edge leading into this vertex, the same argument applies. Note that the Euler path itself guarantees weak connectivity; given any two vertices, there is a path from the one that occurs first along the Euler path to the other, via the Euler path.

Conversely, suppose that the graph meets the degree conditions stated here. By Exercise 8 it cannot have an Euler circuit. If we add one more edge from the vertex of deficient out-degree to the vertex of deficient in-degree, then the graph now has every vertex with its in-degree equal to its out-degree. Certainly the graph is still weakly connected. By Exercise 8 there is an Euler circuit in this new graph. If we delete the added edge, then what is left of the circuit is an Euler path from the vertex of deficient in-degree to the vertex of deficient out-degree.

11. We use the results of Exercise 8 and Exercise 9 and check the in-degrees and out-degrees of the vertices.

   **a)** This directed graph satisfies the condition of Exercise 9. The Euler path must go from $a$ to $d$. One such path is $a, b, d, b, c, d, c, a, d$.

   **b)** The conditions are not met. Vertex $b$, for instance, has out-degree and in-degree differing by 2.

   **c)** The conditions of Exercise 8 are met, so there is an Euler circuit, which is perforce also an Euler path. One such path is $a, d, b, d, e, b, e, c, b, a$.

   **d)** This directed graph satisfies the condition of Exercise 9. The Euler path must go from $a$ to $e$. One such path is $a, d, e, d, b, a, e, c, e, b, c, b, e$.

13. The algorithm is very similar to Algorithm 1. The input is a weakly connected directed multigraph in which either each vertex has in-degree equal to its out-degree, or else all vertices except two satisfy this condition and the remaining vertices have in-degree differing from out-degree by 1 (necessarily once in each direction). We begin by forming a path starting at the vertex whose out-degree exceeds its in-degree by 1 (in the second case) or at any vertex (in the first case). We traverse the edges (never more than once each), forming a path, until we cannot go on. Necessarily we end up either at the vertex whose in-degree exceeds its out-degree (in the first case) or at the starting vertex (in the second case). From then on we do exactly as in Algorithm 1, finding a simple circuit among the edges not yet used, starting at any vertex on the path we already have; such a vertex exists by the weak connectivity assumption. We splice this circuit into the path, and repeat the process until all edges have been used.

15. **a)** Clearly $K_2$ has an Euler path but no Euler circuit. For odd $n > 2$ there is an Euler circuit (since the degrees of all the vertices are $n - 1$, which is even), whereas for even $n > 2$ there are at least 4 vertices of odd degree and hence no Euler path. Thus for no $n$ other than 2 is there an Euler path but not an Euler circuit.

   **b)** Since $C_n$ has an Euler circuit for all $n$, there are no values of $n$ meeting these conditions.

   **c)** A wheel has at least 3 vertices of degree 3 (around the rim), so there can be no Euler path.

   **d)** The same argument applies here as applied in part **(a)**. In more detail, $Q_1$ (which is the same as $K_2$) is the only cube with an Euler path but no Euler circuit, since for odd $n > 1$ there are too many vertices of odd degree, and for even $n > 1$ there is an Euler circuit.

17. Just as a graph with 2 vertices of odd degree can be drawn with one continuous motion, a graph with $2m$ vertices of odd degree can be drawn with $m$ continuous motions.

   **a)** This graph has 4 vertices of odd degree, so it takes 2 continuous motions; in other words, the pencil must be lifted once. We could do this, for example, by first tracing $a, c, d, e, a, b$ and then tracing $c, b, e$.

   **b)** This graph has an Euler circuit, so no lifting is necessary.

   **c)** This graph has an Euler path, so no lifting is necessary.

**d)** This graph has an Euler path, so no lifting is necessary.

**e)** This graph has an Euler circuit, so no lifting is necessary.

**f)** This graph has an Euler path, so no lifting is necessary.

**19. a)** This graph has the Hamilton path $a, b, c, f, d, e$.

**b)** This graph has the Hamilton path $a, b, c, d, e$.

**c)** This graph has the Hamilton path $f, e, d, a, b, c$.

**d)** This graph has no Hamilton path. There are three vertices of degree 1; each of them would have to be an end vertex of any Hamilton path. Since a path has only 2 ends, this is impossible.

**21.** A Hamilton circuit in a bipartite graph must visit the vertices in the parts alternately, returning to the part in which it began. Therefore a necessary condition is certainly $m = n$. Furthermore $K_{1,1}$ does not have a Hamilton circuit, so we need $n \geq 2$ as well. On the other hand, since the complete bipartite graph has all the edges we need, these conditions are sufficient. Explicitly, if the vertices are $a_1, a_2, \ldots, a_n$ in one part and $b_1, b_2, \ldots, b_n$ in the other, with $n \geq 2$, then one Hamilton circuit is $a_1, b_1, a_2, b_2, \ldots, a_n, b_n, a_1$.

**23.** The trick is to use a Gray code for $n$ to build one for $n + 1$. We take the Gray code for $n$ and put a 0 in front of each term to get half of the Gray code for $n + 1$; we put a 1 in front to get the second half. Then we reverse the second half so that the junction at which the two halves meet differ in only the first bit. For a formal proof we use induction on $n$. For $n = 1$ the code is $0, 1$ (which is not really a Hamilton circuit in $Q_1$). Assume the inductive hypothesis that $c_1, c_2, \ldots, c_{2^n}$ is a Gray code for $n$. Then $0c_1, 0c_2, \ldots, 0c_{2^n}, 1c_{2^n}, \ldots, 1c_2, 1c_1$ is a Gray code for $n + 1$.

**25.** Turning this verbal description into pseudocode is straightforward, especially if we allow ourselves lots of words in the pseudocode. We build our *circuit* (which we think of simply as an ordered list of edges) one edge at a time, keeping track of the vertex $v$ we are at; the subgraph containing the edges we have not yet used we will call $H$. We assume that the vertices of $G$ are listed in some order, so that when we are asked to choose an edge from $v$ meeting certain conditions, we can choose the edge to the vertex that comes first in this order among all those edges meeting the conditions. (This avoids ambiguity, which an algorithm is not supposed to have.)

```
procedure fleury(G : connected multigraph with all degrees even)
v := first vertex of G
circuit := the empty circuit
H := G
while H has edges
begin
        Let e be an edge in H with v as one of its endpoints,
                such that e is not a cut edge of H, if such an edge
                exists; otherwise let e be any edge in H with v as
                one of its endpoints.
        v := other endpoint of e
        Add e to the end of circuit
        Remove e from H
end { circuit is an Euler circuit }
```

**27.** If every vertex has even degree, then we can simply use Fleury's algorithm to find an Euler circuit, which is by definition also an Euler path. If there are 2 vertices with odd degree (and the rest with even degree), then we can add an edge between these two vertices and apply Fleury's algorithm (using this edge as the first edge to make it easier to find later), then delete the added edge.

⇒ **SECTION 7.6    Shortest Path Problems**

*In applying Dijkstra's algorithm for finding shortest paths, it is convenient to keep track, as each vertex is labeled, of where the path comes from. You can put this information on the drawing of the graph itself, by placing a little arrow at the vertex, pointing to the vertex causing the new labeling. Remember that the labels (both the values and these arrows) may change as the algorithm proceeds (and shorter paths are found), so you need an eraser to implement the algorithm in this way. The algorithm is quite simple once you see how it goes, and these exercises are not difficult.*

1.  In each case we will use a directed weighted graph, since there is no reason to suppose that travel from stop $A$ to stop $B$ should be the same (in whatever respect) as travel from stop $B$ to stop $A$.

    **a)** We will put an edge from $A$ to $B$ whenever there is a train which travels from $A$ to $B$ without intermediate stops. The weight of that edge will be the time (in seconds, say) required for the trip, including half the stopping time at each end station. This model is not perfect. For example, the time may depend on the time of day. Also, it is not clear that allocating the waiting time at each station in this way is the best way to model the system (but we should not ignore the waiting time).

    **b)** We assume that distance refers to the distance along the subway tracks. If so, this model is straightforward and similar to part **(a)**. We put an edge from $A$ to $B$ whenever there is a train which travels from $A$ to $B$ without intermediate stops. The weight of that edge will be the distance the train travels on that trip.

    **c)** Under the assumption stated, we can model this problem in a manner similar to the previous parts. We put an edge from $A$ to $B$ whenever there is a train which travels from $A$ to $B$ without intermediate stops. The weight of that edge will be the fare required for that trip. Very few subway systems (if any) actually operate under this assumption.

3.  We can answer these questions by applying Dijkstra's algorithm in each case, with the added feature of indicating, when a vertex is given a new label, where the new path to that vertex comes from. We will denote this by making the vertex a superscript to the distance. Then we can reconstruct the path that produces the minimum distance by tracing these superscripts backwards from $z$ to $a$.

    **a)** First $a$ is put into $S$, with label 0, and vertex $b$ is labeled $2^a$, and $c$ is labeled $3^a$. Since $b$ has the smaller label, $b$ is put into $S$ and $d$ is labeled $7^b$, and $e$ is labeled $4^b$. Next $c$ is put into $S$, and no labels are changed. Then $e$ is put into $S$ and the labels of $d$ and $z$ become $5^e$ and $8^e$, respectively. Next $d$ is put into $S$, and the label of $z$ is changed to $7^d$. Finally, $z$ is put into $S$. Now we know that the shortest path, in reverse, is $z, d, e, b, a$; we get this by following the superscripts, starting at $z$. Therefore the shortest path is $a, b, e, d, z$, with length 7.

    **b)** We follow the same procedure as explained in part **(a)**. The shortest path is $a, c, d, e, g, z$, with length 16.

    **c)** We follow the same procedure as in part **(a)**. The graph is bigger, and the algorithm takes longer, but the procedure is the same. We find one shortest path to be $a, b, e, h, l, m, p, s, z$, having length 16. There are some other paths of length 16 as well; which one you come up with depends on which vertex you select when there are ties.

5.  We apply the variation on Dijkstra's algorithm explained in our solution to Exercise 3a. In each case we start at the vertex listed first and can stop once the vertex listed last has been put into $S$.

    a) The shortest path is $a, c, d$, of length 6.

    b) The shortest path is $a, c, d, f$, of length 11.

    c) The shortest path is $c, d, f$, of length 8.

    d) One shortest path is $b, d, e, g, z$, of length 15. Note, though, that when we were labeling vertices adjacent to vertex $c$, we found that vertex $d$ already had the label $5^b$, and yet vertex $d$ could be reached via vertex $c$ by a path of length 5 as well. Thus we could substitute $b, c, d$ for $b, d$ in our path above, without changing the length. In other words, there are two shortest paths here.

7.  In theory we use the variation on Dijkstra's algorithm explained in our solution to Exercise 3a. In each case we start at the vertex listed first and can stop once the vertex listed last has been put into $S$. In practice for a network of this size with the distances having the geometric significance that they do, we solve the problem by inspection (there are usually at most two conceivable solutions, and we compute the smaller of the two).

    a) The shortest trip is, not surprisingly, the direct flight from New York to Los Angeles.

    b) The shortest trip is Boston to New York to San Francisco.

    c) The shortest trip is Miami to Atlanta to Chicago to Denver.

    d) The shortest trip is Miami to New York to Los Angeles.

9.  For solution technique, see the comments for Exercise 7.

    a) The shortest route is Boston to Chicago to Los Angeles.

    b) The shortest route is New York to Chicago to San Francisco.

    c) The shortest route is Dallas to Los Angeles to San Francisco.

    d) The shortest route is Denver to Chicago to New York.

11. For solution technique, see the comments for Exercise 7.

    a) The cheapest route is Boston to Chicago to Los Angeles.

    b) One of the cheapest routes is New York to Chicago to San Francisco.

    c) The cheapest route is Dallas to Los Angeles to San Francisco.

    d) The cheapest route is Denver to Chicago to New York.

13. All we have to do is not stop once $z$ is put into $S$. Thus we change the condition on the **while** statement to something like "$S \neq V$."

15. For solution technique, see the comments for Exercise 7.

    a) The shortest routes are Newark to Woodbridge to Camden, and Newark to Woodbridge to Camden to Cape May. (The map is obviously not drawn to scale.)

    b) The cheapest routes (in terms of tolls) are Newark to Woodbridge to Camden, and Newark to Woodbridge to Camden to Cape May.

17. One application, involving directed graphs, is in project scheduling. The vertices can represent parts of the project, and there is a directed edge from $A$ to $B$ if $B$ cannot be started until $A$ is finished. The weight on an edge is the time required to complete the initial vertex of the edge. A longest path from the start of the project to completion represents the total time required to complete the project. Another application would be in trying to find long routes through a city—something a sightseer, political canvasser, or street cleaner might want to do.

**19.** We can represent the distances with a $6 \times 6$ matrix, with alphabetical order. Initially it is

$$\begin{bmatrix} \infty & 4 & 2 & \infty & \infty & \infty \\ 4 & \infty & 1 & 5 & \infty & \infty \\ 2 & 1 & \infty & 8 & 10 & \infty \\ \infty & 5 & 8 & \infty & 2 & 6 \\ \infty & \infty & 10 & 2 & \infty & 3 \\ \infty & \infty & \infty & 6 & 3 & \infty \end{bmatrix}.$$

After completion of the main inner loops for $i = 1$, the matrix looks like this:

$$\begin{bmatrix} \infty & 4 & 2 & \infty & \infty & \infty \\ 4 & 8 & 1 & 5 & \infty & \infty \\ 2 & 1 & 4 & 8 & 10 & \infty \\ \infty & 5 & 8 & \infty & 2 & 6 \\ \infty & \infty & 10 & 2 & \infty & 3 \\ \infty & \infty & \infty & 6 & 3 & \infty \end{bmatrix}.$$

After completion of the main inner loops for $i = 2$, the matrix looks like this:

$$\begin{bmatrix} 8 & 4 & 2 & 9 & \infty & \infty \\ 4 & 8 & 1 & 5 & \infty & \infty \\ 2 & 1 & 2 & 6 & 10 & \infty \\ 9 & 5 & 6 & 10 & 2 & 6 \\ \infty & \infty & 10 & 2 & \infty & 3 \\ \infty & \infty & \infty & 6 & 3 & \infty \end{bmatrix}.$$

After completion of the main inner loops for $i = 3$, the matrix looks like this:

$$\begin{bmatrix} 4 & 3 & 2 & 8 & 12 & \infty \\ 3 & 2 & 1 & 5 & 11 & \infty \\ 2 & 1 & 2 & 6 & 10 & \infty \\ 8 & 5 & 6 & 10 & 2 & 6 \\ 12 & 11 & 10 & 2 & 20 & 3 \\ \infty & \infty & \infty & 6 & 3 & \infty \end{bmatrix}.$$

After completion of the main inner loops for $i = 4$, the matrix looks like this:

$$\begin{bmatrix} 4 & 3 & 2 & 8 & 10 & 14 \\ 3 & 2 & 1 & 5 & 7 & 11 \\ 2 & 1 & 2 & 6 & 8 & 12 \\ 8 & 5 & 6 & 10 & 2 & 6 \\ 10 & 7 & 8 & 2 & 4 & 3 \\ 14 & 11 & 12 & 6 & 3 & 12 \end{bmatrix}.$$

After completion of the main inner loops for $i = 5$, the matrix looks like this:

$$\begin{bmatrix} 4 & 3 & 2 & 8 & 10 & 13 \\ 3 & 2 & 1 & 5 & 7 & 10 \\ 2 & 1 & 2 & 6 & 8 & 11 \\ 8 & 5 & 6 & 4 & 2 & 5 \\ 10 & 7 & 8 & 2 & 4 & 3 \\ 13 & 10 & 11 & 5 & 3 & 6 \end{bmatrix}.$$

There is no change after the final iteration with $i = 6$. Therefore this matrix represents the distances between all pairs.

**21.** There are two parts to this algorithm. The first part obviously requires $O(n^2)$ operations for bookkeeping and nothing else. The second part obviously requires $O(n^3)$ operations for bookkeeping and the **if...then** statement. Therefore the entire procedure takes $O(n^2 + n^3) = O(n^3)$ steps.

⇒ **SECTION 7.7   Planar Graphs**

*As with Euler and Hamilton circuits and paths, the topic of planar graphs is a classical one in graph theory. The theory (Euler's formula, Kuratowski's theorem, and their corollaries) is quite beautiful. It is easy to ask extremely difficult questions in this area, however—see Exercise 17, for example. In practice, there are very efficient algorithms for determining planarity that have nothing to do with Kuratowski's theorem, but they are quite complicated and beyond the scope of this book. For the exercises here, the best way to show that a graph is planar is to draw a planar imbedding; the best way to show that a graph is nonplanar is to find a subgraph homeomorphic to $K_5$ or $K_{3,3}$.*

1. The question is whether $K_{5,2}$ is planar. It clearly is so, since we can draw it in the $xy$-plane by placing the five vertices in one part along the $x$-axis and the other two vertices on the positive and negative $y$-axis.

3. **a)** This is $K_{3,3}$, with parts $\{a, d, f\}$ and $\{b, c, e\}$. Therefore it is not planar.

   **b)** This graph is easily untangled and drawn in the following planar representation.

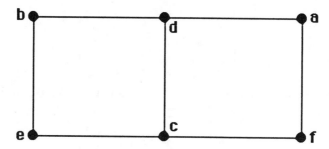

   **c)** This graph can be untangled if we play with it long enough. The following picture gives a planar representation of it.

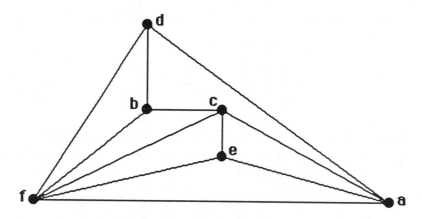

5. We give a proof by contradiction. Suppose there is a planar representation of $K_5$, and let us call the vertices $v_1, v_2, \ldots, v_5$. There must be an edge from every vertex to every other. In particular, $v_1, v_2, \ldots, v_5, v_1$ must form a pentagon. The pentagon separates the plane into two regions, an inside and an outside. The edge from $v_1$ to $v_3$ must be present, and without loss of generality let us assume it is drawn on the inside. Then there is no way for edges $\{v_2, v_4\}$ and $\{v_2, v_5\}$ to be in the inside, so they must be in the outside region. Now this prevents edges $\{v_1, v_4\}$ and $\{v_3, v_5\}$ from being on the outside. But they cannot both be on the inside without crossing. Therefore there is no planar representation of $K_5$.

7. We apply Euler's formula $r = e - v + 2$. Here we are told that $v = 6$. We are also told that each vertex has degree $4$, so that the sum of the degrees is $24$. Therefore by the handshake theorem there are 12 edges, so $e = 12$. Solving, we find $r = 8$.

9. The proof is very similar to the proof of Corollary 1. First note that the degree of each region is at least 4. The reason for this is that there are no loops or multiple edges (which would give regions of degree 1 or 2) and no simple circuits of length 3 (which would give regions of degree 3); and the degree of the unbounded region is at least 4 since we are assuming that $v \geq 3$. Therefore we have, arguing as in the proof of Corollary 1, that $2e \geq 4r$, or simply $r \leq e/2$. Plugging this into Euler's formula, we obtain $e - v + 2 \leq e/2$, which gives $e \leq 2v - 4$ after some trivial algebra.

11. The proof is exactly the same as in Exercise 9, except that this time the degree of each region must be at least 5. Thus we get $2e \geq 5r$, which after the same algebra as before, gives the desired inequality.

13. a) If we remove a vertex from $K_5$, then we get $K_4$, which is clearly planar.

    b) If we remove a vertex from $K_6$, then we get $K_5$, which is not planar.

    c) If we remove a vertex from $K_{3,3}$, then we get $K_{3,2}$, which is clearly planar.

    d) We assume the question means "Is it the case that for every $v$, the removal of $v$ makes the graph planar?" The the answer is no, since we can remove a vertex in the part of size 4 to leave $K_{3,3}$, which is not planar.

15. The instructions are really not fair. It is hopeless to try to use Kuratowski's theorem to prove that a graph *is* planar, since we would have to check hundred of cases to argue that there is no subgraph homeomorphic to $K_5$ or $K_{3,3}$. Thus we will use the theorem to show that the nonplanar graphs shown here are nonplanar, but we will show that the planar ones are planar by giving a planar representation.

    a) This graph is planar; see the picture.

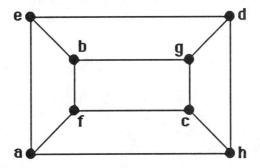

    b) This graph is nonplanar. If we delete the five curved edges outside the big pentagon, then the graph is homeomorphic to $K_5$. We can see this by replacing each vertex of degree 2 and its two edges by one edge.

    c) This graph is nonplanar, since it contains $K_{3,3}$ as a subgraph: the parts are $\{a, g, d\}$ and $\{b, c, e\}$. (Actually it contains $K_{3,4}$, and it even contains a subgraph homeomorphic to $K_5$.)

17. This is an extremely hard problem. We will present parts of the solution; the reader should consult a good graph theory book (such as *Graphs and Digraphs* by Behzad, Chartrand, and Lesniak-Foster, Prindle, Weber & Schmidt, 1979) for references and further details.

First we will state, without proof, what is known about crossing numbers for complete graphs (much is still not known about crossing numbers). If $n \leq 10$, then the crossing number of $K_n$ is given by the following product

$$\frac{1}{4}\left\lfloor\frac{n}{2}\right\rfloor\left\lfloor\frac{n-1}{2}\right\rfloor\left\lfloor\frac{n-2}{2}\right\rfloor\left\lfloor\frac{n-3}{2}\right\rfloor.$$

Thus the answers for parts (a), (b), and (c) are 1, 3, and 9, respectively. The figure below shows $K_6$ drawn in the plane with three crossings, which at least proves that the crossing number of $K_6$ is at most 3. The proof that it is no less than 3 is not easy. The imbedding of $K_5$ with one crossing can be seen in this same picture, by ignoring the vertex at the top.

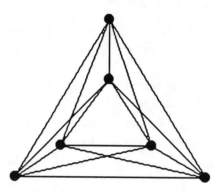

Second, for the complete bipartite graphs, what is known is that if the smaller of $m$ and $n$ is at most 6, then the crossing number of $K_{m,n}$ is given by the following product

$$\left\lfloor\frac{m}{2}\right\rfloor\left\lfloor\frac{m-1}{2}\right\rfloor\left\lfloor\frac{n}{2}\right\rfloor\left\lfloor\frac{n-1}{2}\right\rfloor.$$

Thus the answers for parts (d), (e), and (f) are 2, 4, and 16, respectively. The figure below shows $K_{4,4}$ drawn in the plane with four crossings, which at least proves that the crossing number of $K_{4,4}$ is at most 4. The proof that it is no less than 4 is, again, difficult. It is also easy to see from this picture that the crossing number of $K_{3,4}$ is at most 2 (by ignoring the top vertex).

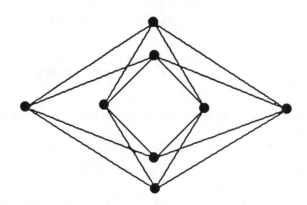

**19.** Each of these graphs is nonplanar; the first three contain $K_5$, and the last three contain $K_{3,3}$. Thus if we can show how to draw each of the graphs in two planes, then we will have shown that the thickness is 2 in each case. The following picture shows that $K_7$ can be drawn in 2 planes, so this takes care of part (a), part (b), and part (c).

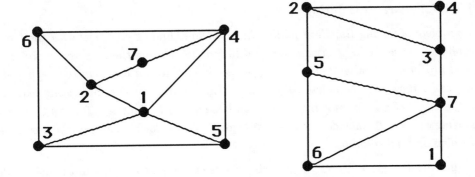

The following picture shows that $K_{5,5}$ can be drawn in 2 planes, so this takes care of part (d), part (e), and part (f).

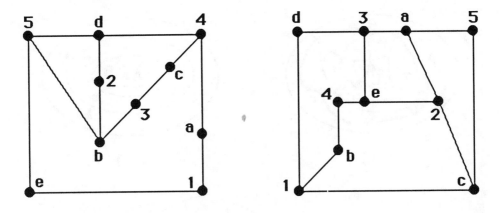

21. We can represent the surface of a torus with a rectangle, thinking of the right-hand edge as being equal to the left-hand edge, and the top edge as being equal to the bottom edge. For example, if we travel out of the rectangle across the right-hand edge about a third of the way from the top, then we immediately reenter the rectangle across the left-hand edge about a third of the way from the top. The picture below shows $K_{3,3}$ drawn on this surface. Note that the edges that seem to leave the rectangle really reenter it from the opposite side.

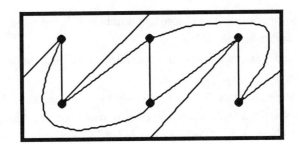

⇒ **SECTION 7.8    Graph Coloring**

*Like the problem of finding Hamilton paths, the problem of finding colorings with the fewest possible colors probably has no good algorithm for its solution. In working these exercises, for the most part you should proceed by trial and error, using whatever insight you can gain by staring at the graph (for instance, finding large complete subgraphs). There are also some interesting exercises here on coloring the edges of graphs—see Exercise 13 and Exercise 14. Exercise 19 through Exercise 21 are worth looking at, as well: they deal with a fast algorithm for coloring a graph which is not guaranteed to produce an optimal coloring.*

1.  We construct the dual graph by putting a vertex inside each region (but not in the unbounded region), and drawing an edge between two vertices if the regions share a common border. The easiest way to do this is illustrated in our answers. First we draw the map, then we put a vertex inside each region and make the connections. The dual graph, then, is the graph with heavy lines in each case.

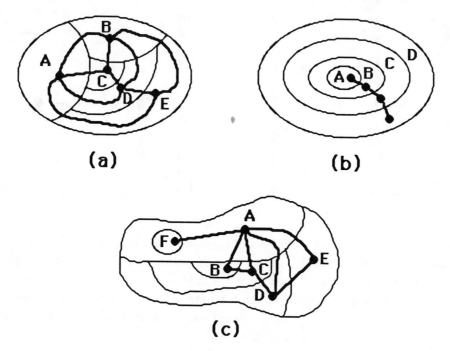

3.  In each case in order to prove that the chromatic number is $k$, we need to find a $k$-coloring and to show that (at least) $k$ colors are needed.

    **a)** Since there is a triangle, at least 3 colors are needed. Clearly 3 colors suffice, since we can color $a$ and $d$ the same color.

    **b)** Since there is a triangle, at least 3 colors are needed. To show that 3 colors suffice, notice that we can color the vertices around the outside alternately using red and blue, and color vertex $g$ green.

    **c)** Since there is a triangle, at least 3 colors are needed. Clearly 3 colors suffice, since we can color $a$ and $c$ the same color.

    **d)** Since there is a triangle, at least 3 colors are needed. The coloring in which $b$ and $c$ are blue, $a$ and $f$ are red, and $d$ and $e$ are green shows that 3 colors suffice.

    **e)** Since there is an edge, at least 2 colors are needed. The coloring in which $b$, $d$, and $e$ are red and $a$ and $c$ blue shows that 2 colors suffice.

    **f)** Since vertices $b$, $c$, $h$, and $i$ form a $K_4$, at least 4 colors are required. A coloring using only 4 colors is (and we can get this by trial and error, without much difficulty) to let $a$ and $c$ be red; $b$, $d$, and $f$, blue; $g$ and $i$, green; and $e$ and $h$, yellow.

5. If a graph has an edge (not a loop, since we are assuming the graphs in this section are simple), then its chromatic number is at least 2. Conversely, if there are no edges, then the coloring in which every vertex receives the same color is proper. Therefore a graph has chromatic number 1 if and only if it has no edges.

7. In Example 3 we saw that the chromatic number of $C_n$ is 2 if $n$ is even and 3 if $n$ is odd. Since the wheel $W_n$ is just $C_n$ with one more vertex, adjacent to all the vertices of the $C_n$ along the rim of the wheel, $W_n$ clearly needs exactly one more color than $C_n$ (for that middle vertex). Therefore the chromatic number of $W_n$ is 3 if $n$ is even and 4 if $n$ is odd.

9. Consider the graph representing this problem. The vertices are the 8 courses, and two courses are joined by an edge if there are students taking both of them. Thus there are edges between every pair of vertices except the 7 pairs listed. It is much easier to draw the complement than to draw this graph itself; it is shown below.

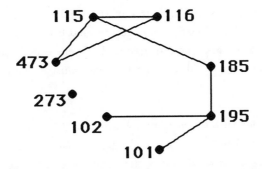

We want to find the chromatic number of the graph whose complement we have drawn; the colors will be the time periods for the exams. First note that since Math 185 and the four CS courses form a $K_5$ (in other words, there are no edges between any two of these in our picture), the chromatic number is at least 5. To show that it equals 5, we just need to color the other three vertices. A little trial and error shows that we can make Math 195 the same color as (i.e., have its final exam at the same time as) CS 101; and we can make Math 115 and 116 the same color as CS 473. Therefore five time slots (colors) are sufficient.

11. We model the problem with the intersection graph of these sets. Note that every pair of these intersect except for $C_4$ and $C_5$. Thus the graph is $K_6$ with that one edge deleted. Clearly its chromatic number is 5, since we need to color all the vertices different colors, except that $C_4$ and $C_5$ may have the same color. In other words, 5 meeting times are needed, since only committees $C_4$ and $C_5$ can meet simultaneously.,

13. Note that the number of colors needed to color the edges is at least as large as the largest degree of a vertex, since the edges at each vertex must all be colored differently. Hence if we can find an edge coloring with that many colors, then we know we have found the answer.
   **a)** There is a vertex of degree 3, so the edge chromatic number is at least 3. On the other hand, we can color $\{a, c\}$ and $\{b, d\}$ the same color, so 3 colors suffice.

**b)** The 6 edges incident to $g$ must all get different colors. On the other hand, it is not hard to complete a proper edge coloring with only these colors (for example, color edge $\{a, f\}$ with the same color as used on $\{d, g\}$), so the answer is 6.

**c)** The answer must be at least 3; it is 3 since edges which appear as parallel line segments in the picture can have the same color.

**d)** Clearly 4 colors are required, since the vertices have degree 4. In fact 4 colors are sufficient. Here is one proper 4-coloring (we denote edges in the obvious shorthand notation): color 1 for $ac$, $be$, and $df$; color 2 for $ae$, $bd$, and $cf$; color 3 for $ab$, $cd$, and $ef$; and color 4 for $ad$, $bf$, and $ce$.

**e)** The answer must be at least 3; it is easy to construct a 3-coloring of the edges by inspection: $\{a, b\}$ and $\{c, e\}$ have the same color, $\{a, d\}$ and $\{b, c\}$ have the same color, and $\{a, e\}$ and $\{c, d\}$ have the same color.

**f)** The largest degree is 6 (vertex $i$ has degree 6); therefore at least 6 colors are required. By trial and error we come up with this coloring using 6 colors (we use the obvious shorthand notation for edges); there are many others, of course. Assign color 1 to $ag$, $cd$, and $hi$; color 2 to $ab$, $cf$, $dg$, and $ei$; color 3 to $bh$, $cg$, $di$, and $ef$; color 4 to $ah$, $ci$, and $de$; color 5 to $bi$, $ch$, and $fg$; and color 6 to $ai$, $bc$, and $gh$.

Despite the appearances of these examples, it is not the case that the edge chromatic number of a graph is always equal to the maximum degree of the vertices in the graph. The simplest example in which this is not true is $K_3$. Clearly its edge chromatic number is 3 (since all three edges are adjacent to each other), but its maximum degree is 2. There is a theorem, however, stating that the edge chromatic number is always equal to either the maximum degree or one more than the maximum degree.

**15.** This problem can be modeled with the intersection graph of the sets of steps during which the variables must be stored. This graph has 7 vertices, $t$ through $z$; there is an edge between the two vertices if the two variables must be stored during some common step. The answer to the problem is the chromatic number of this graph. Rather than considering this graph, we look at its complement (it has a lot fewer edges). Here two vertices are adjacent if the sets (of steps) do not intersect. The only edges are $\{u, w\}$, $\{u, x\}$, $\{u, y\}$, $\{u, z\}$, $\{v, x\}$, $\{x, z\}$. Note that there are no edges in the complement among $\{t, v, w, y, z\}$, so that these vertices form a $K_5$ in the original graph. Thus the chromatic number of the original graph is at least 5. To see that it is 5, note that vertex $u$ can have the same color as $w$, and $x$ can have the same color as $z$ (these pairs appear as edges in the complement). Since the chromatic number is 5, we need 5 registers, with variables $u$ and $w$ sharing a register, and vertices $x$ and $z$ sharing one.

**17.** The set of vertices with one of the colors is one of the parts, and the set of vertices with the other color is the other part. Since no edge can join vertices of the same color, there are no edges between vertices in the same part.

**19.** First we need to list the vertices in decreasing order of degree. This ordering is not unique, of course; we will pick $e, a, b, c, f, h, i, d, g, j$. Next we assign color 1 to $e$, and then to $f$ and $d$, in that order. Now we assign color 2 to $a$, $c$, $i$, and $g$, in that order. Finally, we assign color 3 to $b$, $h$ and $j$, in that order. Thus the algorithm gives a 3-coloring. Since the graph contains triangles, we know that this is the best possible, so the algorithm "worked" here (but it need not always work—see Exercise 21).

**21.** A simple example in which the algorithm may fail to provide a coloring with the minimum number of colors is $C_6$, which of course has chromatic number 2. Since all the vertices are of degree 2, we may order them $v_1$, $v_4$, $v_2$, $v_3$, $v_5$, $v_6$, where the edges are $\{v_1, v_2\}$, $\{v_2, v_3\}$, $\{v_3, v_4\}$, $\{v_4, v_5\}$, $\{v_5, v_6\}$, and $\{v_1, v_6\}$. Then $v_1$ gets color 1, as does $v_4$. Next $v_2$ and $v_5$ get color 2; and then $v_3$ and $v_6$ must get color 3.

⇒ **SUPPLEMENTARY EXERCISES FOR CHAPTER 7**

**1.** The sum of the degrees must be $50 \cdot 100 = 5000$. By the handshake theorem, the graph therefore has $5000/2 = 2500$ edges.

**3. a)** Both graphs have a lot of symmetry to them, and the degrees of the vertices are the same, so we might hope that they are isomorphic. Let us try to form the correspondence $f$. First note that there is a 4-cycle $u_1, u_5, u_2, u_6, u_1$ in the graph on the left. Suppose we try letting it correspond to the 4-cycle $v_1, v_2, v_3, v_4, v_1$ in the graph on the right. Thus we let $f(u_1) = v_1$, $f(u_5) = v_2$, $f(u_2) = v_3$, and $f(u_6) = v_4$. The rest of the assignments are forced: since $u_7$ is the other vertex adjacent to $u_1$, we must let $f(u_7) = v_6$, since $v_6$ is the other vertex adjacent to $v_1$ (which is $f(u_1)$). Similarly, $f(u_3) = v_7$, $f(u_8) = v_8$, and $f(u_4) = v_5$. Now we just have to check that the vertices corresponding to the vertices in the 4-cycle $v_5, v_6, v_7, v_8, v_5$ in the graph on the right form a 4-cycle in that order. Since these vertices form the 4-cycle $u_4, u_7, u_3, u_8, u_4$, our correspondence works.

**b)** Each vertex in the first graph has degree 4. This statement is not true for the second graph. Therefore the graphs cannot be isomorphic.

**5.** It follows immediately from the definition that the complete $m$-partite graph with parts $n_1$, $n_2$, ..., $n_m$ has $n_1 + n_2 + \cdots + n_m = \sum_{i=1}^{m} n_i$ vertices. We will organize the count of the edges by looking at which parts the edges join. Fix $1 \le i < j \le m$, and consider the edges between the $i^{\text{th}}$ part and the $j^{\text{th}}$ part. It is easy to see from the product rule that there are $n_i n_j$ edges. Therefore to get all the edges, we have to add all these products, for all possible pairs $(i, j)$. Thus the number of edges is
$$\sum_{1 \le i < j \le m} n_i n_j .$$

**7. a)** The subgraph induced by $\{a, b, c\}$ consists of those vertices and all the edges that are in the graph and join pairs of them. Thus the induced subgraph is the entire component $G_1$.

**b)** The subgraph induced by $\{a, e, g\}$ consists of those vertices and all the edges joining pairs of them in this graph. Since there are no such edges, the induced subgraph is just the graph with these three vertices and no edges.

**c)** The induced subgraph consists of these five vertices and the edges $\{b, c\}$, $\{f, g\}$, and $\{g, h\}$ (all the edges joining pairs of these five vertices that were in the original graph).

9. In general it is no easy task to find cliques. We need to be careful not to overlook things. We will denote a clique simply by listing the vertices in it, without punctuation.

   **a)** There is one $K_4$, namely $bcef$, and it is the largest clique. There are several $K_3$'s not contained in this $K_4$, and they are all cliques: $abg$, $adg$, $beg$, and $deg$. Since every edge is contained in one of these five cliques (and there are no isolated vertices), there are no smaller cliques, so this list is complete.

   **b)** Some staring at the graph convinces us that there are no $K_6$'s. There is one $K_5$, namely the clique $ceghi$. There are two $K_4$'s not contained in this $K_5$, which therefore are cliques: $abce$, and $cdeg$. All the $K_3$'s not contained in any of the cliques listed so far are also cliques. We find only $aef$ and $efg$. All the edges are in at least one of the cliques listed so far (and there are no isolated vertices), so we are done.

11. These graphs are quite a mess to draw, since they contain so many edges. Instead of drawing them, we describe them in set-theoretic terms. Note that we do not consider a queen on a square to control that square itself, since to do so would give us loops in the graph.

    **a)** The vertex set consists of all pairs $(i, j)$ with $1 \le i \le 3$ and $1 \le j \le 3$. Since a queen in any square controls all the squares in the same row and column, there are edges $\{(i,j),(i,j')\}$ and $\{(i,j),(i',j)\}$ for all $i$, $j$, $i'$ and $j'$ between 1 and 3 inclusive, with $i \ne i'$ and $j \ne j'$. These are not all, though, since we have to put in the diagonal controls. There are 10 such edges: $(1,1)$, $(2,2)$, and $(3,3)$ are all joined to each other; there is an edge between $(1,2)$ and $(2,1)$, and an edge between $(2,3)$ and $(3,2)$; $(1,3)$, $(2,2)$, and $(3,1)$ are all joined to each other; and there is an edge between $(1,2)$ and $(2,3)$, and an edge between $(2,1)$ and $(3,2)$.

    **b)** We do the same sort of thing as in part **(a)**. The vertex set consists of all pairs $(i, j)$ with $1 \le i \le 4$ and $1 \le j \le 4$. Since a queen in any square controls all the squares in the same row and column, there are edges $\{(i,j),(i,j')\}$ and $\{(i,j),(i',j)\}$ for all $i$, $j$, $i'$ and $j'$ between 1 and 4 inclusive, with $i \ne i'$ and $j \ne j'$. Rather than listing the 28 diagonal control edges explicitly, let us use some analytic geometry. The diagonals over which the queen has control all have slope 1 or $-1$. Therefore there are edges between $(i,j)$ and $(i',j')$ if these two vertices are distinct and $i - i' = \pm(j - j')$.

13. **a)** A queen in the center controls the entire board, so the answer is 1.

    **b)** One queen cannot control the entire board, as one can verify by considering the possible cases (there are really only three—corner, noncorner edge, or nonedge). On the other hand 2 queens will do: place one in position $(2,2)$ and the other in position $(4,4)$.

    **c)** Three queens can control the entire board. We can place them at positions $(2,2)$, $(3,4)$, and $(5,1)$, for example. To show that two queens are not enough is tedious. One way to do this is with the help of a computer. For each pair of squares (and there are $C(25,2) = 300$ such pairs), check to see that not all the squares are under control. Such a program will show that two queens can control at most 23 of the 25 squares.

15. Suppose $G$ and $H$ are isomorphic simple graphs, with $f$ the one-to-one and onto function from the vertex set of $G$ to the vertex set of $H$ that gives the isomorphism. By symmetry, it is enough to show in each case that if $G$ has the property, then so does $H$.

    **a)** Assume that $G$ is connected; then for every pair of distinct vertices in $G$ there is a path from one to the other. We want to show that $H$ is connected. Let $u$ and $v$ be two distinct vertices of $H$. Then there is a path in $G$ from $f^{-1}(u)$ to $f^{-1}(v)$, which we can think of as a sequence of vertices. Applying $f$ to each vertex in this path gives us a path from $u$ to $v$ in $H$.

**b)** Suppose $G$ has a Hamilton circuit, which we can think of as a sequence of vertices. Applying $f$ to each vertex in this circuit gives us a Hamilton circuit in $H$.

**c)** This is the same as part **(b)**, replacing "Hamilton" by "Euler."

**d)** The logic of this one is slightly different from the general pattern. Suppose we can imbed $G$ in the plane with $C$ crossings. Then this imbedding clearly gives an imbedding of $H$ in the plane with $C$ crossings as well: we use the same picture, relabeling $u$ by $f(u)$. Therefore the crossing number of $H$ is no bigger than the crossing number of $G$. By symmetry, the crossing number of $G$ can be no bigger than the crossing number of $H$, either. Therefore the crossing numbers are equal.

**e)** If $i_1$, $i_2$, ..., $i_n$ are $n$ isolated vertices in $G$, then $f(i_1)$, $f(i_2)$, ..., $f(i_n)$ are $n$ isolated vertices in $H$.

**f)** If $A$ and $B$ are the parts for $G$, then $f(A)$ and $f(B)$ are the parts for $H$.

17. We need to consider all the possibilities carefully. First suppose that the parts are of size 1 and 3. The only connected bipartite simple graph with parts of these sizes is $K_{1,3}$. The only other possibility is that the parts are each of size 2. Then the graph could be $K_{2,2}$ or $K_{2,2}$ with one edge missing; if more than one edge is deleted, then the result will not be connected. Therefore the answer is 3.

19. **a)** This graph is not orientable because of the cut edge $\{b,c\}$. If we orient it from $b$ to $c$, then there can be no path in the resulting directed graph from $c$ to $b$; if we orient it from $c$ to $b$, then there can be no path in the resulting directed graph from $b$ to $c$.

**b)** This graph is not orientable because of the cut edge $\{c,d\}$, exactly as in part **(a)**.

**c)** This graph is orientable. We can orient the square and each of the triangles in the clockwise direction, for instance. In other words, the edges are $(a,b)$, $(b,c)$, $(c,d)$, $(d,a)$, $(c,e)$, $(e,f)$, $(f,c)$, $(c,g)$, $(g,h)$, and $(h,c)$. There is now a path from any vertex to any other, by traveling clockwise around the appropriate figure to vertex $c$, and then traveling clockwise around the other appropriate figure.

21. Suppose $\{a,b\}$ is a cut edge of the undirected graph $G$. Then $a$ and $b$ are in separate components of $G$ when that edge is removed; in other words, every path from $a$ to $b$ must go through the edge in the $a$ to $b$ direction, and every path from $b$ to $a$ must go through the path in the $b$ to $a$ direction. Suppose we have an orientation of this graph. If $\{a,b\}$ is oriented as $(a,b)$, then by what we have said, there can be no path in the resulting directed graph from $b$ to $a$, so the resulting directed graph is not strongly connected. On the other hand, if $\{a,b\}$ is oriented as $(b,a)$, then there can be no path in the resulting directed graph from $a$ to $b$. Thus by definition $G$ is not orientable. Incidentally, a kind of converse to this result is also true. The ambitious reader should try to construct a proof.

23. Let $n$ be the number of vertices in the tournament. Since for each $u$ different from a given vertex $v$ there is exactly one edge with endpoints $u$ and $v$ (in some order), there are $n-1$ edges involving vertex $v$, so the sum of the in-degree and out-degree of $v$ is $n-1$.

25. We make the vertices the chickens in the flock, and for distinct chickens $u$ and $v$, we have the directed edge $(u,v)$ if and only if $u$ dominates $v$.

27. **a)** No matter how the vertices are labeled, we must have $a_1$ adjacent to $a_5$, so the bandwidth is $5-1=4$.

**b)** The best we can do is to have the vertex of degree 3 as $a_2$. Then the edge between $a_2$ and $a_4$ causes the bandwidth to be $4 - 2 = 2$.

**c)** If we make the vertices in the part with 2 vertices $a_2$ and $a_4$, then the maximum of $|i - j|$ with $a_i$ adjacent to $a_j$ occurs when $i = 1$ and $j = 4$, a maximum of 3. If we carefully consider other possibilities, then we see that there is no way to reduce this difference. Therefore the bandwidth is 3.

**d)** The bandwidth is 4. To see this, assume without loss of generality that $a_1$ is in part $A$. Then if $a_6$ is in part $B$, the maximum difference is 5, which is larger than 4. On the other hand, if $a_6$ is also in part $A$, then the maximum difference is 4, since either $a_2$ or $a_5$ must be in part $B$.

**e)** We can achieve a maximum difference of 4 by labeling the vertices as shown below.

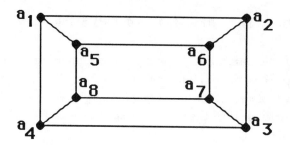

We must show that there is no way to achieve a difference of 3 or less. Now vertex $a_1$ is adjacent to three other vertices. If the difference is going to be 3 or less, then these have to be vertices $a_2$, $a_3$, and $a_4$. Now vertex $a_2$ is adjacent to two vertices besides these four, and therefore the index of one of them must be at least 6, giving a difference of 4.

**f)** The bandwidth cannot be 1, since at least one of the two vertices adjacent to vertex $a_1$ must have subscript at least 3, and $3 - 1 = 2$. On the other hand, if we label the vertices around the cycle as $a_1$, $a_2$, $a_4$, $a_5$, $a_3$ (and back to $a_1$), then the maximum value of $|i - j|$ with $a_i$ and $a_j$ adjacent is 2. Thus the bandwidth equals 2.

**29. a)** Suppose the diameter of $G$ is at least 4, and let $u$ and $v$ be two vertices whose distance apart in $G$ is at least 4. We want to show that the diameter of $\overline{G}$ is at most 2. Let $a$ and $b$ be two distinct vertices of $G$. We need to show that the distance between $a$ and $b$ in $\overline{G}$ is at most 2. If $\{a, b\}$ is not an edge of $G$, then we are done, since then $a$ and $b$ are adjacent (at distance 1) in $\overline{G}$. Thus we assume that $a$ and $b$ are adjacent in $G$. Now it cannot be that $\{u, v\} = \{a, b\}$, since $u$ and $v$ are not adjacent in $G$. Without loss of generality assume that $u$ is not in $\{a, b\}$. Now if $u$ is not adjacent to $a$ and also not adjacent to $b$ in $G$, then we are done, since the path $a, u, b$ in $\overline{G}$ shows that the distance between $a$ and $b$ is 2 in $\overline{G}$. We now show that the other possibility—that $u$ is adjacent (in $G$) to at least one of these—leads either to the conclusion that the distance between $a$ and $b$ is at most 2, or to a contradiction. If $u$ is adjacent to at least one of $a$ and $b$, then $v$ cannot be either $a$ or $b$, because it would be too close to $u$ in $G$. Therefore the same reasoning applies to $v$ as applied to $u$, and either we are done or else we know that $v$ is also adjacent (in $G$) to at least one of $a$ and $b$. But this gives us a path from $u$ to $v$, passing through one or both of $a$ and $b$, of length less than 4, a contradiction.

**b)** The proof is rather similar to that in part **(a)**. Let $u$ and $v$ be vertices at a distance of at least 3 in $G$. Let $a$ and $b$ be arbitrary distinct vertices; we must show that the distance between $a$ and $b$ in $\overline{G}$ is at most 3. Assume not (we will derive a contradiction). Then certainly $a$ and $b$ are adjacent in $G$. Thus at least one of $u$ and $v$ is not equal to either $a$ or $b$; say it is $u$. Now $u$ cannot be adjacent to both $a$ and $b$ in $\overline{G}$, since then the distance between $a$ and $b$ in $\overline{G}$ would be 2. Without loss of generality assume that $u$ is adjacent to $a$ in $G$. Now $v$ cannot be either $a$ or $b$ (it would be too close to $u$ if it were), and it cannot be adjacent to $a$ (in $G$), either, for the same reason. If $v$ is not adjacent to $b$ in $G$, then the path $a, v, b$ in $\overline{G}$ makes the distance between $a$ and $b$ in $\overline{G}$ equal to 2. Thus we can assume that $v$ is adjacent to $b$ in $G$. It follows that $u$ is not adjacent to $b$ in $G$, since that adjacency would again make $u$ too close to $v$. But now we have our contradiction, since there is the path $a, v, u, b$ in $\overline{G}$, of length 3, from $a$ to $b$.

**31.** There are two second shortest paths, both of length 8. One is $a, b, e, z$; the other is $a, d, e, z, e, z$.

**33.** Since the shortest path already went through all the vertices, the answer is that same path: $a, c, b, d, e, z$.

**35.** First we assume that $G$ has exactly 11 vertices. Suppose $G$ is planar. By Corollary 1 to Euler's theorem in Section 7.7, we know that a planar graph with 11 vertices can have at most $3 \cdot 11 - 6 = 27$ edges (if the graph is not connected, then it would have even fewer edges). Therefore $G$ has at most 27 edges. This means that $\overline{G}$ has at least $C(11, 2) - 27 = 28$ edges on its 11 vertices. By Corollary 1, again, this means that $\overline{G}$ is nonplanar, as desired. Now if in fact we were dealing with a graph $G$ with more than 11 vertices, then let us restrict ourselves to the first 11 (in some ordering), and let $H$ be the subgraph of $G$ containing those 11 vertices and all the edges of $G$ between pairs of them. Thus $H$ is a subgraph of $G$, and it is easy to see that $\overline{H}$ is also a subgraph of $\overline{G}$. If $G$ is planar, then so is $H$; by our argument above this means that $\overline{H}$ is not planar, so $\overline{G}$ cannot be planar.

It is actually the case that this result is still true if we replace the number 11 by the number 9. The proof, however, is very hard. The approach used here does not work, since two planes can contain the required *number* of edges. Indeed if we let $G$ have 18 edges, then $\overline{G}$ will also contain $C(9, 2) - 18 = 18$ edges. The corollary to Euler's formula says that a planar graph with 9 vertices can have at most $3 \cdot 9 - 6 = 21$ edges, and $18 < 21$. The subtlety comes with trying to imbed precisely the right edges for $G$ and the right edges for $\overline{G}$, and it can be proved that this cannot be done, no matter what graph on 9 vertices $G$ is.

**37.** Let $n$ be the number of vertices in the graph, $k$ its chromatic number, and $i$ its independence number. Then there is a coloring of the graph with $k$ colors. Since no two vertices in the same color class (i.e., colored the same) are adjacent, each color class is an independent set. Thus there are at most $i$ vertices in each color class. This means there are at most $ki$ vertices in all. In other words, $n \leq ki$, as desired.

# CHAPTER 8
## Trees

⇒ **SECTION 8.1   Introduction to Trees**

*These exercises give the reader experience working with tree terminology, and in particular with the relationships between the height and the numbers of vertices, leaves, and internal vertices of a tree. Exercise 6 should be done: in fact the reader might want to extend it to larger values of $n$. One good way to organize your enumeration of trees (such as all nonisomorphic trees with 5 vertices) is to focus on a particular parameter, such as the length of a longest path in the tree. This makes it easier to include all the trees and not count any of them twice. Review the theorems in this section before working the exercises involving the relationships between the height and the numbers of vertices, leaves, and internal vertices of a tree. For a challenge that gives a good feeling for the flavor of arguments in graph theory, the reader should try Exercise 31. In many ways trees are recursive creatures, and Exercise 33 and Exercise 34 are worth looking at in this regard.*

1. **a)** This graph is connected and has no simple circuits, so it is a tree.
   **b)** This graph is not connected, so it is not a tree.
   **c)** This graph is connected and has no simple circuits, so it is a tree.
   **d)** This graph has a simple circuit, so it is not a tree.
   **e)** This graph is connected and has no simple circuits, so it is a tree.
   **f)** This graph has a simple circuit, so it is not a tree.

3. This is not a full $m$-ary tree for any $m$. It is an $m$-ary tree for all $m \geq 3$, since each vertex has at most 3 children, but since some vertices have 3 children, while others have 1 or 2, it is not full for any $m$.

5. We describe the answers, rather than actually drawing pictures.
   **a)** The subtree rooted at $a$ is Figure 15 itself, since $a$ is the root.
   **b)** The subtree rooted at $c$ is just the vertex $c$, since $c$ has no descendants.
   **c)** The subtree rooted at $e$ consists of three vertices: the root $e$, and children $j$ and $k$ of the root.

7. In each case we find the answer by carefully enumerating the trees, i.e., drawing a full set of nonisomorphic trees. One way to organize this work so as to avoid leaving any trees out or counting the same tree (up to isomorphism) more than once is to list the trees by the length of their longest path from the root.

   **a)** For $n = 3$, the longest path from the root can have length 1 or 2. There is only one tree of each type, so there are exactly 2 nonisomorphic rooted trees with 3 vertices, as shown below.

**b)** For $n = 4$, the longest path from the root can have length 1, 2 or 3. There is only one tree with longest path of length 1 (the other three vertices are at level 1), and only one with longest path of length 3. If the longest path has length 2, then the fourth vertex (after using three vertices to draw this path) can be "attached" to either the root or the vertex at level 1, giving us 2 nonisomorphic trees. Thus there are a total of 4 nonisomorphic trees on 4 vertices, as shown below.

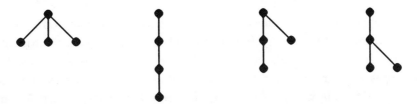

**c)** For $n = 5$, the longest path from the root can have length 1, 2, 3 or 4. There is only one tree with longest path of length 1 (the other four vertices are at level 1), and only one with longest path of length 4. If the longest path has length 3, then the fifth vertex (after using four vertices to draw this path) can be "attached" to either the root or the vertex at level 1 or the vertex at level 2, giving us 3 nonisomorphic trees. If the longest path has length 2, then there are several possibilities for where the fourth and fifth vertices can be "attached." They can both be adjacent to the root; they can both be adjacent to the vertex at level 1; one can be adjacent to the root and the other to the vertex at level 1; or one can be adjacent to the root and the other to this vertex: in all there are 4 possibilities in this case. Thus there are a total of 9 nonisomorphic trees on 4 vertices, as shown below.

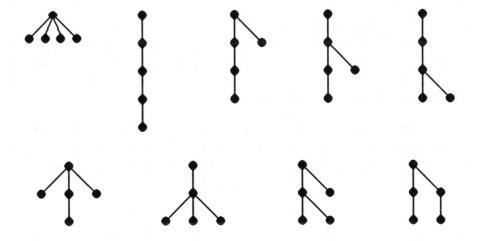

**9.** We will prove this statement by induction on $n$, the number of vertices of $G$. (This exercise can also be done by using Theorem 2, but we will take an entirely different tack.) If $n = 1$, then there is only one possibility for $G$, it *is* a tree, it is connected, and it has $1 - 1 = 0$ edges. Thus the statement is true. Now let us assume that the statement is true for simple graphs with $n$ vertices, and let $G$ be a simple graph with $n + 1$ vertices.

There are two things to prove here. First let us suppose that $G$ is a tree; we must show that $G$ is connected and has $(n+1)-1=n$ edges. Of course $G$ is connected by definition. In order to prove that $G$ has the required number of edges, we need the following fact: a tree with at least one edge must contain a vertex of degree 1. (To see that this is so, let $P$ be a simple path of greatest possible length; since the tree has no simple circuits, such a maximum length simple path exists. The ends of this path must be vertices of degree 1, since otherwise the simple path could be extended.) Let $v$ be a vertex of degree 1 in $G$, and let $G'$ be $G$ with $v$ and its incident edge removed. Now $G'$ is still a tree: it has no simple circuits (since $G$ had none) and it is still connected (the removed edge is clearly not needed to form paths between vertices different from $v$). Therefore by the inductive hypothesis, $G'$, which has $n$ vertices, has $n-1$ edges; it follows that $G$, which has one more edge than $G'$, has $n$ edges.

Conversely, suppose that $G$ is connected and has $n$ edges. If $G$ is not a tree, then it must contain a simple circuit. If we remove one edge from this simple circuit, then the resulting graph (call it $G'$) is still connected. If $G'$ is a tree then we stop; otherwise we repeat this process. Since $G$ had only finitely many edges to begin with, this process must eventually terminate at some tree $T$ with $n+1$ vertices ($T$ has all the vertices that $G$ had). By the paragraph above, $T$ therefore has $n$ edges. But this contradicts the fact that we removed at least one edge of $G$ in order to construct $T$. Therefore our assumption that $G$ was not a tree is wrong, and our proof is complete.

11. Since a tree with $n$ vertices has $n-1$ edges, the answer is 9999.

13. Each internal vertex has exactly 2 edges leading from it to its children. Therefore we can count the edges by multiplying the number of internal vertices by 2. Thus there are $2 \cdot 1000 = 2000$ edges.

15. We can model the tournament as a full binary tree. Each internal vertex represents the winner of the game played by its two children. There are 1000 leaves, one for each contestant. The root is the winner of the entire tournament. By Theorem 4iii, with $m=2$ and $l=1000$, we see that $i=(l-1)/(m-1)=999$. Thus exactly 999 games must be played to determine the champion.

17. Let $P$ be a person sending out the letter. Then 10 people receive a letter with $P$'s name at the bottom of the list (in the sixth position). Later 100 people receive a letter with $P$'s name in the fifth position. Similarly, 1000 people receive a letter with $P$'s name in the fourth position, and so on, until 1,000,000 people receive the letter with $P$'s name in the first position. Therefore $P$ should receive $1,000,000. The model here is a full 10-ary tree.

19. The complete binary tree of height 4 has 5 rows of vertices (levels 0 through 4), with each vertex not in the bottom row having two children). The complete 3-ary tree of height 3 has 4 rows of vertices (levels 0 through 3), with each vertex not in the bottom row having three children).

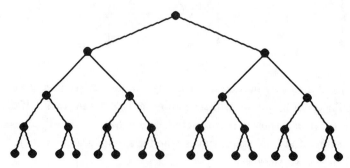

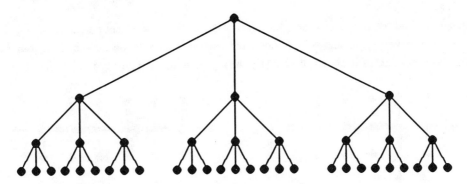

21. For both parts we use algebra on the equations $n = i + l$ (which is true by definition) and $n = mi + 1$ (which is proved in Theorem 3).

    **a)** That $n = mi + 1$ is one of the given equations. For the second equality here, we have $l = n - i = (mi + 1) - i = (m - 1)i + 1$.

    **b)** If we subtract the two given equations, then we obtain $0 = (1 - m)i + (l - 1)$, or $(m - 1)i = l - 1$. It follows that $i = (l - 1)/(m - 1)$. Then $n = i + l = [(l - 1)/(m - 1)] + l = (l - 1 + lm - l)/(m - 1) = (lm - 1)/(m - 1)$.

23. In each of the $t$ trees, there is one fewer edge than there are vertices. Therefore altogether there are $t$ fewer edges than vertices. Thus there are $n - t$ edges.

25. The number of isomers is the number of nonisomorphic trees with the given numbers of atoms. Since the hydrogen atoms play no role in determining the structure (they simply are attached to each carbon atom in sufficient number to make the degree of each carbon atom exactly 4), we need only look at the trees formed by the carbon atoms. In drawing our answers, we will show the tree of carbon atoms in heavy lines, with the hydrogen atom attachments in thinner lines.

    **a)** There is only one tree with three vertices (up to isomorphism), the path of length 2. Thus the answer is 1. The heavy lines in this diagram of the molecule form this tree.

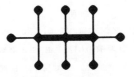

    **b)** There are 3 nonisomorphic trees with 5 vertices: the path of length 4, the "star" $K_{1,4}$, and the tree which consists of a path of length 3 together with one more vertex attached to one of the middle vertices in the path. Thus the answer is 3. Again the heavy lines in the diagrams of the molecules form these trees.

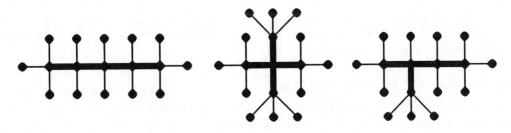

**c)** We need to find all the nonisomorphic trees with 6 vertices, except that we must not count the (one) tree with a vertex of degree 5 (since each carbon can only be attached to four other atoms). The complete set of trees is shown below (the heavy lines in these diagrams). Thus the answer is 5.

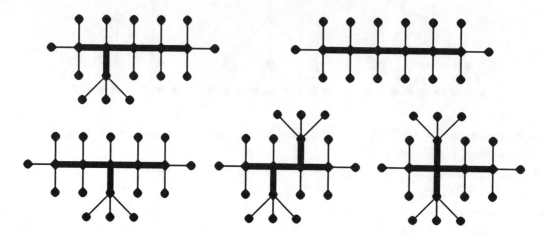

27. **a)** The parent of a vertex $v$ is the directory in which the file or directory represented by $v$ is contained.

**b)** The child of a vertex $v$ (and $v$ must represent a directory) is a file or directory contained in the directory that $v$ represents.

**c)** If $u$ and $v$ are siblings, then the files or directories that $u$ and $v$ represent are in the same directory.

**d)** The ancestors of vertex $v$ are all directories in the path from the root directory to the file or directory represented by $v$.

**e)** The descendants of a vertex $v$ are all the files and directories either contained in $v$, or contained in directories contained in $v$, etc.

**f)** The level of a vertex $v$ tells how far from the root directory is the file or directory represented by $v$.

**g)** The height of the tree is the greatest depth (i.e., level) at which a file or directory is buried in the system.

29. In each case we need to compute the eccentricity of each vertex in order to find the center or centers. In practice, this does not involve much computation, since we can tell at a glance when the eccentricity is large. Intuitively, the center or centers are near the "middle" of the tree.

**a)** The eccentricity of vertex $c$ is 3, and it is the only vertex with eccentricity this small. Indeed, vertices $a$ and $b$ have eccentricity 5 and 4 (look at the paths to $l$); vertices $d$, $f$, $g$, $i$, and $k$ all have eccentricities at least 4 (again look at the paths to $l$); and vertices $e$, $h$, $i$, and $l$ also all have eccentricities at least 4 (look at the paths to $k$). Therefore $c$ is the only center.

**b)** The eccentricity of vertex $e$ is 3, and it is the only vertex with eccentricity this small. Therefore $e$ is the only center.

**c)** The eccentricity of vertices $c$ and $h$ are both 3. The eccentricities of the other vertices are all at least 4. Therefore $c$ and $h$ are the centers.

31. Certainly a tree has at least one center, since the set of eccentricities has a minimum value. First we prove that if $u$ and $v$ are any two distinct centers (say with minimum eccentricity $e$), then $u$ and $v$ are adjacent. Let $P$ be the unique simple path from $u$ to $v$. We will show that $P$ is just $u, v$.

If not, let $c$ be any other vertex on $P$. Since the eccentricity of $c$ is at least $e$, there is a vertex $w$ such that the unique simple path $Q$ from $c$ to $w$ has length at least $e$. This path $Q$ may follow $P$ for awhile, but once it diverges from $P$ it cannot rejoin $P$ without there being a simple circuit in the tree. In any case, $Q$ cannot follow $P$ towards both $u$ and $v$, so suppose without loss of generality that it does not follow $P$ towards $u$. Then the path from $u$ to $c$ and then on to $w$ is simple and of length greater than $e$, a contradiction. Thus no such $c$ exists, and $u$ and $v$ are adjacent.

Finally, to see that there can be no more than two centers, note that we have just proved that any two centers are adjacent. If there were three (or more) centers, then we would have a $K_3$ contained in the tree, contradicting the definition that a tree has no simple circuits.

33. We follow the recursive definition and produce the following pictures for $T_3$ through $T_7$ (of course $T_1$ and $T_2$ are both the tree with just one vertex). For example, $T_3$ has $T_2$ (a single vertex) as its left subtree and $T_1$ (again a single vertex) as its right subtree.

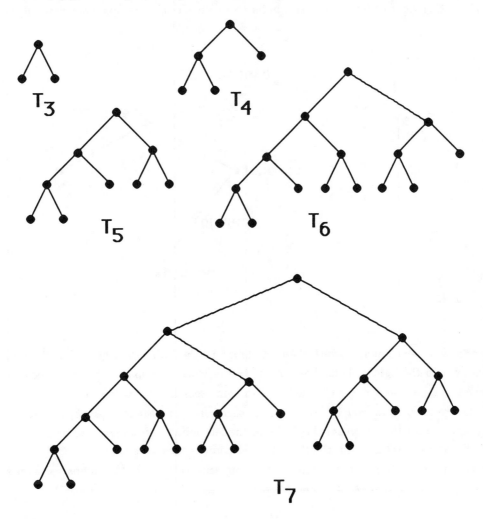

⇒ **SECTION 8.2    Applications of Trees**

*Trees find many applications, especially in computer science. This section and subsequent ones deal with some of these applications. Binary search trees can be built up by adding new vertices one by one; searches in binary search trees are accomplished by moving down the tree until the desired vertex is found, branching either right or left as necessary. Huffman codes provide efficient means of encoding text in which some symbols occur more frequently than others; decoding is accomplished by moving down a binary tree. The coin-weighing problems presented here are but a few of the questions that can be asked. Try making up some of your own and answering them; it is easy to ask quite difficult questions of this type. We will see decision trees again in Section 8.4, applied to sorting.*

1. We first insert *banana* into the empty tree, giving us the tree with just a root, labeled *banana*. Next we insert *peach*, which, being greater than *banana* in alphabetical order, becomes the right child of the root. We continue in this manner, letting each new word find its place by coming down the tree, branching either right or left until it encounters a free position. The final tree is as shown.

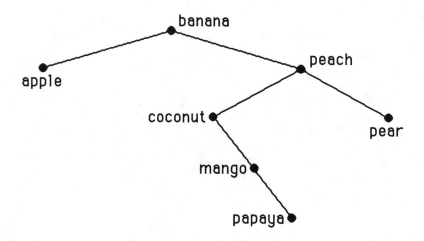

3. **a)** To find *pear*, we compare it with the root (*banana*), then with the right child of the root (*peach*), and finally with the right child of that vertex (*pear*). Thus 3 comparisons are needed.

   **b)** Only 1 comparison is needed, since the item being searched for is the root.

   **c)** We fail to locate *kumquat* by comparing it successively to *banana*, *peach*, *coconut*, and *mango*. Once we determine that *kumquat* should be in the left subtree of *mango*, and find no vertices there, we know that *kumquat* is not in the tree. Thus 4 comparisons were used.

   **d)** This one is similar to part (c), except that 5 comparisons are used. We compare *orange* successively to *banana*, *peach*, *coconut*, *mango*, and *papaya*.

5. We follow exactly the same procedure as in Exercise 1. The only unusual point is that the word "the" appears later in the sentence, after it is already in the tree. The algorithm finds that it is already in the tree, so it is not inserted again. The tree is shown below.

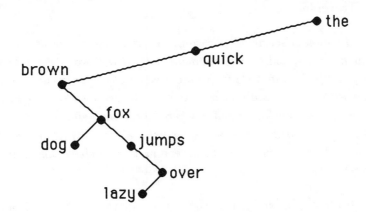

7.  Since there are 4 different outcomes to the testing procedure, we need at least 2 weighings, since one weighing will only give us 3 possible outcomes (a decision tree of height 1 has only 3 leaves). Here is how to find the counterfeit coin with 2 weighings. Let us call the coins $A$, $B$, $C$, and $D$. First compare coins $A$ and $B$. If they balance, then the counterfeit is among the other two. In this case, compare $C$ with $A$; if they balance, then $D$ is counterfeit; if they do not, then $C$ is counterfeit. On the other hand if $A$ and $B$ do not balance, then one of them is the counterfeit. Again compare $C$ with $A$. If they balance, then $B$ is the counterfeit; if they do not, then $A$ is counterfeit.

9.  Since there are 12 different outcomes to the testing procedure, we need at least 3 weighings, since 2 weighings will only give us 9 possible outcomes (a decision tree of height 2 has only 9 leaves). Here is one way to find the counterfeit coin with 3 weighings. Divide the coins into three groups of 4 coins each, and compare two of the groups. If they balance, then the counterfeit is among the other four coins. If they do not balance, then the counterfeit is among the four coins registering lighter. In either case we have narrowed the search to 4 coins. Now by Example 2 we can, in 2 more weighings, find the counterfeit among these four coins and four of the good ones.

11. **a)** This is a prefix code, since no code is the first part of another.
    **b)** This is not a prefix code, since, for instance, the code for $a$ is the first part of the code for $t$.
    **c)** This is a prefix code, since no code is the first part of another.
    **d)** This is a prefix code, since no code is the first part of another.

13. The code for a letter is simply the labels on the edges in the path from the root to that letter. Since the path from the root to $a$ goes through the three edges leading left each time, all labeled 0, the code for $a$ is 000. Similarly the codes for $e$, $i$, $k$, $o$, $p$ and $u$ are 001, 01, 1100, 1101, 11110 and 11111, respectively.

⇒ **SECTION 8.3   Tree Traversal**

*Tree traversal is central to computer science applications. Trees are such a natural way to represent arithmetical and algebraic formulas, and so easy to manipulate, that it would be difficult to imagine how computer scientists could live without them. To see if you really understand the various orders, try Exercise 20 and Exercise 21. You need to make your mind work recursively for tree traversals: when you come to a subtree, you need to remember where to continue after processing the subtree. It is best to think of these traversals in terms of the recursive algorithms (shown as Algorithms 1, 2, and 3). A good bench-mark for testing your understanding of recursive definitions is provided in Exercise 24 through Exercise 28.*

1. The root of the tree is labeled 0. The children of the root are labeled 1, 2, ..., from left to right. The children of a vertex labeled $\alpha$ are labeled $\alpha.1$, $\alpha.2$, ..., from left to right. For example, the two children of the vertex 1 in the first tree are 1.1 and 1.2. We completely label the trees in this manner, from the top down. The labeled trees are shown below.

   **a)** The lexicographic order of the labels is the preorder of the vertices: after each vertex come the subtrees rooted at its children, from left to right. Thus the order is $0 < 1 < 1.1 < 1.2 < 2 < 3$.

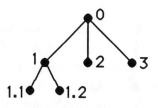

   **b)** This is similar to part (**a**). The order is $0 < 1 < 1.1 < 1.1.1 < 1.1.1.1 < 1.1.1.2 < 1.1.2 < 1.2 < 2$.

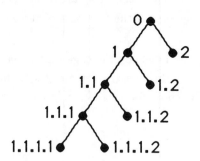

   **c)** This is similar to part (**a**). The order is $0 < 1 < 1.1 < 1.2 < 1.2.1 < 1.2.1.1 < 1.2.1.2 < 1.2.2 < 1.2.3 < 1.2.3.1 < 1.2.3.2 < 1.2.3.2.1 < 1.2.3.2.2 < 1.2.3.3 < 2 < 2.1$.

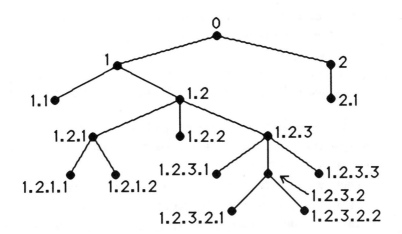

3. The given information tells us that the root has two children. We have no way to tell how many vertices are in the subtree of the root rooted at the first of these children. Therefore we have no way to tell how many vertices are in the tree.

5. **a)** In preorder, the root comes first, then the left subtree in preorder, then the right subtree in preorder. Thus the preorder is $a$, followed by the vertices of the left subtree (the one rooted at $b$) in preorder, then $c$. Recursively, the preorder in the subtree rooted at $b$ is $b$, followed by $d$, followed by the vertices in the subtree rooted at $e$ in preorder, namely $e$, $f$, $g$. Putting this all together, we obtain the answer $a, b, d, e, f, g, c$.

   **b)** The procedure is the same as in part **(a)**, except that some vertices have more than two children here: after listing such a vertex, we list the vertices of its subtrees, in preorder, from left to right. The answer is $a, b, d, e, i, j, m, n, o, c, f, g, h, k, l, p$.

   **c)** This is just like part **(b)**. The answer is $a, b, e, k, l, m, f, g, n, r, s, c, d, h, o, i, j, p, q$.

7. **a)** In postorder, the root comes last, following the left subtree in postorder and the right subtree in postorder. Thus the postorder is the vertices of the left subtree (the one rooted at $b$) in postorder, then $c$, then $a$. Recursively, the postorder in the subtree rooted at $b$ is $d$, followed by the vertices in the subtree rooted at $e$ in postorder, namely $f$, $g$, $e$, followed by $b$. Putting this all together, we obtain the answer $d, f, g, e, b, c, a$.

   **b)** The procedure is the same as in part **(a)**, except that some vertices have more than two children here: before listing such a vertex, we list the vertices of its subtrees, in postorder, from left to right. The answer is $d, i, m, n, o, j, e, b, f, g, k, p, l, h, c, a$.

   **c)** This is just like part **(b)**. The answer is $k, l, m, e, f, r, s, n, g, b, c, o, h, i, p, q, j, d, a$.

9. If we have done Exercise 8, then we can read off the answer simply by listing the vertices of the tree in preorder, postorder, or inorder (with parentheses added). If not, then we can reason as follows.
   **a)** In prefix notation, the operators precede their operands. The outermost operator in the first of these expressions is $+$. Thus the prefix expression consists of $+$ followed by the prefix expression for $x + xy$ followed by the prefix expression for $x/y$. The former is $+ x * x y$ (recursively by the same reasoning), and the latter is $/ x y$. Therefore the answer is $+ + x * x y / x y$. Similarly, the second expression in prefix notation is $+ x / + * x y x y$.
   **b)** In postfix notation, the operators follow their operands. The outermost operator in the first of these expressions is $+$. Thus the postfix expression consists of $+$ following the postfix expression for

$x + xy$ and the postfix expression for $x/y$. The former is $x\,x\,y\,*\,+$ (recursively by the same reasoning), and the latter is $x\,y\,/$. Therefore the answer is $x\,x\,y\,*\,+\,x\,y\,/\,+$. Similarly, the second expression in postfix notation is $x\,x\,y\,*\,x\,+\,y\,/\,+$.

c) The infix expression is just the given expression, fully parenthesized, with an explicit symbol for multiplication. Thus the first is $((x + (x * y)) + (x/y))$, and the second is $(x + (((x * y) + x)/y))$.

11. This exercise is similar to Exercise 9, so we will not go into the details. The only difference is that negation ($\neg$) is a unary operator; it precedes its operand in infix notation, even though it would follow it in an inorder traversal of the expression tree.

   a) The prefix expressions are $\leftrightarrow \neg \wedge p\,q \vee \neg p \neg q$ and $\vee \wedge \neg p \leftrightarrow q \neg p \neg q$.

   b) The postfix expressions are $p\,q \wedge \neg p \neg q \neg \vee \leftrightarrow$ and $p \neg q\,p \neg \leftrightarrow \wedge q \neg \vee$.

   c) The (fully parenthesized) infix expressions are $((\neg(p \wedge q)) \leftrightarrow ((\neg p) \vee (\neg q)))$ and $(((\neg p) \wedge (q \leftrightarrow (\neg p))) \vee (\neg q))$.

13. This exercise is similar to Exercise 9, so we will not go into the details.

   a) The prefix expression is $- \cap A\,B \cup A - B\,A$.

   b) The postfix expression is $A\,B \cap A\,B\,A - \cup -$.

   c) The (fully parenthesized) infix expression is $((A \cap B) - (A \cup (B - A)))$.

15. Either of the four operators can be the outermost one, so there are four cases to consider. If the first operator is the outermost one, then we need to compute the number of ways to fully parenthesize $B - A \cup B - A$. Here there are 5 possibilities: 1 in which the "$\cup$" symbol is the outermost operator and 2 with each of the "$-$" symbols as the outermost operator. If the second operator in our original expression is the outermost one, then the only choice is in the parenthesization of the second of its operands, and there are 2 possibilities. Thus there are a total 7 ways to parenthesize this expression if either of the first two operators are the outermost one. By symmetry there are another 7 if the outermost operator is one of the last two. Therefore the answer to the problem is 14.

17. We show how to do these exercises by successively replacing the first occurrence of an operator immediately followed by two operands with the result of that operation. (This is an alternative to the method suggested in the text, where the *last* occurrence of an operator, which is necessarily preceded by two operands, is acted upon first.) The final number is the value of the entire prefix expression. In part (a), for example, we first replace $*\,2\,2$ by the result of multiplying 2 and 2, namely 4, to obtain the second line. Then we replace $-\,4\,3$ by its answer, 1, which is the final answer.

a)
$$- * 2\,2\,3$$
$$- 4\,3$$
$$1$$

b)
$$\uparrow - * 3\,3 * 4\,2\,5$$
$$\uparrow - 9 * 4\,2\,5$$
$$\uparrow - 9\,8\,5$$

$$\uparrow 1\ 5$$

$$1$$

c)
$$+\ -\ \uparrow\ 3\ 2\ \uparrow\ 2\ 3\ /\ 6\ -\ 4\ 2$$

$$+\ -\ 9\ \uparrow\ 2\ 3\ /\ 6\ -\ 4\ 2$$

$$+\ -\ 9\ 8\ /\ 6\ -\ 4\ 2$$

$$+\ 1\ /\ 6\ -\ 4\ 2$$

$$+\ 1\ /\ 6\ 2$$

$$+\ 1\ 3$$

$$4$$

d)
$$*\ +\ 3\ +\ 3\ \uparrow\ 3\ +\ 3\ 3\ 3$$

$$*\ +\ 3\ +\ 3\ \uparrow\ 3\ 6\ 3$$

$$*\ +\ 3\ +\ 3\ 729\ 3$$

$$*\ +\ 3\ 732\ 3$$

$$*\ 735\ 3$$

$$2205$$

19. We slowly use the clues to fill in the details of this tree, shown below. Since the preorder starts with $a$, we know that $a$ is the root, and we are told that $a$ has four children. Next, since the first child of $a$ comes after $a$ in preorder, we know that this first child is $b$. We are told that $b$ has one child, and it must be $f$, which comes next in the preorder. We are told that $f$ has no children, so we are now finished with the subtree rooted at $b$. Therefore the second child of $a$ must be $c$ (the next vertex in preorder). We continue in this way until we have drawn the entire tree.

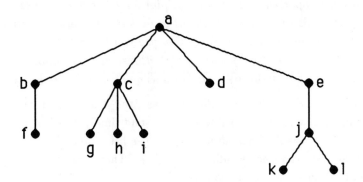

21. We prove this by induction on the length of the list. If the list has just one element, then the statement is trivially true. For the inductive step, consider the end of the list. There we find a sequence of vertices, starting with the last leaf and ending with the root of the tree, each vertex being the last child of its successor in the list. We know where this sequence starts, since we are told the number of children of each vertex: it starts at the last leaf in the list. Now remove this leaf, and decrease the child count of its parent by 1. The result is the postorder and child counts of a tree with one fewer vertex. By the inductive hypothesis we can uniquely determine this smaller tree. Then we can uniquely determine where the deleted vertex goes, since it is the last child of its parent (whom we know).

23. In each case the postorder is $c, d, b, f, g, h, e, a$.

25. We prove this by induction on the recursive definition, in other words, on the length of the formula, i.e., the total number of symbols and operators. The only formula of length 1 arises from the base case of the recursive definition (part (i)), and in that case we have one symbol and no operators, so the statement is true. Assume the statement is true for formulae of length less than $n > 1$, and let $F$ be a formula of length $n$. Then $F$ arises from part (ii) of the definition, so $F$ consists of $*XY$, for some operator $*$ and some formulae $X$ and $Y$. By the inductive hypothesis, the number of symbols in $X$ exceeds the number of operators there by 1, and the same holds for $Y$. If we add and note that there is one more operator in $F$ than in $X$ and $Y$ combined, then we see that the number of symbols in $F$ exceeds the number of operators in $F$ by 1, as well.

27. Any string of length $n$, using these six characters, is a well-formed formula as long as two conditions are met: if we read the string from left to right, the number of symbols is always at least 1 greater than the number of operators; and in all there is one more symbol than operator. We are asked to write down six such strings, with $n \geq 7$. One such set is $xxxx+++$, $xxxxx++++$, $xx+xx++$, $xxxx+xx++++$, $xxx+xx+++$, and $xx+xxx+++$.

⇒ **SECTION 8.4   Trees and Sorting**

*Computers used in business probably spend as much time sorting as doing anything else, so good sorting algorithms are important. It may be helpful for the reader to use a set of about 50 cards (playing cards or file cards with names on them) to perform the various sorting algorithms discussed in this section and exercise set. With a set of this size you begin to get a feeling for the complexity issues involved in sorting. The $O(n^2)$ sorting algorithms, such as bubble sort, are just not feasible with large lists, whereas the $O(n \log n)$ sorts, such as quick sort, are quite fast.*

1. There are 4 passes through the list. On the first pass, the 3 and the 1 are interchanged first, then the next two comparisons produce no interchanges, and finally the last comparison results in the interchange of the 7 and the 4. Thus after one pass the list reads $1, 3, 5, 4, 7$. During the next pass, the 5 and the 4 are interchanged, yielding $1, 3, 4, 5, 7$. There are two more passes, but no further interchanges are made, since the list is now in order.

3. We need to add a Boolean variable to indicate if any interchanges were made during a pass. Initially this variable, which we will call *still_interchanging* is set to **true**. If no interchanges were made, then we can quit. To do this neatly, we turn the outermost loop into a **while** loop that is executed as long as $i < n$ and *still_interchanging* is true. Thus our pseudocode is as follows.

> **procedure** *betterbubblesort*$(a_1, \ldots, a_n)$
> $i := 1$
> *still_interchanging* := **true**
> **while** $i < n$ and *still_interchanging*
> **begin**
>  *still_interchanging* := **false**
>  **for** $j := 1$ **to** $n - i$
>   **if** $a_j > a_{j+1}$ **then**
>   **begin**
>    *still_interchanging* := **true**
>    interchange $a_j$ and $a_{j+1}$
>   **end**
>  $i := i + 1$
> **end** { $a_1, \ldots, a_n$ is in nondecreasing order}

5. We assume that sorting is to be done into alphabetical order. First the list is split into the two lists $b, d, a, f, g$ and $h, z, p, o, k$, and each of these is sorted by merge sort. Let us assume for a moment that this has been done, so the two lists are $a, b, d, f, g$ and $h, k, o, p, z$. Then these two lists are merged into one sorted list, as follows. We compare $a$ with $h$ and find that $a$ is smaller; thus $a$ comes first in the merged list, and we pass on to $b$. Comparing $b$ with $h$, we find that $b$ is smaller, so $b$ comes next in the merged list, and we pass on to $d$. We repeat this process (using Algorithm 2) until the lists are merged into one sorted list, $a, b, d, f, g, h, k, o, p, z$. (It was just a coincidence that every element in the first of these two lists came before every element in the second.)

Let us return to the question of how each of the 5-element lists was sorted. For the list $b, d, a, f, g$, we divide it into the sublists $b, d, a$ and $f, g$. Again we sort each piece by the same algorithm, producing $a, b, d$ and $f, g$, and we merge them into the sorted list $a, b, d, f, g$. Going one level deeper into the recursion, we see that sorting $b, d, a$ was accomplished by splitting it into $b, d$ and $a$, and sorting each piece by the same algorithm. The first of these required further splitting into $b$ and $d$. One element lists are already sorted, of course. Similarly, the other 5-element list was sorted by a similar recursive process. A tree diagram for this problem is displayed below. The top half of the picture is a tree showing the splitting part of the algorithm. The bottom half shows the merging part as an upside-down tree.

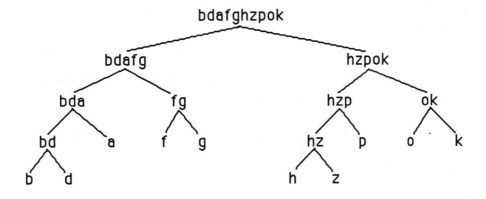

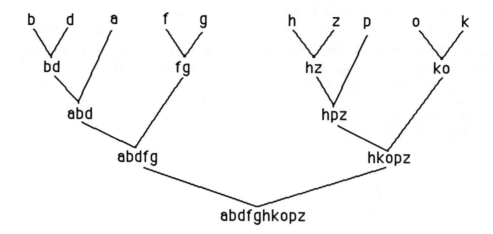

7. All we have to do is to make sure that one of the lists is exhausted only when the other list has only one element left in it. In this case, a comparison is needed to place every element of the merged list into place, except for the last element. Clearly this condition is met if and only if the largest element in the combined list is in one of the initial lists and the second largest element is in the other. One such pair of lists is $\{1, 2, \ldots, m-1, m+n\}$ and $\{m, m+1, \ldots, m+n-1\}$.

9. We assume that when the least element is found at each stage, it is interchanged with the element in the position it wants to occupy.

a) The smallest element is $1$, so it is interchanged with the $3$ at the beginning of the list, yielding $1, 5, 4, 3, 2$. Next, the smallest element among the remaining elements in the list (the second through fifth positions) is $2$, so it is interchanged with the $5$ in position $2$, yielding $1, 2, 4, 3, 5$. One more pass gives us $1, 2, 3, 4, 5$. At this point we find the fourth smallest element among the fourth and fifth positions, namely $4$, and interchange it with itself, again yielding $1, 2, 3, 4, 5$. This completes the sort.

b) The process is similar to part **(a)**. We just show the status at the end of each of the four passes: $1, 4, 3, 2, 5$; $1, 2, 3, 4, 5$; $1, 2, 3, 4, 5$; $1, 2, 3, 4, 5$.

c) Again there are four passes, but all interchanges result in the list remaining as it is.

11. To answer this question exactly requires an explicit algorithm in pseudocode, as is requested in Exercise 10. Absent that, we can argue as follows to find an approximate complexity figure. There are $n-1$ passes, one to place each of the first $n-1$ elements in its correct position (there is no need to place the last item, since it has to be in place if the first $n-1$ elements are in place). In the $i^{\text{th}}$ pass, we need to look through positions $i$ through $n$ of the current list, inclusive, a total of $n-i+1$ numbers. In order to find the largest of these, we need to use $n-i$ comparisons. Thus our answer is $\sum_{i=1}^{n-1} n-i$, which is clearly the same as $\sum_{i=1}^{n-1} i$. We know that this sum is $(n-1)n/2 = O(n^2)$. Of course we have ignored things like comparisons needed for bookkeeping. In any case, the answer is apparently $O(n^2)$, at least with this naive approach.

13. We need to compare every other element with $a_1$. Thus at least $n-1$ comparisons are needed (we will assume for Exercise 15 and Exercise 17 that the answer is exactly $n-1$). The actual number of comparisons depends on the actual encoding of the algorithm. With any reasonable encoding, it should be $O(n)$.

15. In the worst case, the original list splits into lists of length 3 and 0 (with $a_1$ between them); by Exercise 13, this requires $4 - 1 = 3$ comparisons. No comparisons are needed to sort the second of these lists (since it is empty). To sort the first, we argue in the same way: the worst case is for a splitting into lists of length 2 and 0, requiring $3 - 1 = 2$ comparisons. Similarly, $2 - 1 = 1$ comparisons are needed to split the list of length 2 into lists of length 1 and 0. In all, then, $3+2+1 = 6$ comparisons are needed in this worst case. (One can prove that this discussion really does deal with the worst case by looking at what happens in the various other cases.)

17. We claim that the worst case complexity is $n(n-1)/2$ comparisons, and we prove this by induction on $n$. This is certainly true for $n = 1$, since no comparisons are needed. Otherwise, suppose the initial split is into lists of size $k$ and $n - k - 1$. By the inductive hypothesis, it will require $(k(k-1)/2) + ((n-k-1)(n-k-2)/2)$ comparisons in the worst case to finish the algorithm. This quadratic function of $k$ attains its maximum value if $k = 0$ (or $k = n - 1$), namely the value $(n-1)(n-2)/2$. Also, it took $n - 1$ comparisons to perform the first splitting. If we add these two quantities ($(n-1)(n-2)/2$ and $n - 1$) and do the algebra, then we obtain $n(n-1)/2$, as desired. Thus in the worst case the complexity is $O(n^2)$.

19. This recursive algorithm proceeds by splitting the original list into two at the middle, sorting each half, and merging the results. The algorithm can be written with one statement.

> **procedure** *mergesort*$(a_1, \ldots, a_n)$
> **if** $n > 1$ **then**
>     $L := merge\big(mergesort(a_1, \ldots, a_{\lfloor n/2 \rfloor}), mergesort(a_{\lfloor n/2 \rfloor+1}, \ldots, a_n)\big)$
> **else** $L := (a_1)$  {the list with one element is already sorted}
> **end** { $L$ is sorted}

⇒ **SECTION 8.5    Spanning Trees**

*The spanning tree algorithms given here provide systematic methods for searching through graphs, and they are the foundation of many other, more complicated, algorithms. The concept of a spanning tree is quite simple and natural, of course: the problem comes with finding spanning trees efficiently. The reader should pay attention to the excesises on backtracking (Exercise 16 through Exercise 20) to get a feel both for the ideas behind it and for its inefficiency for large problems.*

1. The graph has $m$ edges. The spanning tree has $n - 1$ edges. Therefore we need to remove $m - (n-1)$ edges.

3. In each case we show the original graph and a spanning tree in heavier lines. These were obtained by trial and error. In each case except part **(c)**, our spanning tree is a simple path (but other answers are possible). In part **(c)**, of course, the graph is its own spanning tree.

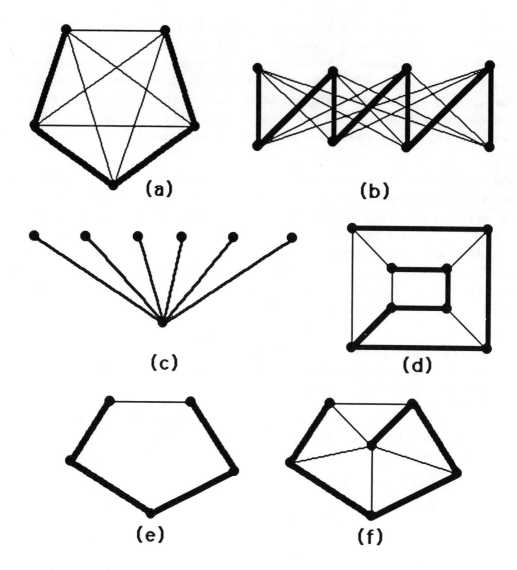

5. We approach this problem in a rather ad hoc way.

a) Every pair of edges in $K_3$ forms a spanning tree, so there are $C(3,2) = 3$ such trees.

b) There are 16 spanning trees; careful counting is required to see this. First, let is note that the trees can take only two shapes: the star $K_{1,3}$ and the simple path of length 3. There are 4 different spanning trees of the former shape, since any of the four vertices can be chosen as the vertex of degree 3. There are $P(4,4) = 24$ orders in which the vertices can be listed in a simple path of length 3, but since the path can be traversed in either of two directions to yield the same tree, there are only 12 trees of this shape. Therefore there are $4 + 12 = 16$ spanning trees of $K_4$ altogether.

c) Note that $K_{2,2} = C_4$. A tree is determined simply by deciding which of the four edges to remove. Therefore there are 4 spanning trees.

d) By the same reasoning as in part (c), there are 5 spanning trees.

7. If we start at vertex $a$ and use alphabetical order, then the depth-first search spanning tree is unique.

a) We start at vertex $a$ and form the path shown in heavy lines to vertex $i$ before needing to backtrack. There are no unreached vertices from vertex $h$ at this point, but there is an unreached vertex $(j)$ adjacent to vertex $g$. Thus the tree is as shown in heavy lines.

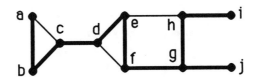

**b)** The tree is shown in heavy lines. It is produced by starting at *a* and continuing as far as possible without backtracking, choosing the first unused vertex (in alphabetical order) at each point. When the path reaches vertex *l*, we need to backtrack. Backtracking to *h*, we can then form the path all the way to *n* without further backtracking. Finally we backtrack to vertex *i* to pick up vertex *m*.

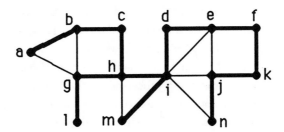

**c)** The procedure is the same as in the previous parts. The spanning tree is shown in heavy lines.

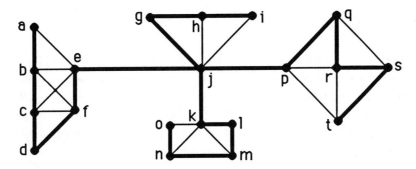

9. The question is simply asking for a spanning tree of the graph shown. There are of course many such spanning trees. One that the airline would probably not like to choose is the tree that consists of the path Bangor, Boston, New York, Detroit, Chicago, Washington, Atlanta, St. Louis, Dallas, Denver, San Diego, Los Angeles, San Francisco, Seattle. All the other 18 flights, then, would be discontinued. This set of flights would not be useful to a New York to Washington flyer, for example, nor to one who wants to fly from Chicago to Seattle. A more practical approach would be to build the tree up from nothing, using key short flights, such as the one between Detroit and Chicago. After 13 such edges had been chosen, without creating any simple circuits, we would have the desired spanning tree, and the other flights would be discontinued.

11. A connected simple graph has only one spanning tree if and only it the graph is itself a tree (and hence its own spanning tree).

13. We can write this algorithm as a recursive procedure *visit* which builds the tree *T* as it visits the vertices. We think of the tree as consisting of vertices and edges. The given connected graph, with vertices $v_1, v_2, \ldots, v_n$, is thought of as a global variable here, as is the tree *T*—all invocations of the procedure have access to them. Initially *T* consists only of one vertex. The pseudocode for *visit* follows. To find the spanning tree we just initialize *T* to be $\{v_1\}$ and call *visit* on $v_1$.

```
        procedure visit(v : vertex of G)
        for each vertex w adjacent to v and not yet in T
        begin
                put vertex w and edge {v, w} into T
                visit(w)
        end
```

15. We prove this statement by induction on the length of a shortest path from $v$ to $u$. If this length is 0, then $v = u$, and indeed, $v$ is at the root of the tree. Assume the statement is true for all vertices $w$ for which a shortest path to $v$ has length $n$, and let $u$ be a vertex for which a shortest path has length $n + 1$. Clearly $u$ cannot be at a level less than $n + 1$, because then a shorter path would be evident in the tree itself. On the other hand, if we let $w$ be the penultimate vertex in a shortest path from $v$ to $u$ of length $n + 1$, then by the inductive hypothesis, we know that $w$ is at level $n$ of the tree. Now when vertex $w$ was being processed by the breadth-first search algorithm, either $u$ was already in the tree (and therefore adjacent to a vertex at level at most $n$) or $u$ was one of the vertices put into the tree adjacent to $w$. In either case, $u$ is adjacent to a vertex at level at most $n$ and therefore is at level at most $n + 1$.

17. Label the squares of the $n \times n$ chessboard with coordinates $(i, j)$, where $i$ and $j$ are integers from 1 to $n$, inclusive.

    a) For the $3 \times 3$ board, we start our search by placing a queen in square $(1, 1)$. The only possibility for a queen in the second column is square $(3, 2)$. Now there is no place to put a queen in the third column. Therefore we backtrack and try placing the first queen in square $(2, 1)$. This time there is no place to put a queen in the second column. By symmetry, we need not consider the initial choice of a queen in square $(3, 1)$ (it will be just like the situation for the queen in square $(1, 1)$, turned upside down). Therefore we have shown that there is no solution.

    b) We start by placing a queen in square $(1, 1)$. The first place a queen might then reside in the second column is square $(3, 2)$, so we place a queen there. Now the only free spot in the third column is $(5, 3)$, the only free spot in the fourth column is $(2, 4)$, and the only free spot in the fifth column is $(4, 5)$. This gives us a solution. Note that we were lucky and did not need to backtrack at all to find this solution.

    c) The portion of the decision tree corresonding to placing the first queen in square $(1, 1)$ is quite large here, and it leads to no solution. For example, the second queen can be in any of the squares $(3, 2)$, $(4, 2)$, $(5, 2)$, or $(6, 2)$. If the second queen is in square $(3, 2)$, then the third can be in squares $(5, 3)$ or $(6, 3)$. After several backtracks we find that there is no solution with one queen in square $(1, 1)$. Next we try square $(2, 1)$ for the first queen. After a few more backtracks, we are led to the solution in which the remaining queens are in squares $(4, 2)$, $(6, 3)$, $(1, 4)$, $(3, 5)$ and $(5, 6)$.

19. Assume the graph has vertices $v_1$, $v_2$, ..., $v_n$. In looking for a Hamilton circuit we may as well start building a path at $v_1$. The general step is as follows. We extend the path if we can, to a new vertex (or to $v_1$ if this will complete the Hamilton circuit) adjacent to the vertex we are at. If we cannot extend the path any further, then we backtrack to the last previous vertex in the path and try other untried extensions from that vertex. The procedure for Hamilton paths is the same, except that we have to try all possible starting vertices, and we do not allow a return to the starting vertex, stopping instead when we have a path of the right length.

21. We know that every component of the graph has a spanning tree. The union of these spanning trees is clearly a spanning forest for the graph, since it contains every vertex and two vertices in the same component are joined by a path in the spanning tree for that component.

23. First we claim that the spanning forest will use $n - c$ edges in all. To see this, let $n_i$ be the number of vertices in the $i^{\text{th}}$ component, for $i = 1, 2, \ldots, c$. The spanning forest uses $n_i - 1$ edges in that component. Therefore the spanning forest uses $\sum (n_i - 1) = (\sum n_i) - c = n - c$ edges in all. Thus we need to remove $m - (n - c)$ edges to form a spanning forest.

25. In effect we use the depth-first search algorithm on each component. Once that algorithm stops, search through the list of vertices in the graph to find one which is not yet in the tree. If there is such a vertex, then repeat the process starting from that vertex. We continue this until all the vertices have been included in the tree.

27. There are five trees here, so there are $C(5, 2) = 10$ questions. Let $T$ be the tree in Figure 3, and let $T_1$ through $T_4$ be the trees in Figure 4, reading from left to right. We will discuss one of the pairs at length and simply report the other answers. Let $d(T, T_1)$ denote the distance between trees $T$ and $T_1$. Note that tree $T_1$ has edges $\{a, e\}$, $\{c, g\}$, and $\{e, f\}$ that tree $T$ does not. Since the trees have the same number of edges, there must also be 3 edges in $T$ that are not in $T_1$ (we do not need to list them). Therefore $d(T, T_1) = 6$. Similarly we have $d(T, T_2) = 4$, $d(T, T_3) = 4$, $d(T, T_4) = 2$, $d(T_1, T_2) = 4$, $d(T_1, T_3) = 4$, $d(T_1, T_4) = 6$, $d(T_2, T_3) = 4$, $d(T_2, T_4) = 2$, and $d(T_3, T_4) = 4$.

29. Let $e_1 = \{u, v\}$. The graph $T_2 \cup \{e_1\}$ contains a (unique) simple circuit $C$ containing edge $e_1$. Now $T_1 - \{e_1\}$ has two components, one of which contains $u$ and the other of which contains $v$. We travel along the circuit $C$, starting at $u$ and not using edge $e_1$ first, until we first reach a vertex in the component of $T_1 - \{e_1\}$ which contains $v$; obviously we must reach such a vertex eventually, since we eventually reach $v$ itself. The edge we last traversed is $e_2$. Clearly $T_2 \cup \{e_1\} - \{e_2\}$ is a tree, since $e_2$ is on $C$. On the other hand, $T_1 - \{e_1\} \cup \{e_2\}$ is also a tree, since $e_2$ reunites the two components of $T_1 - \{e_1\}$.

31. Rooted spanning trees are easy to find in all four figures, as these pictures show. There are of course many other possible correct answers.

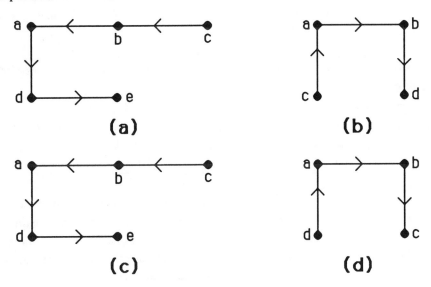

33. By Exercise 8 in Section 7.5, we know that such a directed graph has an Euler circuit. Now we traverse the Euler circuit, starting at some vertex $v$ (which will be our root), and delete from the circuit every edge that has as its terminal vertex a vertex we have already visited on this traversal. The graph that remains is a rooted spanning tree; there is a path from the root to every other vertex, and there can be no simple circuits.

⇒ **SECTION 8.6  Minimal Spanning Trees**

*The algorithms presented here are not hard, once you understand them. The two algorithms are almost identical, the only real difference being in the set of edges available for inclusion in the tree at each step. In Prim's algorithm, only those edges that are adjacent to edges already in the tree (and not completing simple circuits) may be added (so that, as a result, all the intermediate stages are trees). In Kruskal's algorithm, any edge that does not complete a simple circuit may be added (so that the intermediate stages may be forests and not trees). The reader might try to discover other methods for finding minimal spanning trees, in addition to the ones in this section.*

1. We want a minimal spanning tree in this graph. We apply Kruskal's algorithm and pave the following edges: Oasis to Deep Springs, Lida to Gold Point, Lida to Goldfield, Silverpeak to Goldfield, Oasis to Dyer, Oasis to Silverpeak, Manhattan to Tonopah, Goldfield to Tonopah, Gold Point to Beatty, and Tonopah to Warm Springs.

3. Kruskal's algorithm will have us include first the links from Atlanta to Chicago, then Atlanta to New York, then Denver to San Francisco (the cheapest links). The next cheapest link, from Chicago to New York, cannot be included, since it would form a simple circuit. Therefore we next add the link from Chicago to San Francisco, and our network is complete.

5. A graph with one edge obviously cannot be the solution, and a graph with two edges cannot either, since a simple connected graph with two edges must be a tree. On the other hand, if we take a triangle ($K_3$) and weight all the edges equally, then clearly there are three different minimal spanning trees.

7. If we simply replace each of the two occurrences of the word "minimum" with the word "maximum" (and replace the word "minimal" in the comment with the word "maximal") in Algorithm 1, then the resulting algorithm will find a maximal spanning tree.

9. We use an analog of Kruskal's algorithm, adding at each step an edge of greatest weight that does not create a simple circuit.
   a) The answer is unique. It uses edges $\{a,c\}$, $\{b,d\}$, $\{b,e\}$, and $\{c,e\}$.
   b) The answer is unique. It uses edges $\{d,h\}$, $\{d,e\}$, $\{b,f\}$, $\{d,g\}$, $\{a,b\}$, $\{b,e\}$, $\{b,c\}$, and $\{f,i\}$.
   c) There are numerous possible answers. One uses edges $\{a,d\}$, $\{b,f\}$, $\{c,g\}$, $\{d,p\}$, $\{e,f\}$, $\{f,j\}$, $\{g,k\}$, $\{h,l\}$, $\{i,j\}$, $\{i,m\}$, $\{j,k\}$, $\{j,n\}$, $\{k,l\}$, $\{k,o\}$, and $\{o,p\}$.

11. If we want a second "shortest" spanning tree (which may, of course, have the same weight as the "shortest" tree), then we need to use at least one edge not in some minimal spanning tree $T$ that we have found. One way to force this is, for each edge $e$ of $T$, to apply a minimal spanning tree algorithm to the graph with $e$ deleted, and then take a tree of minimum weight among all of these. It cannot equal $T$, and so it must be a second "shortest" spanning tree.

**13.** The proof that Prim's algorithm works shows how to take any minimal spanning tree $T$ and, if $T$ is not identical to the tree constructed by Prim's algorithm, to find another minimal spanning tree with even more edges in common with the Prim tree than $T$ has. The core of the proof is in the last paragraph, where we add an edge $e_{k+1}$ to $T$ and delete an edge $e$. Now if all the edges have different weights, then the result of this process is not another minimal spanning tree but an outright contradiction. We conclude that there are no minimal spanning trees with any edges not in common with the Prim tree, i.e., that the only minimal spanning tree is the Prim tree.

**15.** We simply apply Kruskal's algorithm, starting not from the empty tree but from the tree containing these two edges. We can add the following edges to form the desired tree: $\{c,d\}$, $\{k,l\}$, $\{b,f\}$, $\{c,g\}$, $\{a,b\}$, $\{f,j\}$, $\{a,e\}$, $\{g,h\}$, and $\{b,c\}$.

**17.** The algorithm is identical to Kruskal's algorithm (Algorithm 2), except that we replace the statement "$T :=$ empty graph" by the assignment to $T$ initially of the specified set of edges, and, instead of iterating from 1 to $n-1$, we iterate from 1 to $n-1-s$, where $s$ is the number of edges in the specified set. It is assumed that the specified set of edges forms no simple circuits.

**19. a)** First we need to find the least expensive edges incident to each vertex. These are the links from New York to Atlanta, Atlanta to Chicago, and Denver to San Francisco. The algorithm tells us to choose all of these edges. At the end of this first pass, then, we have a forest of two trees, one containing the three eastern cities, the other containing the two western cities. Next we find the least expensive edge joining these two trees, namely the link from Chicago to San Francisco, and add it to our growing forest. We now have a spanning tree, and the algorithm has finished. Note, incidentally, that this is the same spanning tree that we obtained in Example 3; by the result of Exercise 13, since the weights in this graph are all different, there was only one minimal spanning tree.

**b)** On the first pass, we choose all the edges that are the minimum weight edges at each vertex. This set consists of $\{a,b\}$, $\{b,f\}$, $\{c,d\}$, $\{a,e\}$, $\{c,g\}$, $\{g,h\}$, $\{i,j\}$, $\{f,j\}$, and $\{k,l\}$. At this point the forest has three components. Next we add the lowest weight edges incident to these three components, namely $\{h,l\}$ and $\{b,c\}$, to complete our tree.

**21.** Let $e_1$, $e_2$, ..., $e_{n-1}$ be the edges of the tree $S$ chosen by Sollin's algorithm in the order chosen (arbitrarily order the edges chosen at the same stage). Let $T$ be a minimal spanning tree which contains all the edges $e_1$, $e_2$, ..., $e_k$ for as large a $k$ as possible. Thus $0 \leq k \leq n-1$. If $k = n-1$, then $S = T$ and we have shown that $S$ is a minimal spanning tree. Otherwise we will construct another minimal spanning tree $T'$ which contains edges $e_1$, $e_2$, ..., $e_k$, $e_{k+1}$, contradicting the choice of $T$ and completing the proof.

Let $S'$ be the forest constructed by Sollin's algorithm at the stage before $e_{k+1}$ is added to $S$. Let $u$ be the endpoint of $e_{k+1}$ that is in a component $C$ of $S'$ responsible for the addition of $e_{k+1}$ (i.e., so that $e_{k+1}$ is the minimum weight edge incident to $C$). Let $v$ be the other endpoint of $e_{k+1}$. We let $P$ be the unique simple path from $u$ to $v$ in $T$. We follow $P$ until we come to the first edge $e'$ not in $S'$. Thus $e'$ is also incident to $C$. Since the algorithm chose to add $e_{k+1}$ on behalf of $C$, we know that $w(e_{k+1}) \leq w(e')$, and that $e'$ was added on behalf of the component of its other endpoint. Now if $e'$ is not in $\{e_1, \ldots, e_k\}$, then we go on to the next paragraph. Otherwise, we continue following $P$ until we come to the first edge $e''$ not in $S'$. Thus $e''$ is also incident to $C'$, but was added on behalf of another component $C''$, and $w(e') \leq w(e'')$. We continue in this way until we come to an edge $e^{(r)}$ not in $\{e_1, \ldots, e_k\}$.

Finally, let $T' = T \cup \{e_{k+1}\} - \{e^{(r)}\}$. Then by stringing together the inequalities we have obtained along the way, we know that $w(e_{k+1}) \leq w(e^{(r)})$. It follows that $w(T') \leq w(T)$, so $T'$ is again a minimal spanning tree. Furthermore, $T'$ contains $e_1, e_2, \ldots, e_k, e_{k+1}$, and we have our desired contradiction.

23. Suppose there are $r$ trees in the forest at some intermediate stage of Sollin's algorithm. Each new tree formed during this stage will then contain at least two of the old trees, so there are at most $r/2$ new trees. In other words, we have to reduce the number of trees by at least $r - (r/2) = r/2$. Since each edge added at this stage reduces the number of trees by exactly one, we must add at least $r/2$ edges. Finally, the number of edges added is of course an integer, so it is at least $\lceil r/2 \rceil$.

25. This follows easily from Exercises 23 and 24. After $k$ stages of Sollin's algorithm, since the number of trees begins at $n$ and is at least halved at each stage, there are at most $n/2^k$ trees. Thus if $n \leq 2^k$, then this quantity is less than or equal to 1, so the algorithm has terminated. In other words, the algorithm terminates after at most $k$ stages if $k \geq \log n$, which is what we wanted to prove.

⇒ **SUPPLEMENTARY EXERCISES FOR CHAPTER 8**

1. There are of course two things to prove here. First let us assume that $G$ is a tree. We must show that $G$ contains no simple circuits (which is immediate by definition) and that the addition of an edge connecting two nonadjacent vertices produces a graph that has exactly one simple circuit. Clearly the addition of such an edge $e = \{u, v\}$ produces a graph with a simple circuit, namely $u, e, v, P, u$, where $P$ is the unique simple path joining $v$ to $u$ in $G$. Since $P$ is unique, moreover, this is the only simple circuit that can be formed.

   To prove the converse, suppose that $G$ satisfies the given conditions; we want to prove that $G$ is a tree, in other words, that $G$ is connected (since one of the conditions is already that $G$ has no simple circuits). If $G$ is not connected, then let $u$ and $v$ lie in separate components of $G$. Then edge $\{u, v\}$ can be added to $G$ without the formation of any simple circuits, in contradiction to the assumed condition. Therefore $G$ is indeed a tree.

3. Let $P$ be a longest simple path in a given tree $T$. This path has length at least 1 as long as $T$ has at least one edge, and such a longest simple path exists since $T$ is finite. Now the vertices at the ends of $P$ must both have degree 1 (i.e., be pendant vertices), since otherwise the simple path $P$ could be extended to a longer simple path.

5. Since the sum of the degrees of the vertices is twice the number of edges, and since a tree with $n$ vertices has $n - 1$ edges, the answer is $2n - 2$.

7. One way to prove this is simply to note that the conventional way of drawing rooted trees provides a planar imbedding. Another simple proof is to observe that a tree cannot contain a subgraph homeomorphic to $K_5$ or $K_{3,3}$, since these must contain simple circuits. A third proof, of the fact that a tree can be imbedded in the plane with straight lines for the edges, is by induction on the number of vertices. The base case (a tree with one vertex) is trivial (there are no edges). If tree $T$ contains $n + 1$ vertices, then delete one vertex of degree 1 (which exists by Exercise 3), imbed the remainder (by the inductive hypothesis), and then draw the deleted vertex and reattach it with a short straight line to the proper vertex.

9. Since the colors in one component have no effect on the colors in another component, it is enough to prove this for connected graphs, i.e., trees. In order to color a tree with 2 colors, we simply view the tree as rooted and color all the vertices at even-numbered levels with one color and all the vertices at odd-numbered levels with another color. Since every edge connects vertices at adjacent levels, this coloring is proper.

11. A B-tree of degree $k$ and height $h$ has the most leaves when every vertex not at level $h$ has as many children as possible, namely $k$ children. In this case the tree is simply the complete $k$-ary tree of height $h$, so it has $k^h$ leaves. Thus the best upper bound for the number of leaves of a B-tree of degree $k$ and height $h$ is $k^h$. To obtain a lower bound, we want to have as few leaves as possible. This is accomplished when each vertex has as few children as possible. The root must have at least 2 children. Each other vertex not at level $h$ must have at least $\lceil k/2 \rceil$ children. Thus there are $2\lceil k/2 \rceil^{h-1}$ leaves, so this is our best lower bound. (Of course if $h = 0$, then the tree has exactly 1 leaf.)

13. We follow the recursive definition in drawing these trees. For example, we obtain $S_4$ by taking a copy of $S_3$ (on the left), adding one more child of the root (the right-most one), and putting a copy of $S_3$ rooted at this new child.

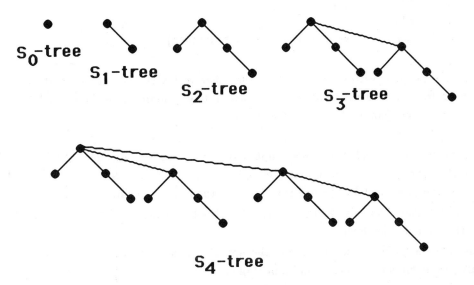

15. We prove this by induction on $k$. If $k = 0$ or $1$, then the result is trivial. Assume the inductive hypothesis that the $S_{k-1}$-tree can be formed in the manner indicated, and let $T$ be an $S_k$-tree. Then $T$ consists of a copy of an $S_{k-1}$ tree $T_{k-1}$ with root $r_{k-1}$, together with another copy of an $S_{k-1}$ tree whose root is made a child of $r_{k-1}$. Now by the inductive hypothesis, this latter $S_{k-1}$-tree can be formed from a handle $v$ and disjoint trees $T_0, T_1, \ldots, T_{k-2}$ by connecting $v$ to $r_0$ and $r_i$ to $r_{i+1}$ for $i = 0, 1, \ldots, k-3$. Since our tree $T$ is formed by then joining $r_{k-2}$ to $r_{k-1}$, our tree is formed precisely in the manner desired, and the proof by induction is complete.

17. Essentially we just want to do a breadth-first search of the tree, starting at the root, and considering the children of a vertex in the order from left to right. Thus the algorithm is to perform breadth-first search, starting at the root of the tree. Whenever we encounter a vertex, we print it out.

19. First we determine the universal addresses of all the vertices in the tree. The root has address $0$. For every leaf address, we include an address for each prefix of that address. For example, if there is a leaf with address 4.3.7.3, then we include vertices with addresses 4, 4.3, and 4.3.7. The tree structure is constructed by making all the vertices with positive integers as their addresses the children of the root, in order, and all the vertices with addresses of the form $A.i$, where $A$ is an address and $i$ is a positive integer, the children of the vertex whose address is $A$, in order by $i$.

21. The most elegant way to do this is by comparing from the end of the list at each stage, rather than from the beginning. That way we can do the moving and the comparing at the same time. To make sure we stop at the head of the list if the item to be inserted is smaller than all the elements of the list, we place an artificial element $-\infty$ as the $0^{\text{th}}$ element of the list.

> **procedure** *insertion*$(a_1, a_2, \ldots, a_n : \text{numbers})$
> $a_0 := -\infty$
> **for** $j := 2$ **to** $n$
> **begin**
> $\quad i := j$
> $\quad$ **while** $a_i < a_{i-1}$
> $\quad$ **begin**
> $\quad\quad$ interchange $a_i$ and $a_{i-1}$
> $\quad\quad i := i - 1$
> $\quad$ **end**
> **end** $\{a_1, a_2, \ldots, a_n$ are now in nondecreasing order$\}$

23. Let $v$ be the pendant vertex, and let $u$ be the other vertex that is an endpoint of $e$. Then every simple path from $u$ to $v$ must end $u, e, v$. Since in any spanning tree there must be a simple path from $u$ to $v$, every spanning tree must include $e$.

25. For convenience, let us define a "very simple circuit" to be a set of edges that form a circuit all of whose vertices are distinct except that (necessarily) the last vertex is the same as the first. Thus a cactus is a graph in which every edge is in no more than one very simple circuit.
    **a)** This is a cactus. The edge at the top is in no simple circuit. The three edges at the bottom are only in the triangle they form.
    **b)** This is not a cactus, since the edge in the upper right-hand corner, for instance, is in more than one very simple circuit: a triangle and a pentagon.
    **c)** This is a cactus. The edges in each of the three triangles are each in exactly one very simple circuit.

27. Adding a very simple circuit (see Exercise 25 for the definition) does not give the graph any more very simple circuits, except for the one being added. Thus the new edges are each in exactly one very simple circuit, and the old edges are still in no more than one.

29. **a)** There is clearly a spanning tree here which is a simple path $(a, b, c, f, e, d$, for instance); since each degree is 1 or 2, this spanning tree meets the condition imposed.
    **b)** The only spanning tree here is the graph itself, and vertex $i$ has degree greater than 3. Thus there is no degree-constrained spanning tree where each vertex has degree less than or equal to 3.
    **c)** There is clearly a spanning tree here which is a simple path $(a, b, c, f, e, d, i, h, g$, for instance); since each degree is 1 or 2, this spanning tree meets the condition imposed.

31. We need to label these trees so that they satisfy the condition. We work by trial and error, using some common sense. For example, the labels 1 and $n$ need to be adjacent in order to obtain the difference $n - 1$.

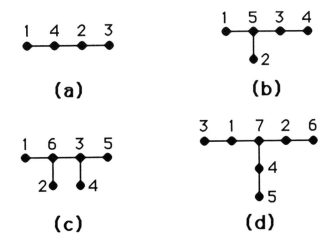

33. We count the caterpillars by drawing them all, using the length of the longest path to organize our work. In fact every tree with six vertices is a caterpillar. They are the five trees shown in our solution to Exercise 25c in Section 8.1, together with the star $K_{1,5}$. Thus the answer is 6.

35. We will not actually draw the trees in question, since they are much too large (each has on the order of 100 vertices). In principle, though, we could draw them. For example, for part (a) there are 5 children of the position shown here, corresponding to the 5 possible moves for X. Each of these vertices has 4 children, and so on. Let us analyze the strategies.

    a) Player X can win by moving in the middle square. This blocks O from winning immediately and gives X a double threat that O cannot counter.

    b) Here X does not have a winning strategy—in fact X will lose if O plays correctly. At this move X must block O by moving in the lower right-hand corner. Then O moves in the center, simultaneously blocking X and creating a fatal double threat.

    c) Here X wins by moving in the middle of the right-hand edge, creating a fatal double threat.

37. Let $T$ be a minimal spanning tree. If $T$ contains $e$, then we are done. If not, then adding $e$ to $T$ creates a simple circuit, and then deleting another edge $e'$ of this simple circuit gives us another spanning tree $T'$. Since $w(e) \leq w(e')$, the weight of $T'$ is no larger than the weight of $T$. Therefore $T'$ is a minimal spanning tree containing $e$.

39. We assume that what is being asked for here is not "a minimal spanning tree of the graph which also happens to satisfy the degree constraint" but rather "a tree of minimum weight among all trees that satisfy the degree constraint."

    a) Since $b$ is a cut vertex we must include at least one of the two edges $\{b, c\}$ and $\{b, d\}$, and one of the other three edges incident to $b$. Thus the best we can do is to include edges $\{b, c\}$ and $\{a, b\}$. It is then easy to see that the unique minimal spanning tree with degrees constrained to be at most 2 consists of these two edges, together with $\{c, d\}$, $\{a, f\}$, and $\{e, f\}$.

    b) Obviously we must include edge $\{a, b\}$. We cannot include edge $\{b, g\}$, because this would force vertex $g$ to have degree greater than 2 in the spanning tree. For a similar reason we cannot include edge $\{b,d\}$. A little more thought shows that the minimal spanning tree under these constraints consists of edge $\{a,b\}$, together with edges $\{b,c\}$, $\{c,d\}$, $\{d,g\}$, $\{f,g\}$, and $\{e,f\}$.

# CHAPTER 9
## Boolean Algebra

⇒ **SECTION 9.1   Boolean Functions**

*The first 20 of these exercises are extremely straightforward and should pose no difficulty. The last 4 relate to the interconnection between duality and DeMorgan's laws; they are a bit subtle. Boolean functions can be proved equal by tables of values (as we illustrate in Exercise 7), by using known identities (as we illustrate in Exercise 5), or by taking duals of equal Boolean functions (Exercise 20 justifies this). To show that two Boolean functions are not equal, we need to find a counterexample, i.e., values of the variables such that give the two functions different values.*

1.  **a)** $1 \cdot \overline{0} = 1 \cdot 1 = 1$
    **b)** $1 + \overline{1} = 1 + 0 = 1$
    **c)** $\overline{0} \cdot 0 = 1 \cdot 0 = 0$
    **d)** $\overline{(1+0)} = \overline{1} = 0$

3.  By looking at the definitions, we see that this equation is satisfied if and only if $x = y$, i.e., $x = y = 0$ or $x = y = 1$.

5.  First we "factor" out an $x$ by using the identity and distributive laws: $x + xy = x \cdot 1 + x \cdot y = x \cdot (1 + y)$. Then we use the commutative law, the dominance law, and finally the identity law again to write this as $x \cdot (y + 1) = x \cdot 1 = x$.

7.  Probably the simplest way to do this is by use of a table, as in Example 4. We list all the possible values for the triple $(x, y, z)$ (there being eight such), and for each compute both sides of this equation. For example, for $x = y = z = 0$ we have $x\overline{y} + y\overline{z} + \overline{x}z = 0 \cdot 1 + 0 \cdot 1 + 1 \cdot 0 = 0 + 0 + 0 = 0$, and similarly $\overline{x}y + \overline{y}z + x\overline{z} = 0$. We do this for all eight lines of the table to conclude that the two functions are equal.

| $x$ | $y$ | $z$ | $x\overline{y} + y\overline{z} + \overline{x}z$ | $\overline{x}y + \overline{y}z + x\overline{z}$ |
|---|---|---|---|---|
| 1 | 1 | 1 | 0 | 0 |
| 1 | 1 | 0 | 1 | 1 |
| 1 | 0 | 1 | 1 | 1 |
| 1 | 0 | 0 | 1 | 1 |
| 0 | 1 | 1 | 1 | 1 |
| 0 | 1 | 0 | 1 | 1 |
| 0 | 0 | 1 | 1 | 1 |
| 0 | 0 | 0 | 0 | 0 |

9.  The idempotent laws state that $x \cdot x = x$ and $x + x = x$. There are only four things to check: $0 \cdot 0 = 0$, $0 + 0 = 0$, $1 \cdot 1 = 1$, and $1 + 1 = 1$, all of which are part of the definitions.

11. The dominance laws state that $x + 1 = 1$ and $x \cdot 0 = 0$. There are only four things to check: $0 + 1 = 1$, $0 \cdot 0 = 0$, $1 + 1 = 1$, and $1 \cdot 0 = 0$, all of which are part of the definitions.

**13.** We can verify the associative laws by constructing the relevant table, which will have eight rows, since there are eight combinations of values for $x$, $y$, and $z$ in the equations $x + (y + z) = (x + y) + z$ and $x(yz) = (xy)z$. Rather than write down these tables, let us observe that in the first case, both sides are equal to 1 unless $x = y = z = 0$ (in which case both sides equal 0), and, dually, in the second case, both sides are equal to 0 unless $x = y = z = 1$ (in which case both sides equal 1).

**15.** We construct the relevant tables (as in Exercise 7) and compute the quantities shown. Since the fourth and seventh columns are equal, we know that $\overline{(xy)} = \overline{x} + \overline{y}$; since the ninth and tenth columns are equal, we know that $\overline{(x + y)} = \overline{x}\,\overline{y}$.

| $x$ | $y$ | $xy$ | $\overline{(xy)}$ | $\overline{x}$ | $\overline{y}$ | $\overline{x} + \overline{y}$ | $x + y$ | $\overline{(x + y)}$ | $\overline{x}\,\overline{y}$ |
|---|---|---|---|---|---|---|---|---|---|
| 1 | 1 | 1 | 0 | 0 | 0 | 0 | 1 | 0 | 0 |
| 1 | 0 | 0 | 1 | 0 | 1 | 1 | 1 | 0 | 0 |
| 0 | 1 | 0 | 1 | 1 | 0 | 1 | 1 | 0 | 0 |
| 0 | 0 | 0 | 1 | 1 | 1 | 1 | 0 | 1 | 1 |

**17.** We could prove these by constructing tables, as in Exercise 15. Instead we will argue directly.
**a)** The left-hand side is equal to 1 if $x \neq y$. In this case the right-hand side is necessarily $1 \cdot 1 = 1$, as well. On the other hand if $x = y = 1$, then the left-hand side is by definition equal to 0, and the right-hand side equals $1 \cdot 0 = 0$; similarly if $x = y = 0$, then the left-hand side is by definition equal to 0, and the right-hand side equals $0 \cdot 1 = 0$.
**b)** The left-hand side is equal to 1 if $x \neq y$. In this case the right-hand side is necessarily $1 + 0 = 1$ or $0 + 1 = 1$, as well. On the other hand if $x = y$, then the left-hand side is by definition equal to 0, and the right-hand side equals $0 + 0 = 0$.

**19. a)** We can prove this by constructing the appropriate table, as in Exercise 15. What we will find is that each side equals 1 if and only if an odd number of the variables are equal to 1. Thus the two functions are equal.
**b)** This is not an identity. If we let $x = y = z = 1$, then the left-hand side is $1 + 0 = 1$, while the right-hand side is $1 \oplus 1 = 0$.
**c)** This is not an identity. If we let $x = y = 1$ and $z = 0$, then the left-hand side is $1 \oplus 1 = 0$, while the right-hand side is $0 + 1 = 1$.

**21.** Let $B$ be a Boolean expression representing $F$, and let $D$ be the dual of $B$. We want to show that for every set of values assigned to the variables $x_1$, $x_2$, ..., $x_n$, the value $D$ equals the opposite of the value of $B$ with the opposites of these values assigned to $x_1$, $x_2$, ..., $x_n$. The trick is to look at $\overline{B}$. Then by DeMorgan's Laws, $\overline{B}$ is the same as the expression obtained by replacing each occurrence of $x_i$ in $D$ by $\overline{x}_i$. Thus for any values of $x_1$, $x_2$, ..., $x_n$, the value of $D$ is the same as the value of $\overline{B}$ for the corresponding value of $\overline{x}_1$, $\overline{x}_2$, ..., $\overline{x}_n$. This tells us that $\overline{B}$ represents the function whose values are exactly those of the function represented by $D$ when the opposites of each of the values of the variables $x_i$ are used, and that is exactly what we wanted to prove.

**23.** Because of the stated condition, we are free to specify $F(1, y, z)$ for all pairs $(y, z)$, but then all the values of $F(0, y, z)$ are thereby determined. There are 4 such pairs $(y, z)$ (each one can be either 0 or 1), and for each such pair we have 2 choices as to the value of $F(1, y, z)$. Therefore the answer is $2^4 = 16$.

$\Rightarrow$ **SECTION 9.2    Representing Boolean Functions**

*The first six exercises are straightforward practice dealing with sum-of-products expansions. These are obtained by writing down one product term for each combination of values of the variables that makes the function have the value 1, and taking the sum of these terms. The dual to the sum-of-products expansion is discussed in Exercise 7 to Exercise 11, and these should be looked at. Since the concept of complete sets of operators plays an important role in the logical circuit design in sections to follow, Exercise 12 to Exercise 20 are also important.*

1.  a) We want $\overline{x}$, $\overline{y}$, and $z$ all to have the value 1; therefore we take the product $\overline{x}\,\overline{y}\,z$. The other parts are similar, so we present only the answers.

    b) $\overline{x}\,y\,\overline{z}$

    c) $\overline{x}\,y\,z$

    d) $\overline{x}\,\overline{y}\,\overline{z}$

3.  a) We want the function to have the value 1 whenever at least one of the variables has the value 1. There are seven minterms that achieve this, so the sum has six summands: $x\,y\,z + x\,y\,\overline{z} + x\,\overline{y}\,z + \overline{x}\,y\,z + x\,\overline{y}\,\overline{z} + \overline{x}\,y\,\overline{z} + \overline{x}\,\overline{y}\,z$.

    b) Here is another way to think about this problem (rather than just making a table and reading off the minterms that make the value equal to 1). If we expand the expression by the distributive law (and use the commutative law), we get $xy+yz$. Now invoking the identity laws, the law that $s+\overline{s} = 1$, and the distributive and commutative laws again, we write this as $xy1 + 1yz = xy(z+\overline{z}) + (x+\overline{x})yz = xyz + xy\overline{z} + xyz + \overline{x}yz$. Finally, we use the idempotent law to collapse the first and third term, to obtain our answer: $xyz + xy\overline{z} + \overline{x}yz$.

    c) We can use either the straightforward approach or the idea used in part (b). The answer is $x\,y\,z + x\,y\,\overline{z} + x\,\overline{y}\,z + x\,\overline{y}\,\overline{z}$.

    d) The method discussed in part (b) works well here, to obtain the answer $x\,\overline{y}\,z + x\,\overline{y}\,\overline{z}$.

5.  We need to list all minterms that have an odd number of the variables without bars (and hence an odd number with bars). There are $C(4,1) + C(4,3) = 8$ terms. The answer is $w\,x\,y\,\overline{z} + w\,x\,\overline{y}\,z + w\,\overline{x}\,y\,z + \overline{w}\,x\,y\,z + w\,\overline{x}\,\overline{y}\,\overline{z} + \overline{w}\,x\,\overline{y}\,\overline{z} + \overline{w}\,\overline{x}\,y\,\overline{z} + \overline{w}\,\overline{x}\,\overline{y}\,z$.

7.  This exercise is dual to Exercise 1.

    a) Note that $\overline{x}$ will have the value 0 if and only if $x = 1$. Similarly, $\overline{y}$ will have the value 0 if and only if $y = 1$. Therefore the expression $\overline{x} + \overline{y} + z$ will have the value 0 precisely in the desired case. The remaining parts are similar, so we list only the answers.

    b) $x + y + z$

    c) $x + \overline{y} + z$

9.  By the definition of "$+$," the sum $y_1 + \cdots + y_n$ has the value 0 if and only if each $y_i = 0$. This happens precisely when $x_i = 0$ for those cases in which $y_i = x_i$ and $x_i = 1$ in those cases in which $y_i = \overline{x}_i$.

11. a) This function is already written in its product-of-sums form.

    b) This function has the value 0 in case $y = 0$ or both $x$ and $z$ equal 0. Therefore we need maxterms $x + y + z$, $x + y + \overline{z}$, $\overline{x} + y + z$, and $\overline{x} + y + \overline{z}$ (to take care of $y = 0$), and also $x + \overline{y} + z$. Therefore the answer is the product of these five maxterms.

**c)** This function has the value 0 in case $x = 0$. Therefore we need four maxterms, and the answer is $(x + y + z)(x + y + \overline{z})(x + \overline{y} + z)(x + \overline{y} + \overline{z})$.

**d)** Let us indicate another way to solve problems like this. In Exercise 3d we found the sum-of-products expansion of this function. Suppose we take take sum-of-products expansion of the function which is the opposite of this one. It will have all the minterms other than the ones in the answer to Exercise 3d, so it will be $x\,y\,z + x\,y\,\overline{z} + \overline{x}\,y\,z + \overline{x}\,y\,\overline{z} + \overline{x}\,\overline{y}\,z + \overline{x}\,y\,z$. If we now take the complement of this (put a big bar over it), then we will have an expression for the function we want. Then we push the complementations inside, using DeMorgan's laws and the fact that $\overline{\overline{s}} = s$. This will give us the desired product-of-sums expansion. Formally, all we do is put parentheses around the minterms, erase all the plus signs, put plus signs between all the variables (where there used to be implied products), and change every complemented variable to its uncomplemented version and vice versa. The answer is thus $(\overline{x} + \overline{y} + \overline{z})(\overline{x} + \overline{y} + z)(x + \overline{y} + \overline{z})(x + \overline{y} + z)(x + y + \overline{z})(x + y + z)$.

13. To do this exercise we need to use DeMorgan's law to replace $st$ by $\overline{(\overline{s} + \overline{t})}$. Thus we just do this formally in the expressions in Exercise 12, and we obtain the answers. It is also good to simplify double complements, of course.

**a)** This is already in the desired form, having no products.

**b)** $x + \overline{y}(\overline{x} + z) = x + \left(\overline{\overline{y} + \overline{(\overline{x} + z)}}\right) = x + \overline{\left(y + \overline{(\overline{x} + z)}\right)}$

**c)** This is already in the desired form, having no products.

**d)** $\overline{x}(x + \overline{y} + \overline{z}) = \left(\overline{\overline{\overline{x}} + \overline{(x + \overline{y} + \overline{z})}}\right) = \overline{\left(x + \overline{(x + \overline{y} + \overline{z})}\right)}$.

15. **a)** We use the definition of $\downarrow$. If $x = 1$, then $x \downarrow x = 0$; and if $x = 0$, then $x \downarrow x = 1$. These are precisely the corresponding values of $\overline{x}$.

**b)** We can construct a table to look at all four cases, as follows. Since the fifth and sixth columns are equal, the expressions are equivalent.

| $x$ | $y$ | $x \downarrow x$ | $y \downarrow y$ | $(x \downarrow x) \downarrow (y \downarrow y)$ | $xy$ |
|---|---|---|---|---|---|
| 1 | 1 | 0 | 0 | 1 | 1 |
| 1 | 0 | 0 | 1 | 0 | 0 |
| 0 | 1 | 1 | 0 | 0 | 0 |
| 0 | 0 | 1 | 1 | 0 | 0 |

**c)** We can construct a table to look at all four cases, as follows. Since the fourth and fifth columns are equal, the expressions are equivalent.

| $x$ | $y$ | $x \downarrow y$ | $(x \downarrow y) \downarrow (x \downarrow y)$ | $x + y$ |
|---|---|---|---|---|
| 1 | 1 | 0 | 1 | 1 |
| 1 | 0 | 0 | 1 | 1 |
| 0 | 1 | 0 | 1 | 1 |
| 0 | 0 | 1 | 0 | 0 |

17. **a)** Since $x + y + z = (x + y) + z$, we first write this as $((x + y) \mid (x + y)) \mid (z \mid z)$, using the identity in Exercise 14c. Then we rewrite $x + y$ as $(x \mid x) \mid (y \mid y)$, using the same identity. This gives us

$$(((x \mid x) \mid (y \mid y)) \mid ((x \mid x) \mid (y \mid y))) \mid (z \mid z).$$

**b)** First we write this as $((x + z) \mid y) \mid ((x + z) \mid y)$, using the identity in Exercise 14b. Then we rewrite $x + z$ as $(x \mid x) \mid (z \mid z)$, using the identity in Exercise 14c. This gives us

$$(((x \mid x) \mid (z \mid z)) \mid y) \mid (((x \mid x) \mid (z \mid z)) \mid y).$$

**c)** There are no operators, so nothing needs to be done; the expression as given is the answer.

**d)** First we write this as $(x \mid \overline{y}) \mid (x \mid \overline{y})$, using the identity in Exercise 14b. Then we rewrite $\overline{y}$ as $y \mid y$, using the identity in Exercise 14a. This gives us $(x \mid (y \mid y)) \mid (x \mid (y \mid y))$.

19. We claim that it is impossible to write a Boolean expression for $\overline{x}$ involving $x$, $+$, and $\cdot$. The reason is that if $x = 1$, then any combination of these two operators applied to $x$ (and the results of previous calculations) can only yield the value 1. But $\overline{1} = 0$. (This problem is somewhat harder if we allow the use of the constants 0 and 1. The argument given here is then no longer valid, since $x \cdot 0 = 0$. Nevertheless it is possible to show that even with these constants allowed, the set $\{+, \cdot\}$ is not functionally complete—i.e., it is impossible to write down a Boolean expression using only the operators $+$ and $\cdot$ (together with $x$, 0, and 1) which is equivalent to $\overline{x}$. What one can do is to prove by induction on the length of the expression that any such Boolean expression which has the value 1 when $x = 0$ must also have the value 1 when $x = 1$.)

⇒ **SECTION 9.3    Logic Gates**

*This section is a brief introduction to circuit design using AND and OR gates and inverters. In real life circuits will have thousands of these components, but you will get some of the flavor in these exercises. Notice particularly Exercise 5, which shows how circuits already constructed can be further combined to give more complex, useful circuits. If we want to get by with fewer types of gates (but more gates), then we can use NOR or NAND gates, as illustrated in Exercise 11 to Exercise 14.*

1. **a)** The output of the OR gate at the top is $x + y$. This and $\overline{y}$ are the inputs to the final AND gate. Therefore the output of the circuit is $(x + y)\overline{y}$.

   **b)** The inputs to the AND gate are $\overline{x}$ and $\overline{y}$. The output is then passed through the inverter. Therefore the final output is $\overline{(\overline{x}\,\overline{y})}$. Note that there is a simpler way to form a circuit equivalent to this one, namely $x + y$.

   **c)** The idea is the same as in the previous parts. The final output is an OR with two inputs. The first of these inputs is the result of inverting $xy$, and the second is $\overline{z} + x$. Therefore the answer is $\overline{(xy)} + (\overline{z} + x)$.

   **d)** This is similar to the others. The output is $\overline{(\overline{x}\,y\,z)}(\overline{x} + y + \overline{z})$.

3. Let $v$, $w$, $x$, $y$, and $z$ be the votes of the five individuals, with a 1 representing a yes vote and a 0 representing a no vote. Then the majority will be a yes vote (represented by an output of 1) if and only if there are at least three yes votes. Thus we make an AND gate for each of the $C(5,3) = 10$ triples of voters, and combine the outputs from these 10 gates with an OR. We turn the picture on its side for convenience.

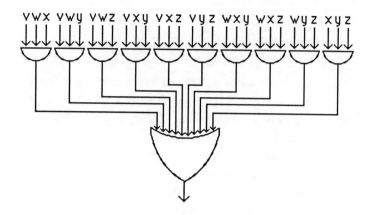

5. The circuit is identical to Figure 10, expanded by two more units to accommodate the two additional bits. To get the computation started, $x_0$ and $y_0$ are the inputs to the half adder. Thereafter, the carry bit from each column is input, together with the next pair $(x_i, y_i)$ to a full adder to find the output and carry for the next column. The final carry bit $(c_4)$ is the final answer bit $(s_5)$.

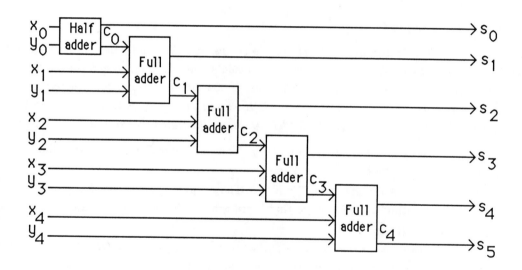

7. We will construct the full subtractor directly. Suppose the inputs bits are $x$, $y$, and $b$, where we are computing $x - y$ with borrow $b$. The output is a bit, $z$, and a borrow from the next column, $b'$. Then by looking at the eight possibilities for the bits $x$, $y$, and $b$, we see that $z = x\,y\,b + x\,\overline{y}\,\overline{b} + \overline{x}\,y\,\overline{b} + \overline{x}\,\overline{y}\,b$; and that $b' = x\,y\,b + \overline{x}\,y\,b + \overline{x}\,y\,\overline{b} + \overline{x}\,\overline{y}\,b$. Therefore a full subtractor can be formed by using *AND* gates, *OR* gates, and inverters to represent these expressions. We obtain the circuits shown below.

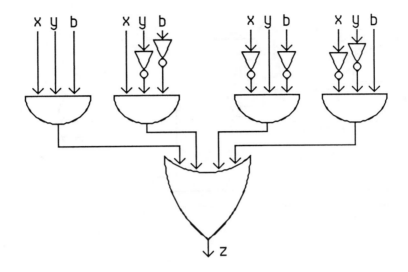

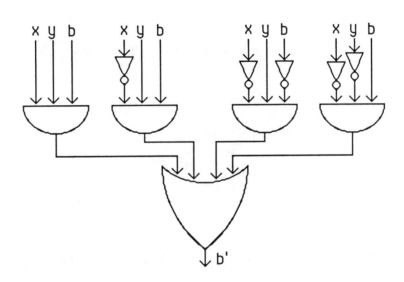

9. The first number is larger than the second if $x_1 > y_1$ (which means $x_1 = 1$ and $y_1 = 0$), or if $x_1 = y_1$ (which means either that $x_1 = 1$ and $y_1 = 1$, or that $x_1 = 0$ and $y_1 = 0$) and also $x_0 > y_0$ (which means $x_0 = 1$ and $y_0 = 0$). We translate this sentence into a circuit in the obvious manner, obtaining the picture shown.

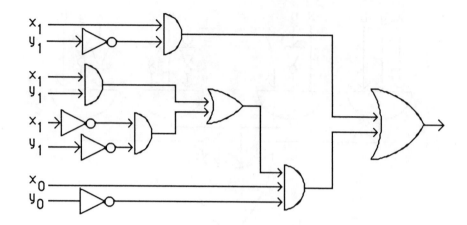

**11. a)** By Exercise 14a in Section 2, $\overline{x} = x \mid x$. Therefore the gate for $\overline{x}$ is as shown below.

**b)** By Exercise 14c in Section 2, $x + y = (x \mid x) \mid (y \mid y)$. Therefore the gate for $x + y$ is as shown below.

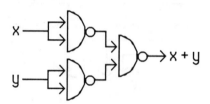

**c)** By Exercise 14b in Section 2, $xy = (x \mid y) \mid (x \mid y)$. Therefore the gate for $xy$ is as shown below.

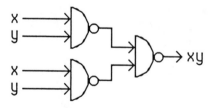

**d)** First we note that $x \oplus y = x\,\overline{y} + \overline{x}\,y = \overline{((x\,\overline{y})\,(\overline{x}\,y))} = \overline{(x\,\overline{y})} \mid \overline{(\overline{x}\,y)} = (x \mid \overline{y}) \mid (\overline{x} \mid y)$. We constructed the gate for inverting in part (a). Therefore the gate for $xy$ is as shown below.

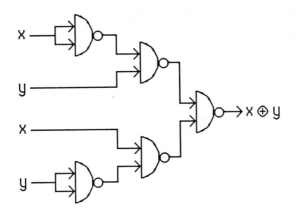

**13.** We know that the sum bit in the half adder is $s = x\overline{y} + \overline{x}y$. The answer to Exercise 11d shows precisely this gate constructed from *NAND* gates, so it gives us this part of the answer. Also, the carry bit in the half adder is $s = xy$. The answer to Exercise 11c shows precisely this gate constructed from *NAND* gates, so it gives us this part of the answer.

⇒  **SECTION 9.4    Minimization of Circuits**

*The two methods presented here for minimizing circuits are really the same, just looked at from two different points of view—one geometric (Karnaugh maps) and one algebraic (the Quine-McCluskey method). In each case the idea is to get larger blocks, which represent simpler terms, to cover several minterms. The calculations can get very messy, but if you follow the examples and organize your work carefully, you should not have trouble with them. The hard part in these algorithms from a theoretical point of view is finding the set of products which cover all the minterms. In these small examples, this tends not to be a problem.*

**1.  a)** The Karnaugh map we draw here has the variable $x$ down the side and variable $y$ across the top.

|  | y | $\overline{y}$ |
|---|---|---|
| x |  |  |
| $\overline{x}$ | 1 |  |

**b)** The upper left-hand corner square (whose minterm is $x\,y$) and the lower right-hand corner square (whose minterm is $\overline{x}\,\overline{y}$) are adjacent to this square.

**3.** The 2 × 2 square is used in each case. We put a 1 in those squares whose minterms are listed.

|  | y | $\overline{y}$ |
|---|---|---|
| x |  | 1 |
| $\overline{x}$ |  |  |

**(a)**

|  | y | $\overline{y}$ |
|---|---|---|
| x | 1 |  |
| $\overline{x}$ |  | 1 |

**(b)**

|  | y | $\overline{y}$ |
|---|---|---|
| x | 1 | 1 |
| $\overline{x}$ | 1 | 1 |

**(c)**

**5. a)** We can draw a Karnaugh map for three variables in the manner shown here, with the $x$ variable down the side and the $y$ and $z$ variables across the top, in the order shown. We have placed a 1 in the requested position.

|  | yz | yz̄ | ȳz̄ | ȳz |
|---|---|---|---|---|
| x |  |  |  |  |
| x̄ |  | 1 |  |  |

**b)** There are three squares adjacent to every square (since there are three variables). The minterms of the adjacent squares can be read off the picture: $\overline{x}\,y\,z$, $x\,y\,\overline{z}$, and $\overline{x}\,\overline{y}\,\overline{z}$.

**7.** The $2 \times 4$ square is used in each case. We put a 1 in those squares whose minterms are listed.

|  | yz | yz̄ | ȳz̄ | ȳz |
|---|---|---|---|---|
| x |  |  | 1 |  |
| x̄ |  |  |  |  |

**(a)**

|  | yz | yz̄ | ȳz̄ | ȳz |
|---|---|---|---|---|
| x |  |  |  |  |
| x̄ | 1 |  | 1 |  |

**(b)**

|  | yz | yz̄ | ȳz̄ | ȳz |
|---|---|---|---|---|
| x | 1 | 1 |  |  |
| x̄ |  | 1 |  | 1 |

**(c)**

**9. a)** We can draw a Karnaugh map for four variables in the manner shown here, with the $w$ and $x$ variables down the side and the $y$ and $z$ variables across the top, in the order shown. We have placed a 1 in the requested position.

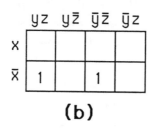

|  | yz | yz̄ | ȳz̄ | ȳz |
|---|---|---|---|---|
| w x |  |  |  |  |
| w x̄ |  |  |  |  |
| w̄ x̄ |  |  |  |  |
| w̄ x |  | 1 |  |  |

**b)** There are four squares adjacent to every square (since there are four variables). The minterms of the adjacent squares can be read off the picture: $\overline{w}\,x\,y\,z$, $\overline{w}\,\overline{x}\,y\,\overline{z}$, $\overline{w}\,x\,\overline{y}\,\overline{z}$, and (recalling that the top row is adjacent to the bottom row) $w\,x\,y\,\overline{z}$.

**11. a)** There are clearly $2^n$ squares in a Karnaugh map for $n$ variables, since in specifying a minterm each variable can appear either complemented or uncomplemented. Thus the answer is $2^5 = 32$.

**b)** There are $n$ squares adjacent to each square in the Karnaugh map for $n$ variables, because each of the variables can be changed (from complemented to uncomplemented or vice versa) to produce an adjacent square. Thus the answer is 5. The fact that this answer is greater than 4 makes it difficult to draw useful pictures of Karnaugh maps with five variables (but not impossible, if the drawings are interpreted correctly).

**13.** We could ignore the stated condition, but then our circuit would be more complex than need be. If we use the condition then there are really only three inputs; let us call them $x$, $y$, and $z$, where $z$ represents Marcus's vote and $x$ and $y$ represent the votes of the unnamed people. Since Smith and Jones always vote against Marcus, a majority will occur if either Marcus assents with both of the other two (i.e., the minterm $x\,y\,z$), or else if Marcus votes no but at least one of the other two vote yes (which we can represent by $(x+y)\overline{z}$). Thus we design our circuit to be the *OR* of these two expressions.

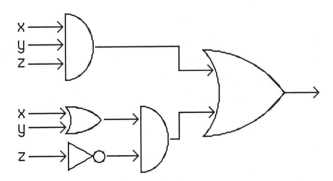

**15.** We organize our work as in the text.

**a)**

|   | Term | String | Step 1 Term | String |
|---|------|--------|------|--------|
| 1 | $\overline{x}\,y\,z$ | 011 | $(1,2)\,\overline{x}\,z$ | 0–1 |
| 2 | $\overline{x}\,\overline{y}\,z$ | 001 | | |

In this case we have one product that covers both of the minterms, so that $(\overline{x}\,z)$ is our answer.

**b)**

|   | Term | String | Step 1 Term | String | Step 2 Term | String |
|---|------|--------|------|--------|------|--------|
| 1 | $x\,y\,z$ | 111 | $(1,2)\,x\,y$ | 11– | $(1,2,3,4)\,y$ | –1– |
| 2 | $x\,y\,\overline{z}$ | 110 | $(1,3)\,y\,z$ | –11 | | |
| 3 | $\overline{x}\,y\,z$ | 011 | $(2,4)\,y\,\overline{z}$ | –10 | | |
| 4 | $\overline{x}\,y\,\overline{z}$ | 010 | $(3,4)\,\overline{x}\,y$ | 01– | | |

Again we have one product that covers all the minterms, so that is our answer $(y)$.

**c)**

|   | Term | String | Step 1 Term | String |
|---|------|--------|------|--------|
| 1 | $x\,y\,\overline{z}$ | 110 | $(1,4)\,x\,\overline{z}$ | 1–0 |
| 2 | $x\,\overline{y}\,z$ | 101 | $(2,4)\,x\,\overline{y}$ | 10– |
| 3 | $\overline{x}\,y\,z$ | 011 | $(2,5)\,\overline{y}\,z$ | –01 |
| 4 | $x\,\overline{y}\,\overline{z}$ | 100 | $(3,5)\,\overline{x}\,z$ | 0–1 |
| 5 | $\overline{x}\,\overline{y}\,z$ | 001 | | |

(Note that we reordered the minterms so that the number of 1's decreased as we went down the list.) No further combinations are possible at this point, so there are four products that must be used to cover our five minterms, each product covering two minterms. Clearly, then, two of these are not enough, but it is easy to find three whose sum covers all the minterms. One possible answer is to choose the first, third, and fourth of the products, namely $x\,\overline{z}+\overline{y}\,z+\overline{x}\,z$.

d)

| | Term | String | Step 1 Term | String |
|---|---|---|---|---|
| 1 | $x\,y\,z$ | 111 | $(1,2)\,x\,z$ | 1–1 |
| 2 | $x\,\overline{y}\,z$ | 101 | $(1,3)\,y\,z$ | –11 |
| 3 | $\overline{x}\,y\,z$ | 011 | $(2,4)\,x\,\overline{y}$ | 10– |
| 4 | $x\,\overline{y}\,\overline{z}$ | 100 | $(3,5)\,\overline{x}\,y$ | 01– |
| 5 | $\overline{x}\,y\,\overline{z}$ | 010 | $(4,6)\,\overline{y}\,\overline{z}$ | –00 |
| 6 | $\overline{x}\,\overline{y}\,\overline{z}$ | 000 | $(5,6)\,\overline{x}\,\overline{z}$ | 0–0 |

(Note that we reordered the minterms so that the number of 1's decreased as we went down the list.) No further combinations are possible at this point, so there are six products that must be used to cover our six minterms, each product covering two minterms. Clearly, then, two of these are not enough, but it is not hard to find three whose sum covers all the minterms. One possible answer is to choose the first, fourth, and fifth of the products, namely $x\,z + \overline{x}\,y + \overline{y}\,\overline{z}$.

**17.** We follow the procedure and notation given in the text.

a)

| | Term | String | Step 1 Term | String |
|---|---|---|---|---|
| 1 | $w\,x\,y\,z$ | 1111 | $(1,2)\,w\,x\,z$ | 11–1 |
| 2 | $w\,x\,\overline{y}\,z$ | 1101 | $(2,3)\,w\,x\,\overline{y}$ | 110– |
| 3 | $w\,x\,\overline{y}\,\overline{z}$ | 1100 | $(2,5)\,w\,\overline{y}\,z$ | 1–01 |
| 4 | $w\,\overline{x}\,y\,\overline{z}$ | 1010 | | |
| 5 | $w\,\overline{x}\,\overline{y}\,z$ | 1001 | | |

The three products in the last column as well as minterm #4 are possible products in the desired expansion, since they are not contained in any other product. We make a table of which products cover which of the original minterms.

| | 1 | 2 | 3 | 4 | 5 |
|---|---|---|---|---|---|
| $w\,x\,z$ | X | X | | | |
| $w\,x\,\overline{y}$ | | X | X | | |
| $w\,\overline{y}\,z$ | | X | | | X |
| $w\,\overline{x}\,y\,\overline{z}$ | | | | X | |

Since only the first of our products covers minterm #1, it must be included. Similarly, the other three products must be included since they are the only ones which cover minterms #3, #4, and #5. If we do include them all, then of course all the minterms are covered. Therefore our answer is $w\,x\,z + w\,x\,\overline{y} + w\,\overline{y}\,z + w\,\overline{x}\,y\,\overline{z}$.

b)

| | Term | String | Step 1 Term | String |
|---|---|---|---|---|
| 1 | $w\,x\,y\,\overline{z}$ | 1110 | $(2,4)\,x\,\overline{y}\,z$ | –101 |
| 2 | $w\,x\,\overline{y}\,z$ | 1101 | $(4,6)\,\overline{w}\,\overline{y}\,z$ | 0–01 |
| 3 | $w\,\overline{x}\,y\,z$ | 1011 | | |
| 4 | $\overline{w}\,x\,\overline{y}\,z$ | 0101 | | |
| 5 | $\overline{w}\,\overline{x}\,y\,\overline{z}$ | 0010 | | |
| 6 | $\overline{w}\,\overline{x}\,\overline{y}\,z$ | 0001 | | |

Since minterms #1, #3, and #5 are not contained in any others, these, along with the two products in the last column, are the products which we look at to cover the original minterms. It is not hard to see that all five are needed to cover all the original minterms.  Therefore the answer is $x\,\overline{y}\,z + \overline{w}\,\overline{y}\,z + w\,x\,y\,\overline{z} + w\,\overline{x}\,y\,z + \overline{w}\,\overline{x}\,y\,\overline{z}$.

**c)**

| | Term | String | | Step 1 Term | String | Step 2 Term | String |
|---|------|--------|---|------|--------|------|--------|
| 1 | $w\,x\,y\,z$ | 1111 | $(1,2)$ | $w\,x\,y$ | 111– ⇐ | $(3,4,5,8)\,\overline{y}\,z$ | ––01 |
| 2 | $w\,x\,y\,\overline{z}$ | 1110 | $(1,3)$ | $w\,x\,z$ | 11–1 ⇐ | | |
| 3 | $w\,x\,\overline{y}\,z$ | 1101 | $(3,4)$ | $w\,\overline{y}\,z$ | 1–01 | | |
| 4 | $w\,\overline{x}\,\overline{y}\,z$ | 1001 | $(3,5)$ | $x\,\overline{y}\,z$ | –101 | | |
| 5 | $\overline{w}\,x\,\overline{y}\,z$ | 0101 | $(4,6)$ | $w\,\overline{x}\,\overline{y}$ | 100– ⇐ | | |
| 6 | $w\,\overline{x}\,\overline{y}\,\overline{z}$ | 1000 | $(4,8)$ | $\overline{x}\,\overline{y}\,z$ | –001 | | |
| 7 | $\overline{w}\,\overline{x}\,y\,\overline{z}$ | 0010 | $(5,8)$ | $\overline{w}\,\overline{y}\,z$ | 0–01 | | |
| 8 | $\overline{w}\,\overline{x}\,\overline{y}\,z$ | 0001 | | | | | |

The product in the last column, as well as the products in Step 1 that are marked with an arrow, as well as minterm #7, are possible products in the desired expansion, since they are not contained in any other product. We make a table of which products cover which of the original minterms.

| | 1 | 2 | 3 | 4 | 5 | 6 | 7 | 8 |
|---|---|---|---|---|---|---|---|---|
| $\overline{y}\,z$ | | | X | X | X | | | X |
| $w\,x\,y$ | X | X | | | | | | |
| $w\,x\,z$ | X | | | X | | | | |
| $w\,\overline{x}\,\overline{y}$ | | | | X | | X | | |
| $\overline{w}\,\overline{x}\,y\,\overline{z}$ | | | | | | | X | |

In order to cover minterms #5, #2, #6, and #7, we need the first, second, fourth, and fifth of the products in this table. If we include these four, then all the minterms are covered, and we do not need the third one. Therefore our answer is $\overline{y}\,z + w\,x\,z + w\,\overline{x}\,\overline{y} + \overline{w}\,\overline{x}\,y\,\overline{z}$.

**d)**

| | Term | String | | Step 1 Term | String | Step 2 Term | String |
|---|------|--------|---|------|--------|------|--------|
| 1 | $w\,x\,y\,z$ | 1111 | $(1,2)$ | $w\,x\,y$ | 111– | $(1,2,4,6)\,w\,y$ | 1–1– |
| 2 | $w\,x\,y\,\overline{z}$ | 1110 | $(1,3)$ | $w\,x\,z$ | 11–1 ⇐ | $(1,4,5,7)\,y\,z$ | ––11 |
| 3 | $w\,x\,\overline{y}\,z$ | 1101 | $(1,4)$ | $w\,y\,z$ | 1–11 | $(4,6,7,8)\,\overline{x}\,y$ | –01– |
| 4 | $w\,\overline{x}\,y\,z$ | 1011 | $(1,5)$ | $x\,y\,z$ | –111 | | |
| 5 | $\overline{w}\,x\,y\,z$ | 0111 | $(2,6)$ | $w\,y\,\overline{z}$ | 1–10 | | |
| 6 | $w\,\overline{x}\,y\,\overline{z}$ | 1010 | $(4,6)$ | $w\,\overline{x}\,y$ | 101– | | |
| 7 | $\overline{w}\,\overline{x}\,y\,z$ | 0011 | $(4,7)$ | $\overline{x}\,y\,z$ | –011 | | |
| 8 | $\overline{w}\,\overline{x}\,y\,\overline{z}$ | 0010 | $(5,7)$ | $\overline{w}\,y\,z$ | 0–11 | | |
| 9 | $\overline{w}\,\overline{x}\,\overline{y}\,z$ | 0001 | $(6,8)$ | $\overline{x}\,y\,\overline{z}$ | –010 | | |
| | | | $(7,8)$ | $\overline{w}\,\overline{x}\,y$ | 001– | | |
| | | | $(7,9)$ | $\overline{w}\,\overline{x}\,z$ | 00–1 ⇐ | | |

The product in the last column, as well as the products in Step 1 that are marked with an arrow, are possible products in the desired expansion, since they are not contained in any other product. We make a table of which products cover which of the original minterms.

|       | 1 | 2 | 3 | 4 | 5 | 6 | 7 | 8 | 9 |
|-------|---|---|---|---|---|---|---|---|---|
| $w\,y$ | X | X |   | X |   | X |   |   |   |
| $y\,z$ | X |   |   | X | X |   | X |   |   |
| $\overline{x}\,y$ |   |   |   | X |   | X | X | X |   |
| $w\,x\,z$ | X |   | X |   |   |   |   |   |   |
| $\overline{w}\,\overline{x}\,z$ |   |   |   |   |   |   | X |   | X |

In order to cover minterms #2, #5, #8, #3, and #9, we need the first, second, third, fourth, and fifth of the products in this table, respectively—i.e., all of them. Therefore our answer is $w\,y + y\,z + \overline{x}\,y + w\,x\,z + \overline{w}\,\overline{x}\,z$.

19. Using the method of Exercise 18, we draw the following picture, putting a 0 in each square that represent a maxterm in our product-of-sums expansion.

We then combine them into larger blocks, as shown, obtaining two large blocks: the entire first row, which represents the factor $x$, and the entire first column, which represents the factor $(y + z)$. Since neither of these blocks alone covers all the maxterms, we need to use both. Therefore the simplified product is $x(y + z)$.

⇒ **SUPPLEMENTARY EXERCISES FOR CHAPTER 9**

1. **a)** Suppose the equation holds. If at least one of the variables equals 1, then the left-hand side is 1; therefore the right-hand side must be 1, as well, and that forces $y$ and $z$ to be 1. Similarly, if $x = 0$, then equality holds if and only if $y = z = 0$. Therefore the only solutions are $(1,1,1)$ and $(0,0,0)$.
**b)** If $x = 1$, then the right-hand side equals 1, so in order for there to be equality we need $y + z = 1$, whence $y = 1$ or $z = 1$. Thus $(1,1,0)$, $(1,0,1)$, and $(1,1,1)$ are all solutions. If $x = 0$, then the left-hand side is 0, so we need $yz = 0$ in order for equality to hold, whence $y = 0$ or $z = 0$. Thus $(0,0,0)$, $(0,0,1)$, and $(0,1,0)$ are also solutions.
**c)** There are no solutions here. If any of the variables equals 1, then the left-hand side is 0 and the right-hand side is 1; if all the variables are 0, then the left-hand side is 1 and the right-hand side is 0.

3. In each case we form $\overline{F(\overline{x}_1, \ldots, \overline{x}_n)}$ and simplify. If we get back to what we originally started with, then the function is self-dual; if what we obtain is not equivalent to what we began with, then the function is not self-dual. The simplification is done using the identities for Boolean algebra, especially DeMorgan's laws.
**a)** $\overline{\overline{x}} = x$, so the function is self-dual.
**b)** $\overline{(\overline{x}\,\overline{y} + \overline{\overline{x}\,\overline{y}})} = \overline{(\overline{x}\,\overline{y} + x\,y)}$, which is the complement of what we originally had. Thus this is as far from being self-dual as it can possibly be.
**c)** $\overline{(\overline{x} + \overline{y})} = \overline{\overline{x}}\,\overline{\overline{y}} = x\,y$, which is certainly not equivalent to $x + y$. Therefore this is not self-dual.
**d)** We first simplify the expression, using the distributive law and the fact that $x + \overline{x} = 1$ to rewrite our function as $F(x, y) = y$. Now, as in part (a), we see that it is indeed self-dual.

5. The reasoning here is essentially the same as in Exercise 23 in Section 9.1. To specify all the values of a self-dual function, we are free to specify the values of $F(1, x_2, x_3, \ldots, x_n)$, and we can do this in $2^{2^{n-1}}$ ways, since there are $2^{n-1}$ different elements at which we can choose to make the function value either 0 or 1. Once we have specified these values, the values of $F(0, x_2, x_3, \ldots, x_n)$ are all determined by the definition of self-duality, so no further choices are possible. Therefore the answer is $2^{2^{n-1}}$.

7. **a)** At any point in the domain, it is certainly the case that if $F(x_1, \ldots, x_n) = 1$, then $(F + G)(x_1, \ldots, x_n) = F(x_1, \ldots, x_n) + G(x_1, \ldots, x_n) = 1 + G(x_1, \ldots, x_n) = 1$, no matter what value $G$ has at that point. Thus by definition $F \leq F + G$.
   **b)** This is dual to the first part. At any point in the domain, it is certainly the case that if $F(x_1, \ldots, x_n) = 0$, then $(FG)(x_1, \ldots, x_n) = F(x_1, \ldots, x_n)G(x_1, \ldots, x_n) = 0 \cdot G(x_1, \ldots, x_n) = 0$, no matter what value $G$ has at that point. The contrapositive of this statement is that if $(FG)(x_1, \ldots, x_n) = 1$, then $F(x_1, \ldots, x_n) = 1$. Thus by definition $FG \leq F$.

9. We need to show that this relation is reflexive, antisymmetric, and transitive. That $F \leq F$ (reflexivity) is simply the tautology "if $F(x_1, \ldots, x_n) = 1$, then $F(x_1, \ldots, x_n) = 1$." For antisymmetry, suppose $F \leq G$ and $G \leq F$. Then the definition of the relation says that $F(x_1, \ldots, x_n) = 1$ if and only if $G(x_1, \ldots, x_n) = 1$, which is the definition of equality between functions, so $F = G$. Finally, for transitivity, suppose $F \leq G$ and $G \leq H$. We want to show that $F \leq H$. So suppose $F(x_1, \ldots, x_n) = 1$. Then by the first inequality $G(x_1, \ldots, x_n) = 1$, whence by the second inequality $H(x_1, \ldots, x_n) = 1$, as desired.

11. None of these are identities. The counterexample $x = 1$, $y = z = 0$ works for all three.
    **a)** We have $1 \mid (0 \mid 0) = 1 \mid 1 = 0$, whereas $(1 \mid 0) \mid 0 = 1 \mid 0 = 1$.
    **b)** We have $1 \downarrow (0 \downarrow 0) = 1 \downarrow 1 = 0$, whereas $(1 \downarrow 0) \downarrow (1 \downarrow 0) = 0 \downarrow 0 = 1$.
    **c)** We have $1 \downarrow (0 \mid 0) = 1 \downarrow 1 = 0$, whereas $(1 \downarrow 0) \mid (1 \downarrow 0) = 0 \mid 0 = 1$.

13. This is clear from the definitions. The given operation applied to $x$ and $y$ is defined to be 1 if and only if $x = y$, while *XOR* applied to $x$ and $y$ is defined (preamble to Exercise 16 in Section 9.1) to be 1 if and only if $x \neq y$.

15. We show this with a table. For typographical reasons we denote the operator here by $\odot$. Since the fifth and seventh columns are equal, the equation is an identity.

| $x$ | $y$ | $z$ | $x \odot y$ | $(x \odot y) \odot z$ | $y \odot z$ | $x \odot (y \odot z)$ |
|---|---|---|---|---|---|---|
| 1 | 1 | 1 | 1 | 1 | 1 | 1 |
| 1 | 1 | 0 | 1 | 0 | 0 | 0 |
| 1 | 0 | 1 | 0 | 0 | 0 | 0 |
| 1 | 0 | 0 | 0 | 1 | 1 | 1 |
| 0 | 1 | 1 | 0 | 0 | 1 | 0 |
| 0 | 1 | 0 | 0 | 1 | 0 | 1 |
| 0 | 0 | 1 | 1 | 1 | 0 | 1 |
| 0 | 0 | 0 | 1 | 0 | 1 | 0 |

17. In each case we can actually list all the functions.
    **a)** The only function values we can get are $x$, $y$, 0, 1, $\overline{x}$, and $\overline{y}$, since applying complementation twice does not give us anything new. Therefore the answer is 6.

**b)** Since $s \cdot s = s$, $s \cdot 1 = s$, and $s \cdot 0 = 0$ for all $s$, the only functions we can get are $x$, $y$, $0$, $1$, and $x\,y$. Therefore the answer is $5$.

**c)** By duality the answer here has to be the same as the answer to part **(b)**, namely $5$.

**d)** We can get the 6 distinct functions $x$, $y$, $0$, $1$, $x\,y$ and $x + y$. Any further applications of these operations, however, returns us to one of these functions. For example, $x\,y + x = x$.

**19.** The sum bit is the exclusive *OR* of the inputs, and the carry bit is their product. Therefore we need only two gates to form the half adder if we allow an *XOR* gate and an *AND* gate.

**21.** We need to figure out which combinations of values for $x_1$, $x_2$, and $x_3$ cause the inequality $-x_1 + x_2 + 2x_3 \geq 1/2$ to be satisfied. Clearly this will be true if $x_3 = 1$. If $x_3 = 0$, then it will be true if and only if $x_2 = 1$ and $x_1 = 0$. Thus a Boolean expression for this function is $x_3 + \overline{x}_1 x_2$.

**23.** We prove this by contradiction. Suppose $a$, $b$, and $T$ are such that $ax + by \geq T$ if and only if $x \oplus y = 1$, i.e., if and only if either $x = 1$ and $y = 0$, or else $x = 0$ and $y = 1$. Thus for the first case we need $a \geq T$, and for the second we need $b \geq T$. Since we need $ax + by < T$ for $x = y = 0$, we know $T > 0$. Hence in particular $b$ is positive. Therefore we have $a + b > a \geq T$, which contradicts the fact that $1 \oplus 1 = 0$ (requiring $a + b \leq T$).

# CHAPTER 10
# Modeling Computation

⇒ **SECTION 10.1   Languages and Grammars**

*There is no magical way to come up with the grammars to generate a language described in English. In particular, Exercise 11 and Exercise 12 are challenging and very worthwhile. Exercise 15 shows how grammars can be combined. In constructing grammars, we observe the rule that every production must contain at least one nonterminal symbol on the left. This allows us to know when a derivation is completed—namely, when the string we have generated contains no nonterminal symbols.*

1. The following sequences of lines show that each is a valid sentence.

    **a)** sentence
    **noun phrase   intransitive verb phrase**
    **article   adjective   noun   intransitive verb phrase**
    **article   adjective   noun   intransitive verb**
    *the*   **adjective   noun   intransitive verb**
    *the   happy*   **noun   intransitive verb**
    *the   happy   hare*   **intransitive verb**
    *the   happy   hare   runs*

    **b)** sentence
    **noun phrase   intransitive verb phrase**
    **article   adjective   noun   intransitive verb phrase**
    **article   adjective   noun   intransitive verb   adverb**
    *the*   **adjective   noun   intransitive verb   adverb**
    *the   sleepy*   **noun   intransitive verb   adverb**
    *the   sleepy   tortoise*   **intransitive verb   adverb**
    *the   sleepy   tortoise   runs*   **adverb**
    *the   sleepy   tortoise   runs   quickly*

    **c)** sentence
    **noun phrase   transitive verb phrase   noun phrase**
    **article   noun   transitive verb phrase   noun phrase**
    **article   noun   transitive verb   noun phrase**
    **article   noun   transitive verb   article   noun**
    *the*   **noun   transitive verb   article   noun**
    *the   tortoise*   **transitive verb   article   noun**
    *the   tortoise   passes*   **article   noun**
    *the   tortoise   passes   the*   **noun**
    *the   tortoise   passes   the   hare*

    **d)** sentence
    **noun phrase   transitive verb phrase   noun phrase**

article  adjective  noun  transitive verb phrase   noun phrase
article  adjective  noun  transitive verb   noun phrase
article  adjective  noun  transitive verb   article  adjective   noun
*the*   adjective  noun  transitive verb   article  adjective   noun
*the*   *sleepy*  noun  transitive verb   article  adjective   noun
*the*   *sleepy*  *hare*  transitive verb   article  adjective   noun
*the*   *sleepy*  *hare*  *passes*  article   adjective  noun
*the*   *sleepy*  *hare*  *passes*  *the*   adjective  noun
*the*   *sleepy*  *hare*  *passes*  *the*   *happy*   noun
*the*   *sleepy*  *hare*  *passes*  *the*   *happy*   *tortoise*

3. Since *runs* is only an **intransitive verb**, it can only occur in a sentence of the form **noun phrase intransitive verb phrase**. Such a sentence cannot have anything except an **adverb** after the **intransitive verb**, and *the sleepy tortoise* cannot be an **adverb**.

5. We write the derivation in the obvious way. $S \Rightarrow 0S1 \Rightarrow 00S11 \Rightarrow 000S111 \Rightarrow 000111$. We used the rule $S \to 0S1$ in the first three steps and $S \to \lambda$ in the last step.

7. **a)** Using $G_1$, we can add 0's on the left or 1's on the right of $S$. Thus we have $S \Rightarrow 0S \Rightarrow 00S \Rightarrow 00S1 \Rightarrow 00S11 \Rightarrow 00S111 \Rightarrow 00S1111 \Rightarrow 001111$.

**b)** In this grammar we must add all the 0's first to $S$, then change to an $A$ and add the 1's, again on the left. Thus we have $S \Rightarrow 0S \Rightarrow 00S \Rightarrow 001A \Rightarrow 0011A \Rightarrow 00111A \Rightarrow 001111$.

9. First we apply the first rule twice and the rule $S \to \lambda$ to get $00ABAB$. We can then apply the rule $BA \to AB$, to get $00AABB$. Now we can apply the rules $0A \to 01$ and $1A \to 11$ to get $0011BB$; and then the rules $1B \to 12$ and $2B \to 22$ to end up with $001122$, as desired.

11. **a)** We need to add the 0's two at a time. Thus we can take the rules $S \to S00$ and $S \to \lambda$.

**b)** We can use the same first rule as in part **(a)**, namely $S \to S00$, to increase the number of 0's. Since the string must begin 10, we simply adjoin to this the rule $S \to 10$.

**c)** We need to add 0's and 1's two at a time. Furthermore, we need to allow for 0's and 1's to change their order. Since we cannot have a rule $01 \to 10$ (there being no nonterminal symbol on the left), we make up nonterminal analogs of 0 and 1, calling them $A$ and $B$, respectively. Thus our rules are as follows: $S \to AAS$, $S \to BBS$, $AB \to BA$, $BA \to AB$, $S \to \lambda$, $A \to 0$, and $B \to 1$. (There are also totally different ways to approach this problem, which are just as effective.)

**d)** This one is fairly simple: $S \to 0000000000A$, $A \to 0A$, $A \to \lambda$. This assures at least 10 zeros and allows for any number of additional zeros.

**e)** We need to invoke the trick used in part **(c)** to allow 0's and 1's to change their order. Furthermore, since we need at least one extra 0, we use $S \to A$ as our vanishing condition, rather than $S \to \lambda$. Our solution, then, is $S \to AS$, $S \to ABS$, $S \to A$, $AB \to BA$, $BA \to AB$, $A \to 0$, and $B \to 1$.

**f)** This is identical to part **(e)**, except that the vanishing condition is $S \to \lambda$, rather than $S \to A$, and there is no rule $S \to AS$.

**g)** We just put together two copies of a solution to part **(e)**, one in which there are more 0's than 1's, and one in which there are more 1's than 0's. The rules are as follows: $S \to ABS$, $S \to T$, $S \to U$, $T \to AT$, $T \to A$, $U \to BU$, $U \to B$, $AB \to BA$, $BA \to AB$, $A \to 0$, and $B \to 1$.

**13. a)** This is a type 2 grammar, because the left-hand side of each production has a single nonterminal symbol. It is not a type 3 grammar, because the right-hand side of the productions are not of the required type.

**b)** This meets the definition of a type 3 grammar.

**c)** This is only a type 0 grammar; it is not of type 1 since the second production decreases the length of the string.

**d)** This is a type 2 grammar, because the left-hand side of each production has a single nonterminal symbol. It is not a type 3 grammar, because the right-hand side of the productions are not of the required type.

**e)** This meets the definition of a type 2 grammar. It is not of type 3, because of the production $A \to B$.

**f)** This is only a type 0 grammar; it is not of type 1 since the third production decreases the length of the string.

**g)** This meets the definition of a type 3 grammar.

**h)** This is only a type 0 grammar; it is not of type 1 since the second production decreases the length of the string.

**i)** This is a type 2 grammar because each left-hand side is a single nonterminal. It is not type 3 because of the production $B \to \lambda$.

**j)** This is a type 2 grammar because each left-hand side is a single nonterminal. It is not type 3; each of the productions violates the conditions imposed for a type 3 grammar.

**15.** Let us assume that the nonterminal symbols of $G_1$ and $G_2$ are disjoint. (If they are not, we can give those in $G_2$, say, new names so that they will be; obviously this does not change the language that $G_2$ generates.) Call the start symbols $S_1$ and $S_2$. In each case we will define $G$ by taking all the symbols and rules for $G_1$ and $G_2$, a new symbol $S$, which will be the start symbol for $G$, and the rules listed below.

**a)** Since we want strings that either $G_1$ or $G_2$ generate, we add the rules $S \to S_1$ and $S \to S_2$.

**b)** Since we want strings that consist of a string that $G_1$ generates followed by a string that $G_2$ generates, we add the rule $S \to S_1 S_2$.

**c)** This time we add the rules $S \to S_1 S$ and $S \to \lambda$. This clearly gives us all strings that consist of the concatenation of any number of strings that $G_1$ generates.

**17.** We simply translate the derivations we gave in the solution to Exercise 1 to tree form, obtaining the following pictures.

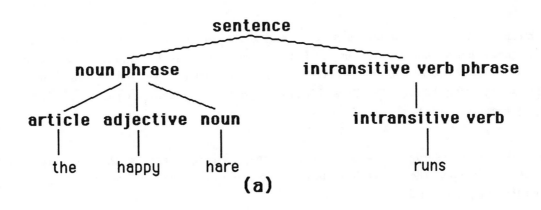

**(a)**

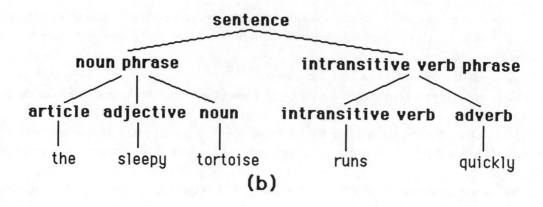

**(b)**

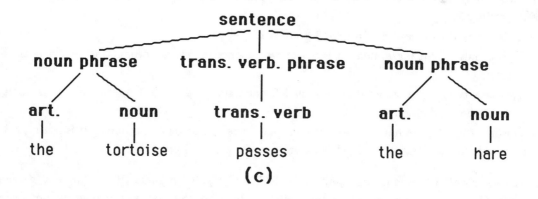

**(c)**

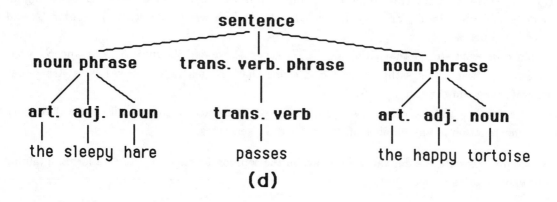

**(d)**

**19.** We can assume that the derivation starts $S \Rightarrow AB \Rightarrow CaB \Rightarrow cbaB$, or $S \Rightarrow AB \Rightarrow CaB \Rightarrow baB$. This shows that neither the string in part **(b)** nor the string in part **(d)** is in the language, since they do not begin $cba$ or $ba$. In order to derive the string in part **(a)**, we need to turn $B$ into $ba$, and this is easy, using the rule $B \rightarrow Ba$ and then the rule $B \rightarrow b$. Finally, for part **(c)**, we again simply apply these two rules to change $B$ into $ba$.

**21.** This is straightforward. The $-$ is the sign and the 109 is an integer, so the tree starts at shown. Then we decompose the integer 109 into the digit 1 and the integer 09, then in turn to the digit 0 and the integer (digit) 9.

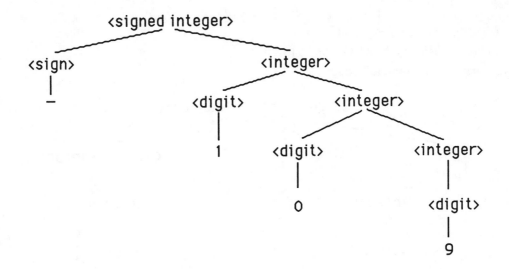

**23. a)** Note that a string such as "34." is not allowed by this definition, but a string such as $-0.780$ is. This is pretty straightforward using the following rules. As can be seen, we are using $\langle integer \rangle$ to stand for a nonnegative integer.

$S \rightarrow \langle sign \rangle \langle integer \rangle$

$S \rightarrow \langle sign \rangle \langle integer \rangle . \langle positive\ integer \rangle$

$\langle sign \rangle \rightarrow +$

$\langle sign \rangle \rightarrow -$

$\langle integer \rangle \rightarrow \langle integer \rangle \langle digit \rangle$

$\langle integer \rangle \rightarrow \langle digit \rangle$

$\langle positive\ integer \rangle \rightarrow \langle integer \rangle \langle nonzero\ digit \rangle \langle integer \rangle$

$\langle positive\ integer \rangle \rightarrow \langle integer \rangle \langle nonzero\ digit \rangle$

$\langle positive\ integer \rangle \rightarrow \langle nonzero\ digit \rangle \langle integer \rangle$

$\langle positive\ integer \rangle \rightarrow \langle nonzero\ digit \rangle$

$\langle digit \rangle \rightarrow \langle nonzero\ digit \rangle$

$\langle digit \rangle \rightarrow 0$

$\langle nonzero\ digit \rangle \rightarrow 1$

$\langle nonzero\ digit \rangle \rightarrow 2$

$\langle nonzero\ digit \rangle \rightarrow 3$

$\langle nonzero\ digit \rangle \rightarrow 4$

$\langle nonzero\ digit \rangle \rightarrow 5$

$\langle nonzero\ digit \rangle \rightarrow 6$

$\langle nonzero\ digit \rangle \rightarrow 7$

$\langle nonzero\ digit \rangle \rightarrow 8$

$\langle nonzero\ digit \rangle \rightarrow 9$

**b)** We combine rows of the previous answer with the same left-hand side, and we change the notation to produce the answer to this part.

$\langle signed\ decimal\ number \rangle ::= \langle sign \rangle \langle integer \rangle \mid \langle sign \rangle \langle integer \rangle . \langle positive\ integer \rangle$

$\langle sign \rangle ::= + \mid -$

$\langle integer \rangle ::= \langle integer \rangle \langle digit \rangle \mid \langle digit \rangle$

$\langle positive\ integer \rangle ::= \langle integer \rangle \langle nonzero\ digit \rangle \langle integer \rangle \mid \langle integer \rangle \langle nonzero\ digit \rangle$

$$| \langle nonzero\ digit \rangle \langle integer \rangle\ |\ \langle nonzero\ digit \rangle$$
$$\langle digit \rangle ::= \langle nonzero\ digit \rangle\ |\ 0$$
$$\langle nonzero\ digit \rangle ::= 1\ |\ 2\ |\ 3\ |\ 4\ |\ 5\ |\ 6\ |\ 7\ |\ 8\ |\ 9$$

**c)** We easily produce the following tree.

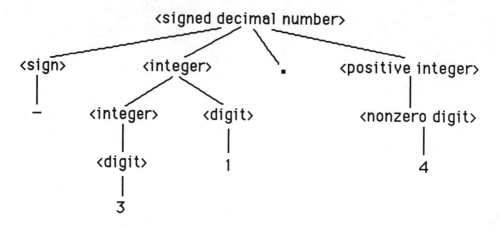

**25.** The definition of "derivable from" says that it is the reflexive, transitive closure of the relation "directly derivable from." Indeed, taking $n = 0$ in that definition gives us the fact that every string is derivable from itself; and the existence of a sequence $w_0 \Rightarrow w_1 \Rightarrow \cdots \Rightarrow w_n$ for $n \geq 1$ means that $(w_0, w_n)$ is in the transitive closure of the relation $\Rightarrow$ (see Theorem 2 in Section 6.4).

$\Rightarrow$ **SECTION 10.2   Finite-State Machines with Output**

*Finding finite-state machines to do specific tasks is in essence computer programming. There is no set method for doing this. You have to think about the problem for awhile, ask yourself what it might be useful for the states to represent, and then very carefully proceed to construct the machine. Expect to have several false starts. "Bugs" in your machines are also very common. There are of course many machines that will accomplish the same task. The reader should look at Exercise 16 through Exercise 21 to see that it is also possible to build finite-state machines with the output associated with the states, rather than the transitions.*

**1.** We draw the state diagrams by making a node for each state and a labeled arrow for each transition. In part **(a)**, for example, since under input 1 from state $s_2$ we are told that we move to state $s_1$ and output a 0, we draw an arrow from $s_2$ to $s_1$ and label it $1, 0$. It is assumed that $s_0$ is always the start state.

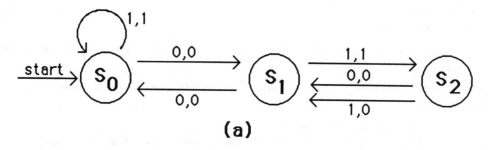

**(a)**

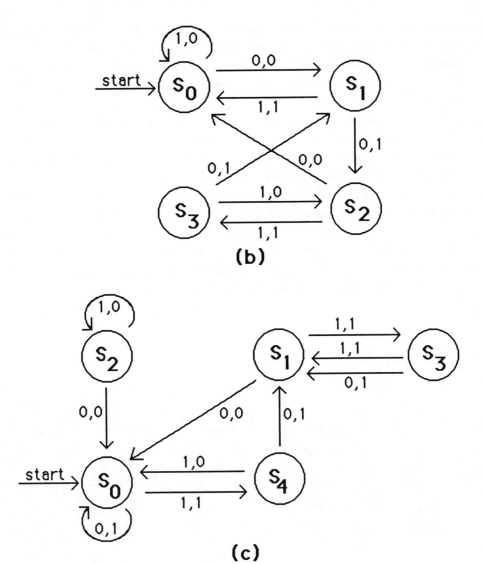

**(b)**

**(c)**

3. **a)** The machine starts in state $s_0$. Since the first input symbol is 0, the machine moves to state $s_1$ and gives 1 as output. (This is what the arrow from $s_0$ to $s_1$ with label 0, 1 means.) The next input symbol is 1. Because of the edge from $s_1$ to $s_0$, the machine moves to state $s_0$ and gives 1 as output. The next input is 1. Because of the loop at $s_0$, the machine stays in state $s_0$ and gives output 0. The same thing happens on the fourth input symbol. Therefore the output is 1100 (and the machine ends up in state $s_0$).

**b)** This is similar to part (a). The first two symbols of input cause the machine to output two 0's and remain in state $s_0$. The third symbol causes an output of 1 as the machine moves into state $s_1$. The fourth input takes us back to state $s_0$ with output 1. The next four symbols of input cause the machine to give output 0110 as it goes to states $s_0$, $s_1$, $s_0$, and $s_0$, respectively. Therefore the output is 00110110.

**c)** This is similar to the other parts. The machine alternates between states $s_0$ and $s_1$, outputting 1 for each input. Thus the output is 11111111111.

5. We model this machine as follows. There are four possible inputs, which we denote by 5, 10, 25, and

*b*, standing for a nickel, a dime, a quarter, and a button labeled by a kind of soda pop, respectively. (Actually the model is a bit more complicated, since there are three kinds of pop, but we will ignore that; to incorporate the kind of pop into the model, we would simply have three inputs in place of just *b*.) The output can either be an amount of money in cents—0, 5, 10, 15, 20, or 25—or can be a can of soda pop, which we denote *c*. There will be eight states. Intuitively, state $s_i$ will represent the state in which the machine is indebted to the customer by $5i$ cents. Thus $s_0$, the start state, will represent that the machine owes the customer nothing; state $s_1$ will represent that the machine has accepted 5 cents from the customer, and so on. State $s_7$ will mean that the machine owes the customer 35 cents, which will be paid with a can of soda pop, at which time the machine will return to state $s_0$, owing nothing. The following picture is the state diagram of this machine, simplified even further in that we have eliminated quarters entirely for sake of readability. For example, the transition from state $s_6$ (30 cents credit) on input of a dime is to state $s_7$ (35 cents credit) with the return of 5 cents in change. We have also used *a* to stand for any monetary input: if you deposit any amount when the machine already has your 35 cents, then you get that same amount back. Thus the transition *a, a* really stands for three transitions: 5, 5 and 10, 10 and 25, 25.

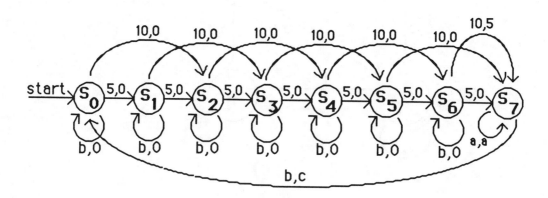

7. We draw the diagram for this machine. Intuitively, we need four states, corresponding to the four possibilities for what the last two bits have been. In our picture, state $s_1$ corresponds to the last two bits having been 00; state $s_2$ corresponds to the last two bits having been 01; state $s_3$ corresponds to the last two bits having been 10; state $s_4$ corresponds to the last two bits having been 11. We also need a state $s_0$ to get started, to account for the delay. Let us see why some of the transitions are what they are. If you are in state $s_3$, then the last two bits have been 10. If you now receive an input 0, then the last two bits will be 00, so we need to move to state $s_1$. Furthermore, since the bit received two pulses ago was a 1 (we know this from the fact that we are in state $s_3$), we need to output a 1. Also, since we are told to output 00 at the beginning, it is right to have transitions from $s_0$ as shown.

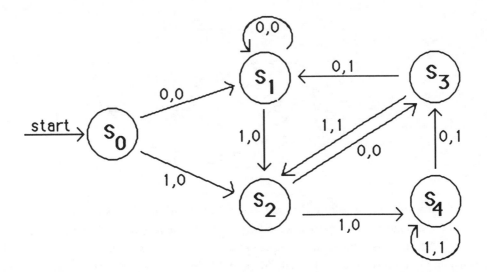

If we look at this machine now, we observe that states $s_0$ and $s_1$ are equivalent, i.e., they cause exactly the same transitions and outputs. Therefore a simpler answer would be a machine like this one, but without state $s_0$, where state $s_1$ is the start state.

9. This machine is really only part of a machine; we are not told what happens after a successful log-on. Also, the machine is really much more complicated than we are indicating here, because we really need a separate state for each user. We assume that there is only one user. We also assume that an invalid user ID is rejected immediately, without a request for a password. (The alternate assumption is also reasonable, that the machine requests a password whether or not the ID is valid. In that case we obtain a different machine, of course.) We need only two states. The initial state waits for the valid user ID. We let $i$ be the valid user ID, and we let $j$ be any other input. If the input is valid, then we enter state $s_1$, outputting the message $e$: "enter your password." If the input is not valid, then we remain in state $s_0$, outputting the message $t$: "invalid ID; try again." From state $s_1$ there are only two relevant inputs: the valid password $p$ and any other input $q$. If the input is valid, then we output the message $w$: "welcome" and proceed. If the input is invalid, then we output the message $a$: "invalid password; enter user ID again" and return to state $s_0$ to await another attempt at logging-on.

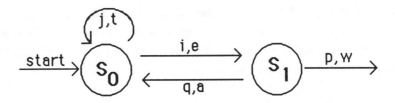

11. This exercise is similar to Exercise 5. We let state $s_i$ for $i = 0, 1, 2, 3, 4$ represent the fact that $5i$ cents has been deposited. When at least 25 cents has been deposited, we return to state $s_0$ and open the gate. Nickels (input 5), dimes (input 10) and quarters (input 25) are available. We let $o$ and $c$ be the outputs: the gate is opened (for a limited time, of course), or remains closed. After the gate is opened, we return to state $s_0$.

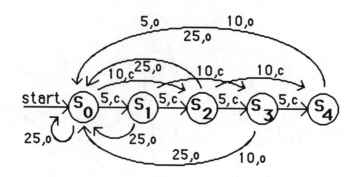

13. We interpret this problem as asking that a 1 be output if the conditions are met, and a 0 be output otherwise. For this machine, we need to keep track of what the last two inputs have been, and we need four states to "store" this information. Let the states $s_3$, $s_4$, $s_5$, and $s_6$ be the states corresponding to the last two inputs having been 00, 10, 01, and 11, respectively. We also need some states to get started—to get us into one of these four states. There are only two cases in which the output is 1: if we are in states $s_3$ or $s_5$ (so that the last two inputs have been 00 or 01) and we receive a 1 as input. The transitions in our machine are the obvious ones. For example, if we are in state $s_5$, having just read 01, and receive a 0 as input, then the last two symbols read are now 10, so we move to state $s_4$.

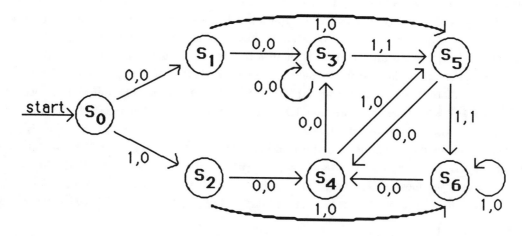

As in Exercise 7, we can actually get by with a smaller machine. Note that here states $s_1$ and $s_4$ are equivalent, as are states $s_2$ and $s_6$. Thus we can merge each of these pairs into one state, producing a machine with only five states. At that point, furthermore, state $s_0$ is equivalent to the merged $s_2$ and $s_6$, so we can omit state $s_0$ and make this other state the start state. The reader is urged to draw the diagram for this simpler machine.

15. We need some notation to make our picture readable. The alphabet has 26 symbols in it. If $\alpha$ is a letter, then by $\overline{\alpha}$ we mean any letter other than $\alpha$. Thus an arrow labeled $\overline{\alpha}$ really stands for 25 arrows. The output is to be 1 when we have just finished reading the word *computer*. Thus we need eight states, to stand for the various stages of having read part of that word. The picture below gives the details, except that we have omitted all the outputs except on inputs $r$ and $\overline{r}$; all the omitted ones are intended to be 0. The reader might contemplate why this problem would have been harder if the word in question were something like *baboon*.

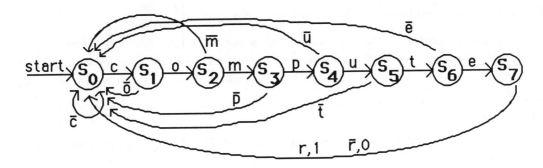

**17.** We construct the state table by having one row for each state. The arrows tell us what the values of the transition function are. For example, since there is an arrow from $s_0$ to $s_1$ labeled 0, the transition from $s_0$ on input 0 is to $s_1$. Similarly, the transition from $s_0$ on input 1 is to $s_2$. The output function values are shown next to each state. Thus the output for state $s_0$ is 1, the output for state $s_1$ is 1, and the output for state $s_2$ is 0. The table is therefore as shown here.

| State | Input 0 | Input 1 | Output |
|-------|---------|---------|--------|
| $s_0$ | $s_1$ | $s_2$ | 1 |
| $s_1$ | $s_1$ | $s_0$ | 1 |
| $s_2$ | $s_1$ | $s_2$ | 0 |

**19. a)** The input drives the machine successively to states $s_1$, $s_0$, $s_1$, and $s_0$. The output is the output of the start state, followed by the outputs of these four states, namely 11111.

**b)** The input drives the machine to state $s_2$, where it remains because of the loop. The output is the output of the start state, followed by the output at state $s_2$ six times, namely 1000000.

**c)** The states visited after the start state are, in order, $s_2$, $s_2$, $s_2$, $s_1$, $s_0$, $s_2$, $s_2$, $s_1$, $s_0$, $s_2$, and $s_2$. Therefore the output is 100011001100.

**21.** We can use a machine with just two states, one to indicate that there is an even number of 1's in the input string, the other to indicate that there is an odd number of 1's in the string. Since the empty string has an even number of 1's, we make $s_0$ (the start state) the state for an even number of 1's. The output for this state will be 1, as directed. The output from state $s_1$ will be 0 to indicate an odd number of 1's. The input 1 will drive the machine from one state to the other, while the input 0 will keep the machine in its current state. The diagram below gives the desired machine.

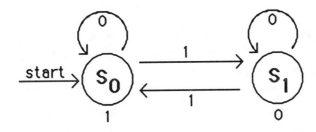

⇒ **SECTION 10.3   Finite-State Machines with No Output**

*As in the previous section, many of these exercises are really exercises in programming. There is no magical way to become a good programmer, but experience helps. The converse problem is also hard—finding a good verbal description of the set recognized by a given finite-state automaton.*

1. **a)** This is the set of all strings $ab$, where $a \in A$ and $b \in B$. Thus it contains precisely 000, 001, 1100, and 1101.

   **b)** This is the set of all strings $ba$, where $a \in A$ and $b \in B$. Thus it contains precisely 000, 0011, 010, and 0111.

   **c)** This is the set of all strings $a_1 a_2$, where $a_1 \in A$ and $a_2 \in A$. Thus it contains precisely 00, 011, 110, and 1111.

   **d)** This is the set of all strings $b_1 b_2 b_3$, where each $b_i \in B$. Thus it contains precisely 000000, 000001, 000100, 000101, 010000, 010001, 010100 and 010101.

3. Two possibilities are of course to let $A$ be this entire set and let $B = \{\lambda\}$, and to let $B$ be this entire set and let $A = \{\lambda\}$. Let us find more. With a little experimentation we see that $A = \{\lambda, 10\}$ and $B = \{10, 111, 1000\}$ also works, and it can be argued that there are no other solutions in which $\lambda$ appears in either set. Finally, there is the solution $A = \{1, 101\}$ and $B = \{0, 11, 000\}$. It can be argued that there are no more. (Here is how the first of these arguments goes. If $\lambda \in A$, then necessarily $\lambda \notin B$. Hence the shortest string in $B$ has length at least 2, from which it follows that $10 \in B$. Now since the only other string in $AB$ that ends with 10 is 1010, the only possible other string in $A$ is 10. This leads to the third solution mentioned above. On the other hand, if $\lambda \in B$, then $\lambda \notin A$, so it must be that the shortest string in $A$ is 10. This forces 111 to be in $A$, and now there can be no other strings in $B$. The second argument is similar.)

5. **a)** One way to write this answer is $\{(10)^n \mid n = 0, 1, 2, \dots\}$. It is the concatenation of zero or more copies of the string 10.

   **b)** This is like part (**a**). This set consists of all copies of zero of more concatenations of the string 111. In other words, it is the set of all strings of 1's of length a multiple of 3. In symbols, it is $\{(111)^n \mid n = 0, 1, 2, \dots\} = \{1^{3n} \mid n = 0, 1, 2, \dots\}$.

   **c)** A little thought will show that this consists of all bit strings in which every 1 is immediately preceded by a 0. No other restrictions are imposed, since $0 \in A$.

   **d)** Because the 0 appears only in 101, the strings formed here have the property that there are at least two 1's between every pair of 0's in the string, and the string begins and ends with a 1. All strings satisfying this property are in $A^*$.

7. This follows directly from the definition. Any string $w$ in $A^*$ consists of the concatenation of one or more strings from $A$. Since $A \subseteq B$, all of these strings are also in $B$, so $w$ is the concatenation of one or more strings from $B$, i.e., is in $B^*$.

9. **a)** This set contains all bit strings, so of course the answer is yes.

   **b)** This set contains all strings consisting of any number of 1's, followed by any number of 0's, followed by any number of 1's. Since 11101 is such a string, the answer is yes.

   **c)** The answer is yes again. Just take the * to equal 1. In other words, the string 11101 consists of the string 11 followed by one copy of the string 1, followed by the string 01.

**d)** All the strings in this set must in particular have even length. The given string has odd length, so the answer is no.

**e)** The answer is yes again. Just take one copy of each of the strings 111 and 0, together with the required string 1.

**f)** The answer is yes again. Just take 111 from the first set and 01 from the second.

11. **a)** The set in question is the set of all strings of zero or more 0's. Since the machine in Figure 1 has $s_0$ as a final state, and since there is a transition from $s_0$ to itself on input 0, any string of zero or more 0's will leave the machine in state $s_0$ and will therefore be accepted. Therefore the answer is yes.

**b)** Since this set is a subset of the set in part (**a**), the answer must be yes.

**c)** One string in this set is the string 1. Since an input of 1 drives the machine to the nonfinal state $s_1$, not every string in this set is accepted. Therefore the answer is no.

**d)** One string in this set is the string 01. Since an input of 01 drives the machine to the nonfinal state $s_1$, not every string in this set is accepted. Therefore the answer is no.

**e)** The answer here is no for exactly the same reason as in part (**d**).

**f)** The answer here is no for exactly the same reason as in part (**c**).

13. In general it is quite hard to describe succinctly languages recognized by machines. An ad hoc approach is usually best.

**a)** There is only one final state, $s_2$, and only three ways to get there, namely on input 0, 01, or 11. Therefore the language recognized by this machine is $\{0, 01, 11\}$.

**b)** The empty string is accepted, since the start state is final. No other string drives the machine to state $s_0$, so the only other accepted strings are the ones that can drive the machine to state $s_1$. Clearly the strings 0 and 1 do so. Also, any string of one or more 1's can drive the machine to state $s_2$, after which a 0 will take it to state $s_1$. Therefore all the strings of the form $1^n 0$ for $n \geq 1$ are also accepted. Thus the answer is $\{\lambda, 0, 1\} \cup \{1^n 0 \mid n \geq 1\}$. (This can also be written as $\{\lambda, 1\} \cup \{1^n 0 \mid n \geq 0\}$, since $0 = 1^0 0$.)

**c)** As in part (**b**), the empty string is accepted. There are essentially two ways to get to the final state $s_2$. We can go through state $s_1$, and any string of the form $0^n 1^m$, where $n$ and $m$ are positive integers, will take us through state $s_1$ on to $s_2$. We can also bypass state $s_1$, and any string of the form $01^m$ for $m \geq 0$ will take us directly to $s_2$. Thus our answer is $\{\lambda\} \cup \{0^n 1^m \mid n, m \geq 1\} \cup \{01^m \mid m \geq 0\}$. Note that this can also be written as $\{\lambda, 0\} \cup \{0^n 1^m \mid n, m \geq 1\}$.

**d)** First it is easy to see that all strings of the form $10^n$ for $n \geq 0$ can drive the machine to the final state $s_1$. Next we see that all strings of the form $10^n 10^m$ for $n, m \geq 0$ can drive the machine to state $s_3$. No other strings can drive the machine to a final state. Therefore the answer is $\{10^n \mid n \geq 0\} \cup \{10^n 10^m \mid n, m \geq 0\}$.

15. **a)** We want to accept only the string 0. Let $s_1$ be the only final state, where we reach $s_1$ on input 0 from the start state $s_0$. Make a "graveyard" state $s_2$, and have all other transitions (there are five of them in all) lead there.

**b)** This uses the same idea as in part (**a**), but we need a few more states. The graveyard state is $s_4$. See the picture for details.

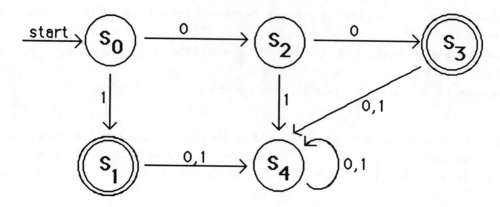

c) In the picture of our machine, we show a transition to the graveyard state whenever we encounter a 0. The only final state is $s_2$, which we reach after 11 and remain at as long as the input consists just of 1's.

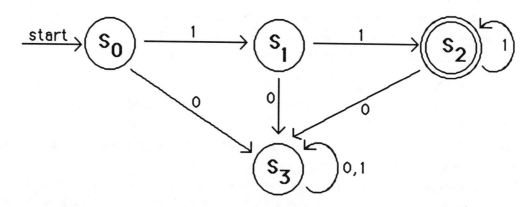

⇒ **SECTION 10.4    Language Recognition**

*Finding good verbal descriptions of the set of strings generated by a regular expression is not easy; neither is finding a good regular expression for a given verbal description. What Kleene's theorem says is that these problems of "programming" in regular expressions are really the same as the programming problems for machines discussed in the previous section. The **pumping lemma**, discussed in Exercise 14 and the three exercises that follow it, is an important technique for proving that certain sets are not regular.*

1. **a)** This regular expression generates all strings consisting of zero or more 1's, followed by a lone 0.

   **b)** This regular expression generates all strings consisting of zero or more 1's, followed by one or more 0's.

   **c)** This set has only two elements, 111 and 001.

   **d)** This set contains all strings in which the 0's come in pairs.

   **e)** This set consists of all strings in which every 1 is preceded by at least one 0, with the proviso that the string ends in a 1 if it is not the empty string.

   **f)** This gives us all strings of length at least 3 which end 00.

**3. a)** We can translate "one or more 0's" into $00^*$. Therefore the answer is $00^*1$.

**b)** We can translate "two or more symbols" into $(0 \cup 1)(0 \cup 1)(0 \cup 1)^*$. Therefore the answer is $(0 \cup 1)(0 \cup 1)(0 \cup 1)^*0000^*$.

**c)** A little thought tells us that we want all strings in which all the 0's come before all the 1's or all the 1's come before all the 0's. Thus the answer is $0^*1^* \cup 1^*0^*$.

**d)** The string of 1's can be represented by $11(111)^*$; the string of 0's, by $(00)^*$. Thus the answer is $11(111)^*(00)^*$.

**5.** We can prove this by induction on the length of a regular expression for $A$. If this expression has length 1, then it is either $\emptyset$ or $\lambda$ or $x$ (where x is some symbol in the alphabet). In each case $A$ is its own reversal, so there is nothing to prove. There are three inductive steps. If the regular expression for $A$ is $\mathbf{BC}$, then $A = BC$, where $B$ is the set generated by $\mathbf{B}$ and $C$ is the set generated by $\mathbf{C}$. By the inductive hypothesis, we know that there are regular expressions $\mathbf{B}'$ and $\mathbf{C}'$ that generate $B^R$ and $C^R$, respectively. Now $A^R = (BC)^R = (C^R)(B^R)$. Therefore a regular expression for $A^R$ is $\mathbf{C}'\mathbf{B}'$. The case of union is handled similarly. Let the regular expression for $A$ be $\mathbf{B} \cup \mathbf{C}$, with $B$, $C$, $\mathbf{B}'$, and $\mathbf{C}'$ as before. Then a regular expression for $A^R$ is $\mathbf{B}' \cup \mathbf{C}'$, since clearly $(B \cup C)^R = (B^R) \cup (C^R)$. Finally, if the regular expression for $A$ is $\mathbf{B}^*$, then, with the same notation as before, it is easy to see that $(\mathbf{B}')^*$ is a regular expression for $A^R$.

**7. a)** We can build machines to recognize $0^*$ and $1^*$ as shown in the second row of Figure 3. Next we need to put these together to make a machine which recognizes $0^*1^*$. We place the first machine on the left and the second machine on the right. We make each final state in the first machine nonfinal (except for the start state, since $\lambda \in 0^*1^*$), but leave the final states in the second machine final. Next we copy each transition to a state which was formerly final in the first machine into a transition (on the same input) to the start state of the second machine. Lastly, since $\lambda \in 0^*$, we add the transition from the start state to the state to which there is a transition from the start state of the machine for $1^*$. The result is as shown. (In all parts of this exercise we have not put names on the states in our state diagrams.)

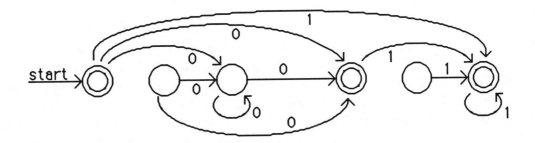

**b)** This machine is quite messy. The upper portion is for $0$, and the lower portion is for $11$. They are combined to give a machine for $0 \cup 11$. Finally, to incorporate the Kleene star, we added a new start state (on the far left), and adjusted the transitions according to the procedure shown in Figure 2.

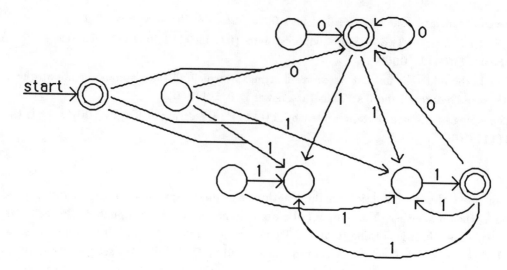

**c)** This is similar to the other parts. We grouped the expression as **01\* ∪ (00\*)1**. The answer is as shown.

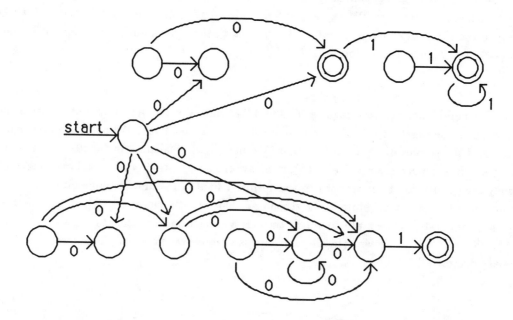

9. In each case, we choose as the nonterminal symbols corresponding to states $s_0$, $s_1$, and $s_2$ (and $s_3$ in part (**c**)) the symbols $S$, $A$, and $B$ (and $C$ in part (**c**)), respectively. Thus $S$ is always our start symbol. The terminal symbols are of course 0 and 1. We construct the rules for our grammars by following the procedure described in the proof of the second half of Theorem 2: putting in rules of the form $X \to aY$ for each transition from the state corresponding to $X$ to the state corresponding to $Y$, on input $a$; putting in rules of the form $X \to a$ for each transition from the state corresponding to $X$ to any final state, on input $a$; and putting in a rule $S \to \lambda$ if $s_0$ is a final state.

**a)** Since there is a transition from $s_0$ to $s_1$ on input 0, we include the rule $S \to 0A$. Similarly, the other transitions give us the rules $S \to 1B$, $A \to 0B$, $A \to 1B$, $B \to 0B$, and $B \to 1B$. Also, the transition to the final state from $S$ on input 0 gives rise to the rule $S \to 0$. Thus our grammar contains these seven rules.

**b)** The transitions between states cause us to put in the rules $S \to 0A$, $S \to 1B$, $A \to 0B$, $A \to 1A$, $B \to 0B$, and $B \to 1A$. The transitions to final states cause us to put in the rules $S \to 0$, $A \to 1$, and $B \to 1$. Finally, since $s_0$ is a final state, we add the rule $S \to \lambda$.

**c)** This is similar to the other parts. The set of rules contains $S \to 0C$, $S \to 1A$, $A \to 1A$, $A \to 0C$, $B \to 0B$, $B \to 1B$, $C \to 0C$, $C \to 1B$, $S \to 1$, $A \to 1$, $B \to 0$, $B \to 1$, and $C \to 1$.

**11.** This is clear, since the operation of the machine is exactly mimicked by the grammar. If the current string in the derivation in the grammar is $v_1 v_2 \ldots v_k A_s$, then the machine has seen input $v_1 v_2 \ldots v_k$ and is currently in state $s$. If the current string in the derivation in the grammar is $v_1 v_2 \ldots v_k$, then the machine has seen input $v_1 v_2 \ldots v_k$ and is currently in some final state. Hence the machine accepts precisely those strings that the grammar generates. (The empty string does not fit this discussion, but it is handled separately—and correctly—since we take $S \to \lambda$ as a production if and only if we are supposed to.)

**13.** First suppose that the language recognized by $M$ is infinite. Then the length of the words recognized by $M$ must be unbounded, since there are only a finite number of symbols. Thus $l(x)$ is greater than the finite number $|S|$ for some word $x \in L(M)$.

Conversely, let $x$ be such a word, and let $s_0$, $s_{i_1}$, $s_{i_2}$, $\ldots$, $s_{i_n}$ be the sequence of states that the machine goes through on input $x$, where $n = l(x)$ and $s_{i_n}$ is a final state. By the pigeonhole principle, some state occurs twice in this sequence, i.e., there is a loop from this state back to itself during the computation. Let $y$ be the substring of $x$ that causes the loop, so that $x = uyv$. Then for every nonnegative integer $k$, the string $uy^k v$ is accepted by the machine $M$ (i.e., is in $L(M)$), since the computation is the same as the computation on input $x$, except that the loop is traversed $k$ times. Thus $L(M)$ is infinite.

**15.** We apply the pumping lemma in a proof by contradiction. Suppose that this set were regular. Then the pumping lemma tells us that $uv^i w$, with $v \neq \lambda$, is in our set for every $i$. Now if $v$ contains both 0's and 1's, then $uv^2 w$ cannot be in the set, since it would have a 0 following a 1, which no string in our set has. On the other hand, if $v$ contains only 0's (or only 1's), then for large enough $i$, it is clear that $uv^i w$ has more than (or less than) twice as many 0's as 1's, again contradicting the definition of our set. Thus the set cannot be regular.

**17.** We will give a proof by contradiction, using the pumping lemma. Following the hint, let $x$ be the palindrome $0^N 10^N$, for some fixed $N > |S|$, where $S$ is the set of states in a machine that recognizes palindromes. By the lemma, we can write $x = uvw$, with $l(uv) \leq |S|$ and $l(v) \geq 1$, so that for all $i$, $uv^i w$ is a palindrome. Now since $0^N 10^N = uvw$ and $l(uv) \leq |S| < N$, it must be the case that $v$ is a string consisting solely of 0's, with the 1 lying in $w$. Then $uv^2 w$ cannot be a palindrome, since it has more 0's before its sole 1 than it has 0's following the 1.

$\Rightarrow$ **SUPPLEMENTARY EXERCISES FOR CHAPTER 10**

**1. a)** We simply need to add two 0's on the left and three 1's on the right at the same time. Thus the rules can be $S \to 00S111$ and $S \to \lambda$.

**b)** We need to add two 0's for every 1 and also allow the symbols to change places at will. Following the trick in our solution to Exercise 11c in Section 10.1, we let $A$ and $B$ be nonterminal symbols representing 0 and 1, respectively. Our rules are $S \to AABS$, $AB \to BA$, $BA \to AB$, $A \to 0$, $B \to 1$, and $S \to \lambda$.

**c)** Our trick here is first to generate a string that looks like $Ew(w^R)$, with $A$ in the place of 0, and $B$ in the place of 1, in the second half. The rules $S \to ET$, $T \to 0TA$, $T \to 1TB$, and $T \to \lambda$ will accomplish this much. Then we force the $A$'s and $B$'s to march to the left, across all the 0's and 1's, until they bump into the left-hand wall ($E$), at which point they turn into their terminal counterparts. Finally, the wall disappears. The rules for doing this are $0A \to A0$, $1A \to A1$, $0B \to B0$, $1B \to B1$, $EA \to E0$, $EB \to E1$, and $E \to \lambda$.

**3.** For part **(a)** note that $(())$ can come from $(B)$, which in turn can come from $(A)$, which can come from $B$, and we can start $S \Rightarrow A \Rightarrow B$. Thus the tree can be as shown in the first picture. For part **(b)** we need to use the rule $A \to AB$ early in the derivation, with the $A$ turning into $()$, and the $B$ turning into $(())$. The ideas in part **(c)** are similar.

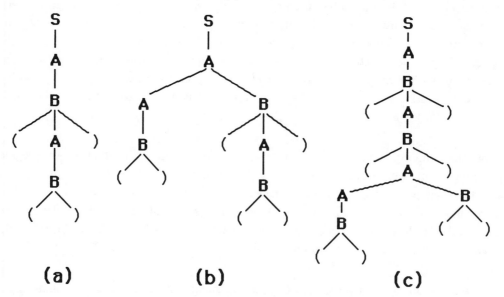

**(a)**                    **(b)**                    **(c)**

**5.** The idea is that the rules enable us to add 0's to either the right or the left. Thus we can get three 0's in many ways, depending on which side we add the 0's on.

**7.** It is not true that $|AB|$ is always equal to $|A| \cdot |B|$, since a string in $AB$ may be formed in more than one way. After a little experimentation, we might come up with the following example to show that $|AB|$ need not equal $|BA|$. Let $A = \{0, 00\}$, and let $B = \{01, 1\}$. Then $AB = \{01, 001, 0001\}$ (there are only three elements, since $001$ can be formed in two ways), whereas $BA = \{010, 0100, 10, 100\}$ has its full complement of four elements.

**9.** This is clearly not necessarily true. For example, we could take $A = V^*$ and $B = V$. Then $A^*$ is again $V^*$, so it is true that $A^* \subseteq B^*$, but of course $A \not\subseteq B$ (for one thing, $A$ is infinite and $B$ is finite).

**11.** In each case we apply the definition to rewrite $h(E)$ in terms of $h$ applied to the strings that make up $E$.
**a)** $h(0^*1) = \max(h(0^*), h(1)) = \max(h(0) + 1, 0) = \max(0 + 1, 0) = 1$
**b)** $h(0^*1^*) = \max(h(0^*), h(1^*)) = \max(h(0) + 1, h(1) + 1) = \max(0 + 1, 0 + 1) = 1$
**c)** $h((0^*01)^*) = h(0^*01) + 1 = 1 + 1 = 2$
**d)** This is similar to part (c); the answer is $3$.
**e)** There are three "factors," and by the definition we need to find the maximum value that $h$ takes on them. It is easy to compute that these values are $1$, $2$, and $2$, respectively, so the answer is $2$.
**f)** A calculation similar to that in part (c) shows that the answer is $4$.

**13.** We need to have states to represent the number of 1's read in so far. Thus $s_i$, for $i = 0, 1, 2, 3$, will "mean" that we have seen exactly $i$ 1's so far, and $s_4$ will signify that we have seen at least four 1's. We draw only the finite-state automaton; the machine with output is exactly the same, except that instead of a state being designated final, there is an output for each transition; all the outputs are $0$ except for the outputs to our final state, and all of the outputs to this final state are $1$.

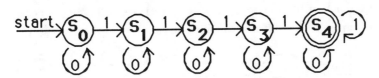

**15.** This is similar to Exercise 13, except that we need to return to the starting state whenever we encounter a $0$, rather than merely remaining in the same state. As in Exercise 13, we draw only the automaton, since the machine with output is practically the same.

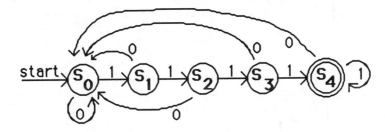

**17. a)** To specify a machine, we need to pick a start state (this can be done in $n$ ways), and for each pair (state, input) (and there are $nk$ such pairs), we need to choose a state and an output. By the product rule, therefore, the answer is $n \cdot n^{nk} \cdot m^{nk}$. (We are answering the question as it was asked.

A much harder question is to determine how many "really" different machines there are, since two machines which really do the same thing and just have different names on the states should perhaps be considered the same. We will not pursue this question.)

b) This is just like part (a), except that we do not need to choose an output for each transition, only an output for each state. Thus the term $m^{nk}$ needs to be replaced by $m^n$, and the answer is $n \cdot n^{nk} \cdot m^n$.

19. This machine has no final states. Therefore no strings are accepted. Any deterministic machine with no final states will be equivalent to this one. We show one such machine below.

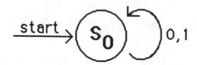

21. The answers are not unique, of course. There are two ways to approach this exercise. We could simply apply the algorithm inherent in the proof of Kleene's theorem, but that would lead to machines much more complicated than they need to be. Alternately, we just try to be clever and make the machines "do what the expressions say." This is essentially computer programming, and it takes experience to be able to do it well. In part (a), for example, we want to accept any string of 0's, so we make the start state a final state, with returns to this state on input 0; and we want to accept any string that has this beginning and then consists of any number of copies of 10—which is precisely what the rest of our machine does. These pictures can either be viewed as nondeterministic machines, or else for all the missing transitions we assume a transition to a new state (the graveyard), which is not final and which has transitions to itself on both inputs. Also, as usual, having two labels on an edge is an abbreviation for two edges, one with each label.

a) This one is pretty simple. State $s_0$ represents the condition that only 0's have been read so far; it is final. After we have read in as many 0's as desired, we still want to accept the string if we read in any number of copies of 10. This is accomplished with the other two states.

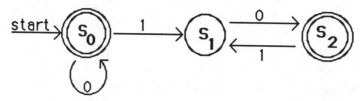

b) In this machine, we keep returning to $s_0$ as long as we are reading 01 or 111, corresponding to the first factor in our regular expression. Then we move to $s_4$ for the term $10^*$, and finally to $s_5$ for the factor $(0 \cup 1)$.

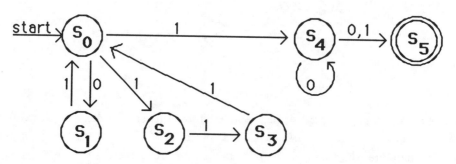

**c)** Note that the inner star in this regular expression is irrelevant; we get the same set whether it is there or not. Our machine returns us to $s_0$ after we have read either 001 or 11, so we accept any string consisting of any number of copies of these strings.

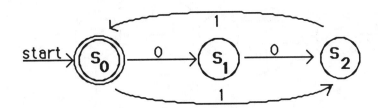

**23.** We invoke the power of Kleene's theorem here. If $A$ is a regular set, then there is a deterministic finite automaton which accepts $A$. If we take the same machine but make all the final states nonfinal and all the nonfinal states final, then the result will accept precisely $\overline{A}$. Therefore $\overline{A}$ is regular.

**25.** See the comments for Exercise 21. Here the problem is even harder, since we are given just verbal descriptions of the sets. Thus there *is* no general algorithm we can invoke. We just have to be clever programmers. See the comments on the solution to Exercise 21 for how to interpret missing transitions.

**a)** The top part of our machine (as drawn) takes us to a graveyard if there are more than three consecutive 0's at the beginning. The rest assures that there are at least two consecutive 1's.

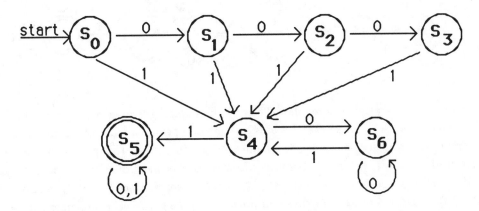

**b)** This one is rather complicated. The states represent what has been seen recently in the input. For example, states $s_2$ and $s_6$ represent the condition in which the last two symbols have been 10. Thus if we encounter a 1 from either of these states, we move to a graveyard. (Note that we could have combined states $s_3$ and $s_7$ into one, or, under our conventions, we could have omitted them altogether; the answers to these exercises are by no means unique.) States $s_0$, $s_2$ and $s_5$ all represent conditions in which an even number of symbols have been read in, whereas $s_1$, $s_4$ and $s_6$ represent conditions in which an odd number of symbols have been read.

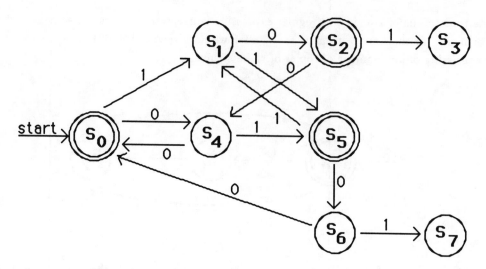

**c)** This one is really not as bad as it looks. The first row in our machine (as drawn) represents conditions before any 0's have been read; the second row after one 0, and the third row after two or more 0's. The horizontal direction takes care of looking for the blocks of 1's.

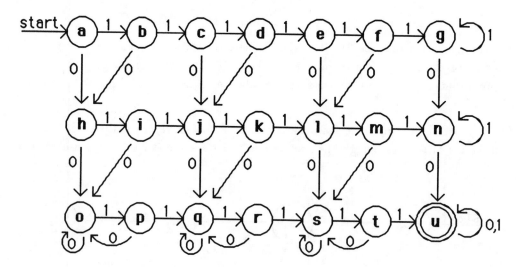

**27.** Suppose that $\{1^p \mid p \text{ is prime}\}$ is regular. Then by the pumping lemma, we can find a prime $p$ such that $1^p = uvw$, with $l(v) \geq 1$, so that $uv^i w$ is a string of a prime number of 1's for all $i$. If we let $a$ be the number of 1's in $uw$ and $b > 0$ the number of 1's in $v$, then this means that $a + bi$ is prime for all $i$. In other words, the gap between two consecutive primes (once we are looking at numbers greater than $a$) is at most $b$. This contradicts reality, however, since for every $n$, all the numbers from $n! + 2$ through $n! + n$ are not prime—in other words the gaps between primes can be arbitrarily large (see Example 17 in Section 3.1).

# APPENDICES

⇒ **APPENDIX 1    Exponential and Logarithmic Functions**

*This material should all be familiar from high school algebra. When working with exponents it is important to remember the rules $b^x b^y = b^{x+y}$ and $(b^x)^y = b^{xy}$. When working with logarithms it is important to remember that $\log_b(xy) = \log_b x + \log_b y$ and $\log_b x^y = y \log_b x$.*

1. **a)** We use the facts that $2^1 = 2$ and $2^{x+y} = 2^x \cdot 2^y$. Thus we have $2 \cdot 2^2 = 2^1 \cdot 2^2 = 2^{1+2} = 2^3$.

   **b)** We use the second part of Theorem 1 to write $(2^2)^3 = 2^{(2 \cdot 3)} = 2^6$.

   **c)** There is no way to use a rule of exponents to simplify this. However, since $2^2 = 4$, we can write this as $2^4$.

3. **a)** We use Theorem 3. Thus $\log_2 x = (\log_4 x)/(\log_4 2) = (\log_4 x)/(1/2) = 2 \log_4 x = 2y$.

   **b)** This is just like part **(a)**. We have $\log_8 x = (\log_4 x)/(\log_4 8) = (\log_4 x)/(3/2) = (2 \log_4 x)/3 = 2y/3$.

   **c)** This is just like part **(a)**. We have $\log_{16} x = (\log_4 x)/(\log_4 16) = (\log_4 x)/2 = y/2$.

5. We can draw these graphs by plotting points, following the general shape shown in Figure 1. For part **(a)** the graph is similar to the graph of $f(x) = 2^x$. For part **(b)** the graph is similar to the graph of $f(x) = (1/2)^x$. Finally for part **(c)** the function is constant, since $1^x = 1$ for all $x$.

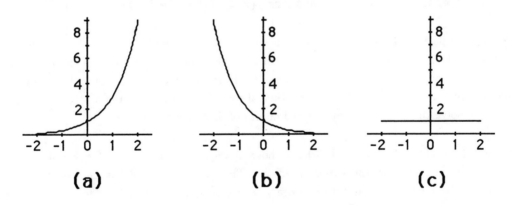

**(a)**          **(b)**          **(c)**

⇒ **APPENDIX 2    Pseudocode**

*Obviously the text cannot give an entire course in programming in just a few pages. One nice thing about pseudocode is that it is readable even when the reader has no specialized knowledge of the conventions being followed.*

1. In the first case, the value of $a$ is first set to the value of $b$, and then the value of $b$ is changed. Thus the final value of $a$ is the same as the original value of $b$. In the second case, the value of $b$ is changed first (to the original value of $c$), then this new value is assigned to $a$. Thus the final value of $a$ is the same as the original value of $c$.

3. According to the definition, the way this loop is executed is that first $i$ is assigned the *initial value*. Then as long as $i$ is less than or equal to *final value*, the statement in the loop is executed, and the value of $i$ is incremented by 1. Thus the code is equivalent to the following code.

```
i := initial value
while i ≤ final value
begin
        statement
        i := i + 1
end
```

⇒ **APPENDIX 3    Generating Functions**

*Entire books can be written on generating functions, so this section is but the briefest introduction. Try following the examples in using recurrence relations for modeling counting problems and for solving recurrence relations. For a more complete exposition, see, for example, C. L. Liu, Introduction to Combinatorial Mathematics, McGraw-Hill, 1968.*

1. By definition we want the function $f(x) = 2 + 2x + 2x^2 + 2x^3 + 2x^4 + 2x^5 = 2(1 + x + x^2 + x^3 + x^4 + x^5)$. From Example 1, we see that the expression in parentheses can also be written as $(x^6 - 1)/(x - 1)$. Thus we can write the answer more simply as $f(x) = 2(x^6 - 1)/(x - 1)$.

3. Following the pattern of Example 7, we want to find the coefficient of $x^{10}$ in the expansion of $(x^2 + x^3 + x^4)^4$. (The reason that we stop the sum in each factor at $x^4$ is that if each child gets at least two balloons, then none of the four children can possibly receive more than four balloons out of the ten to be distributed.) If we multiply this out, then the coefficient of $x^{10}$ turns out to be 10. In practice, the way to solve this problem is by the techniques of Section 4.5.

5. We want the coefficient of $x^k$ to be the number of ways to make change for $k$ dollars. One-dollar bills contribute 1 each to the exponent of $x$. Thus we can model the choice of the number of one-dollar bills by a choice of a term from $1 + x + x^2 + x^3 + \cdots$. Two-dollar bills contribute 2 each to the exponent of $x$. Thus we can model the choice of the number of two-dollar bills by a choice of a term from $1 + x^2 + x^4 + x^6 + \cdots$. Similarly, five-dollar bills contribute 5 each to the exponent of $x$, so we can model the choice of the number of five-dollar bills by a choice of a term from $1 + x^5 + x^{10} + x^{15} + \cdots$. Similar reasoning applies to ten-dollar bills. Thus the generating function is $f(x) = (1 + x + x^2 + x^3 + \cdots)(1 + x^2 + x^4 + x^6 + \cdots)(1 + x^5 + x^{10} + x^{15} + \cdots)(1 + x^{10} + x^{20} + x^{30} + \cdots)$, which can also be written as

$$f(x) = \frac{1}{(1 - x)(1 - x^2)(1 - x^5)(1 - x^{10})}.$$

7. We follow the method of Example 6. The restriction on $x_1$ gives us the factor $x^2 + x^3 + \cdots$. The restriction on $x_2$ gives us the factor $1 + x + x^2 + x^3$. The restriction on $x_3$ gives us the factor $x^2 + x^3 + x^4 + x^5$. Thus the answer is the product of these: $(x^2 + x^3 + \cdots)(1 + x + x^2 + x^3)(x^2 + x^3 + x^4 + x^5)$. We can use algebra (transfer the factor $x^2$ from the first of these three terms to the second) to rewrite this in closed form as $(x^2 + x^3 + x^4 + x^5)^2/(1 - x)$.

9. **a)** From Example 3 we know that the generating function when each $a_k = 1$ is $f(x) = 1/(1 - x)$. Thus the answer is $f(x) = 3/(1 - x)$.

   **b)** We want to find a simple expression for $1 + 5x + 5^2 x^2 + 5^3 x^3 + \cdots$. This is the same as $1 + (5x) + (5x)^2 + (5x)^3 + \cdots$. From Example 3 we know that this can be written as $1/(1 - 5x)$. Thus our answer is $f(x) = 1/(1 - 5x)$.

   **c)** We found precisely this sequence in Example 5. Thus the answer is $f(x) = 1/(1 - x)^2$.

11. This problem is identical to Example 9, with 7 in place of 3, and 5 in place of 2. Mimicking the analysis there gives us the answer $a_k = 5 \cdot 7^k$.

13. This problem is very much like Example 10. Let $G$ be the generating function for $a_k$, so that $G(x) = \sum_{k=0}^{\infty} a_k x^k$. Let us rewrite the recurrence relation as $a_k - 3a_{k-1} - 4^{k-1} = 0$. The generating function for $4^{k-1}$ is $\dfrac{x}{1 - 4x}$. Thus

$$G(x) - 3xG(x) - \frac{x}{1 - 4x} = \sum_{k=0}^{\infty} a_k x^k - \sum_{k=1}^{\infty} 3a_{k-1} x^k - \sum_{k=1}^{\infty} 4^{k-1} x^k$$

$$= a_0 + \sum_{k=1}^{\infty} (a_k - 3a_{k-1} - 4^{k-1}) x^k$$

$$= 1.$$

Now we apply algebra to solve this equation for $G$.

$$(1 - 3x)G(x) = 1 + \frac{x}{1 - 4x}$$

$$(1 - 3x)G(x) = \frac{1 - 3x}{1 - 4x}$$

$$G(x) = \frac{1}{1 - 4x} = \sum_{k=0}^{\infty} 4^k x^k$$

Therefore $a_k = 4^k$.

15. In principle this exercise is similar to the examples and previous exercises. In fact, the algebra is quite a bit messier. We want to solve the recurrence relation $f_k = f_{k-1} + f_{k-2}$, with initial conditions $f_0 = 0$ and $f_1 = 1$. Let $G$ be the generating for $f_k$, so that $G(x) = \sum_{k=0}^{\infty} f_k x^k$. We look at $G(x) - xG(x) - x^2 G(x)$ in order to take advantage of the recurrence relation:

$$G(x) - xG(x) - x^2 G(x) = \sum_{k=0}^{\infty} f_k x^k - \sum_{k=1}^{\infty} f_{k-1} x^k - \sum_{k=2}^{\infty} f_{k-2} x^k$$

$$= f_0 + f_1 x - f_0 x + \sum_{k=2}^{\infty} (f_k - f_{k-1} - f_{k-2}) x^k$$

$$= 0 + x - 0 + 0 = x.$$

Thus $G$ satisfies the equation

$$G(x) = \frac{x}{1 - x - x^2}.$$

To write this more usefully, we need to use partial fractions. The roots of the denominator are $r_1 = (-1 + \sqrt{5})/2$ and $r_2 = (-1 - \sqrt{5})/2$. We want to find constants $A$ and $B$ such that

$$\frac{x}{1 - x - x^2} = \frac{-x}{x^2 + x - 1} = \frac{A}{x - r_1} + \frac{B}{x - r_2}.$$

This means that $A$ and $B$ have to satisfy the simultaneous equations $A + B = -1$ and $r_2 A + r_1 B = 0$ (multiply the last displayed equation through by the denominator and equate like powers of $x$). Solving we obtain $A = (1 - \sqrt{5})/(2\sqrt{5})$ and $B = (-1 - \sqrt{5})/(2\sqrt{5})$. Now we have

$$\begin{aligned}
G(x) &= \frac{A}{x - r_1} + \frac{B}{x - r_2} \\
&= \frac{-A}{r_1} \frac{1}{1 - (x/r_1)} + \frac{-B}{r_2} \frac{1}{1 - (x/r_2)} \\
&= \frac{-A}{r_1} \sum_{k=0}^{\infty} \left(\frac{1}{r_1}\right)^k x^k + \frac{-B}{r_2} \sum_{k=0}^{\infty} \left(\frac{1}{r_2}\right)^k x^k.
\end{aligned}$$

Therefore

$$\begin{aligned}
f_k &= -A \left(\frac{1}{r_1}\right)^{k+1} - B \left(\frac{1}{r_2}\right)^{k+1} \\
&= \frac{1}{\sqrt{5}} \left(\frac{2}{-1 + \sqrt{5}}\right)^k - \frac{1}{\sqrt{5}} \left(\frac{2}{-1 - \sqrt{5}}\right)^k.
\end{aligned}$$

We can check our answer by computing the first few terms with a calculator, and indeed we find that $f_2 = 1$, $f_3 = 2$, $f_4 = 3$, $f_5 = 5$, and so on.